To Mike:
God Bless
+ Family
Sincerely,
[signature] 6·25·22

VICTIMS
OF
CIRCUMSTANCE

A YOUNG MAN'S JOURNEY TO REDEMPTION

BY FRANK A. ROSSI

DORRANCE
PUBLISHING CO
EST. 1920
PITTSBURGH, PENNSYLVANIA 15238

Dorrance Publishing Co
585 Alpha Drive
Pittsburgh, PA 15238
Visit our website at *www.dorrancebookstore.com*

ISBN: 978-1-6491-3768-5
eISBN: 978-1-6491-3956-6

CONTENTS

PART III

PROLOGUE

The hour was late and the road ahead clear. Nick yelled out of his open sunroof, "Time to take a little ride, Nicky!" He put the sports car in gear and gunned the engine. The back tires spun out of control as the car jolted forward. He raced down Route 5 knowing it was a one-way ticket.

Nick stepped on the gas. The engine roared as the vehicle sped along in the night. Nick's heart raced faster than the seventy-five-mph needle on the car dashboard. Unsatisfied, he popped a couple more uppers and washed them down with a swig of vodka. Nick streaked into a small village along the lake and quickly approached an intersection. The light changed to yellow, then promptly to red. "No stopping for this guy." Nick snarled to himself. He braced himself and stepped hard on the accelerator. The car hurtled through to the surprise of the drivers in the crossing lane. Nick laughed. In the span of a few minutes, he repeated the scene through every town and village along the route, nearly colliding with a half dozen vehicles along the way. "Not even one cop," he said grinning. "Never one around when you need them."

As he approached the city, Nick could see the elevated Buffalo Skyway lit up in the dark night. The bridge spanned over a mile long and towered a hundred feet above the Buffalo River. It was his destination. Nick accelerated up the ramp onto the bridge and raced along at a blistering speed. At the center of the span he slammed on the brakes. The sports car fishtailed violently before coming to a screeching halt.

Nick shifted the car into park. He reached into his back pocket, pulled out his wallet, and threw it onto the dashboard. "Won't be needing this anymore," he said. Nick grabbed his bottle of vodka and exited the car. Perspiration poured off his brow. No cars could be seen coming down the Skyway behind him. Feeling the effects of the pills and alcohol, Nick staggered over to the four-foot high retainer wall and stood atop a small concrete support beam. He glanced over at the glowing city skyline and lowered his head. Nick stared down into the dark waters below. He took another swig of vodka and extended his arm. He let go of the bottle and watched it fall straight down and disappear into the swirling darkness with a muffled swoosh.

"I guess I'm next," he said to himself. Nick climbed to the topmost of the wall and stood out on the ledge. He grabbed a steel girder to steady himself as a cool breeze came in off Lake Erie. Nick looked into the night sky and howled in despair. "All right, old man, I'm ready whenever you are. Send me to heaven or send me to hell...because I ain't staying here!" A gust of wind blew. Nick held on tightly to the girder for support. He gazed down into the black emptiness below which reflected how he felt inside. With tears now streaming down his cheeks, he asked himself, "How did I end up here? How did everything become so fucked up?"

CHAPTER 1
THE ESCAPE

(Three Months Earlier)

The sun crept atop the pristine mountains. Embedded in the valley below sat the Clinton Correctional Facility. The maximum-security prison located in Dannemora, New York. An imposing structure which boasted an unblemished escape record extending well over a century. The facility referred to by its inmates as "Hotel California," the nickname originating from an old Eagles song written in 1977—because *one could check out anytime they want, but they could never leave.*

On the afternoon of June 5, 2015, the chaotic scene in the colossal Clinton prison yard had turned eerily quiet. Inside the guard towers, dozens of trained snipers stood frozen, their fingers still poised on their AR-15s' triggers. The yard below them was finally desolate. All that remained was the piercing sound of the escape horn and great mass of footprints left behind in the dirt from the three thousand angry inmates on lockdown inside their cells.

Outside the prison's thirty-foot high concrete walls, scores of local and state police fanned out on the ghostlike streets. The officers were determined to protect Dannemora's five thousand inhabitants. A robo-call blasted its way into each neighborhood home and business. "This is an important message from the New York State Police…the search continues for two men who escaped from the Clinton Correctional Facility…police are reminding residents to please remain on alert…"

On the local news, an austere looking reporter continued her dire warning. "Hundreds of officers are now on a massive manhunt for convicted murderers, Richard Matt and David Sweat. Matt, nicknamed *Hacksaw* by his fellow inmates, was serving a twenty-five to life sentence for the brutal 1997 slaying of his former boss, whose body he then dismembered, throwing the pieces into the Niagara River. The torso was later discovered by a local fisherman. Sweat was serving a life sentence without parole for the violent 2002 death of a Broome County sheriff's deputy who confronted Sweat and an accomplice after a robbery. The deputy had been shot fifteen times and run over with their car."

On screen, the stark mugshots of the two inmates in their prison greens peered into every home watching the telecast. The striking image of Ricky Matt demanded your attention. The forty-eight-year-old possessed old-school movie star good looks. He was rugged and handsome with masculine features which projected a youthful char despite his middle age. They also masked an intense, predatory gaze which unsettled many—like peeking into the cold, lifeless eyes of a shark out for the kill. The effect was one of unmistakable menace. In contrast, David Sweat looked almost boyish. He was slim with soft features making him appear much younger than his thirty-four years. His youthful look easily attracted others into his orbit and often caused one to drop their guard. Something he routinely used to his advantage.

A second newscaster glanced up at the teleprompter. "…authorities believe the two men had access to power tools and hacksaw blades—cutting their way through their cell walls and a steel drainage pipe. It is believed they made their way through the drainage pipe exiting a manhole cover a hundred feet from the prison. They are now fugitives on the run. Authorities consider both men armed and dangerous."

The truth was, Ricky Matt was very dangerous. He had a chip on his shoulder. A chip fueled by anger growing more pronounced with each minute he was on the run. Ricky had now achieved a seven-hour head start. He could be almost anywhere.

Three hundred and fifty miles away, police sirens flooded the western New York countryside. One long steady scream reflecting their sense of urgency. Erie County and New York State Trooper vehicles, along with federal agents, converged on the small town of Angola, New York. They were minutes away from the ill-kempt home on the corner of Tree Hollow and Lakeshore Road. In its front yard, an above-ground pool in obvious disrepair, begged for attention while the dilapidated garage in back appeared abandoned and was sealed shut. Inside the house, the only source of light emanated from a large flat screen TV. It displayed the haunting image of Ricky Matt.

Vee Harris, fifty-three, stood hunched over her walker, enveloped in a thick shroud of cigarette smoke. The mother of two was wearing old sweats and a coffee-stained T-shirt. She had been struggling with the identities of a baggie filled with different colored prescription pills and not having much success. The Fentanyl patch she had on probably didn't help. They often made her drowsy and disorientated. A small price to pay to mask the pain.

Vee looked much older than her years. The daughter of a former fashion model and a beauty once herself, her youthful look had long since faded. She had put on extra weight, and her skin was now tracked with crisscrossing wrinkles.

A series of debilitating medical issues with her shoulder and neck left her body a shell of its former self. She was now ravaged by chronic pain which often left her on the verge of tears. It also made her permanently hunched over, requiring the support of a walker to get around. Vee felt the weight of her current condition especially hard. She had always been a person on the go. She had worked as a nurse for over twenty years and was accustomed to pulling double shifts and sixty-hour work weeks. But all that had changed. Now, an effort was needed just to get from room to room.

The intense pain in her back and neck had finally subsided. Her medications had officially kicked in. Vee used her newfound strength to wobble on her walker into the kitchen. She grabbed her large coffee, took a sip, and smiled at the simple pleasure. Tim Horton's coffee with three creams and four Splenda had become one of the few remaining bright spots in her day. A little ritual that reminded her of her former life. Vee collected two jars from the countertop along with a loaf of bread and made herself a peanut butter and jelly sandwich. It had become the staple of her diet the past few months, and today was no different. She took a bite and enjoyed another sip of coffee.

As she ate, Vee started to hear the high-pitched sounds of the sirens coming from outside, which sounded like they were getting close. She struggled over to the kitchen window and looked out. Several police cars had lined up along the street outside her home. More pulled into her driveway. Sirens and flashers were going full throttle. Vee let out a sigh as shock turned to resignation. She threw her one good arm into the air in defiance and said to herself, "Oh, what the hell? If you're coming to get me, then come and get me. You boys would be doing me a favor." Vee thought her doctor shopping for prescriptions had finally caught up to her. It was plain bad luck. Resigned to her fate but still rebellious, Vee sat down on the walker, determined to finish her breakfast. That's when she glanced over at the TV in the living room and saw Ricky on the screen.

⤜⬩⧓⬩⤛

Upstairs in the back bedroom, seated on the floor with his legs folded, was the twenty-three-year-old son of Vee Harris. Nick had long hair with a stubble beard and was wearing expensive designer jeans and a polo T-shirt. He had been chasing the dragon off a Fentanyl patch and had just inhaled the last of the smoke through a straw. In his self-induced stupor, he thought he had heard sirens. He slowly stood up and shuffled his way into the bathroom. He glanced out the window and observed the line of police cars in front of his house. The sirens were no longer wailing, but the barrage of red lights was still flashing. Their message loud and clear.

4

Nick's heart skipped a beat. A sense of panic snuck in, and his mind began to race. He dropped to the bathroom floor and quickly crawled to one corner. He pulled up a tiny flap of the linoleum floor which concealed a small space. Inside were two clear plastic bags. They contained cocaine and heroin—well over four ounces. Knowing he didn't have much time, Nick ripped open the bags. He took a couple of quick snorts of the cocaine and glared at the bags one last time. He emptied the powdery contents into the toilet and flushed. With an irritated grin, Nick watched twenty thousand dollars of pure profit go down the drain.

If possession was nine tenths of the law, then Nick no longer possessed. He ran back into the bedroom and dove under his bed. He retrieved a large shoebox and opened the lid. Two thousand and four hundred dollars in cash glared back at him. Nick knew the DEA boys would let that go if they found it. Still, he didn't want any of it lifted *accidentally* during a search, so he slid the money into his pocket. He still had fifteen thousand dollars in cash safely hidden in the attic. Even if it was discovered, storing money wasn't illegal.

Nick stepped up to the window and witnessed numerous officers converging on the house. They were heavily armed. He grabbed a few OxyContin off the dresser and swallowed them. His heart was already beating rapidly from the cocaine. The Oxy's would slow it down to a snail's crawl. Nothing like speed balling before an arrest. If he was going to jail, being high for the first two days suited him just fine.

By force of habit, Nick walked over to his bed and grabbed a six-inch knife from under the mattress. He tucked it in his sock just in case. Now he was ready. He stood in front of a wall easily visible from the room's entrance and assumed an arrest position. He raised his arms and placed his hands on the wall, spreading his feet wide apart. Nick waited. Downstairs, he could hear the sounds of people entering through the front door. The rapid trampling of feet as they went from room to room. Followed by the loud thuds on the steps as they rushed up the stairs. Nick could feel the tension in his neck. He heard someone step into the room and come up behind him. A steely voice asked, "Are you the son of Richard Matt?"

CHAPTER 2
Going Down
Memory Lane

Nick's head was spinning. He took his hands of the wall and slowly turned around. The agent stood there stoically, waiting for a response. All Nick could muster was a confused, "What?" FBI Special Agent Frank Maggio looked sternly into Nick's eyes. He knew why Nick thought he was there. Maggio laid it out. "Last night after bed check, Richard Matt escaped from the Clinton Correctional Facility. We think he might be headed back this way. Has he tried to contact you or your mom." Even with the Oxys he had taken, Nick could feel his heart rate soar. A wave of fear swept through him. He anxiously looked back at Maggio and just shook his head from side to side.

┄•┄ ▆◆▆ ┄•┄

The day had turned to night. It was several hours since the feds had left. They had searched the inside of the house and surrounding property. There was no sign of Ricky. A solid contingent of law enforcement remained outside. The media had also begun to arrive en masse. Despite the growing number of people huddled outside his door, Nick

7

began to feel consumed by a sense of helplessness. He felt like death was coming for him, and all he could do now was wait. He finished off the last of a sandwich and helped his mom to the black leather couch in the living room.

Nick grabbed a pack of cigarettes and slid two Marlboro lights into his shirt pocket. He set the pack down on the coffee table and glanced at Vee. "He'll be coming for us. He'll be coming for both of us." Vee rocked off the couch. The lit cigarette falling from her mouth. "He can kill me, Nicky. But that bastard touches one hair on your head and I'll cut his balls off!"

Nick let out a nervous laugh. "I believe you would, Vee Harris... I believe you would." Nick kissed his mom and headed up the stairs.

Inside his room, Nick desperately searched for a stash of China-White to squelch his anxiety. He could sense the inner demons coming. A brief glimpse of his own terrified image staring back at him in the mirror all but confirmed it. Shivering, he finally located a hit of heroin hidden inside an old Bic pen. He grabbed a lighter and a piece of tinfoil. As the powder vaporized from the heat, Nick inhaled and waited for the euphoria.

A short time later, he was feeling much more relaxed. The smack had done its job—the anxieties had skipped. He grabbed a beer from the fridge and walked towards the TV. On a shelf nearby was a group of old VHS tapes. They were videos of his dad. He often felt compelled to watch them but rarely did. The few times he had he was high. Maybe that's what was needed to tip the scales between fear and curiosity. Tonight, he felt inspired. Nick grabbed one of the tapes and popped it in the video player. He sat down in the recliner and said to himself, "Bring it on, Ricky."

The TV image flickered as the old video crackled in the night. A handsome thirty-one-year-old Ricky Matt appeared on screen with short, perfectly groomed hair. He was clad in white dress pants, black suspenders, and a long-sleeve button down shirt. Ricky sat in a chair, holding a blow gun and a long dart. :This is my friend, Ricky Matt. He's a freaking crazy lunatic," a voice said off screen. Adding, "And this is the face of that lunatic." The camera zoomed in on Ricky's smiling face. Nick sat there staring at the screen in silence.

Ricky stood up and displayed the blow gun. Then said in his gruff voice, "This is a South American blow gun...and we're going to demonstrate it." Ricky held the dart and showed the needle close-up. "We're gonna dip these in AIDS blood and put a patent on them. Then sell them as a deadly weapon. Whadda you think?"

"I think you're one deranged motherfucker is what I think," Nick responded back to the screen.

Ricky slid the dart into the gun and offered it towards the camera. "I loaded it for you." He grinned. The camera had been placed on a stationary mount. Ricky stood in the center of the room with his bare left arm extended out. To the left, the end of the gun could be seen extending into the frame directed toward Ricky.

"We're about to shoot the dart into Ricky Matt's arm," quivered the off-screen voice. There was a sudden twang and quick whining sound. The dart entered Ricky's left forearm. He barely flinched. Just growled into the camera and winked. A close up of Ricky's forearm showed the wound.

"Went in there. Started to come out there," he described matter-of-factly.

The video stopped. The screen went blank. Nick sat there in the dark wondering if this would be his fate. Would he become like his dad? *The apple does not fall far from the tree.* Thinking about it made him nervous and frightened. Nick slipped a Lortab capsule into his mouth and took a long swig of his beer. He leaned his head back in the recliner and closed his eyes—comforted by the darkness.

The next few days Nick spent in his room trying to shield himself from his own thoughts and fears. Having the cops and media vultures camped outside did not make it any easier. He occasionally made trips downstairs, returning each time with a Fentanyl patch or some other suitable prescription from his mom's supply. She was well stocked and wouldn't miss them. Vee spent most of each day on the couch submerged in a mental fog watching TV. If there was a silver lining to the continuous news coverage of Ricky, it was that it helped take the focus off Vee's chronic pain.

For a brief time, Nick's attention shifted to the three cell phones on the nightstand inside his bedroom. They were now screaming at him.

Their desperate cries all one in the same. "Answer the phone, Nick!" "I need my prescription!" "Don't let me down, Nicky Boy…" "I can't make it 'til Monday!" Nick had always responded quickly to their urgent cries for help or gnashing of teeth. It was good for business. But things were different now. Their desperate pleas would go unanswered.

A couple days passed without incident. The feds were no closer in apprehending the two fugitives. The central air in the house had gone on the fritz, and the summer heat was suffocating. Nick had just started smoking his second cocaine and marijuana joint of the evening when he decided to watch another tape. He was perspiring noticeably when he finally slid a video into the VCR. On the screen played an episode of the tabloid show *Current Affair* from 1992. Not long after Nick had been born. Dressed in a black tux, a spruced-up Ricky Matt strutted down the staircase of a plush home. A glass of champagne filled his left hand. Beluga caviar his right. He was being interviewed for his alleged role as a hitman in a failed murder for hire plot. The producers were playing it up for all it was worth.

Thinking about how his dad came to be on the show made Nick angry. Ricky had been jailed for a violent assault on Vee and unable to make the high bail. Awaiting his trial, Ricky had befriended a wealthy inmate whose wife was the granddaughter of some former big-name Hollywood producer. The inmate allegedly asked Nick's dad if he would be interested in killing his wife in exchange for bail. Ricky was free a week later. Apparently, he had agreed. However, instead of killing the wife, Ricky phoned her and exposed the plot. He hoped by doing so, he could reduce his own sentence if convicted of the assault charge. The feds swooped in to ask questions. The tabloid shows came calling because of the Hollywood connection. Ricky accepted the invitation from *Current Affair*. He desperately needed the appearance fee. He ended up on national television dressed in a tuxedo.

The entire ordeal had a foul stink to it. It made Nick nauseous. In a fury, he ripped the tape from the VCR and rushed to the open window. He flung the tape out and watched it land in a small pond in back of the house. Nick grabbed another beer and returned to his chair. A steely gaze suggested he was unwilling to go along with the charade a minute longer.

CHAPTER 3
A VISIT FROM A FRIEND

Nick was asleep in his recliner. He had been dressed in the same outfit for three days running and looked haggard. He was surrounded by empty beer cans and leftover trash. His eyes suddenly opened, awakened by instinct. *Footsteps?* He knew the Evans Police Department had him under surveillance. Nick listened intently for a few seconds but heard nothing. He let out a deep sigh and drifted back into his slumber. His instincts shook him awake again. This time he was staring into the face of Jake Donald. Jake was standing near the recliner glaring down at him with a smirk. Nick jumped from his chair and gave him a big bear hug. "I knew you'd come back...my big brother would never let me down." Jake released himself gently, looked into Nick's eyes, and said, "And it's time for you not to let me down, Nicky."

Jake had journeyed three thousand miles from Los Angeles to be at the side of a man he had once considered his brother. He had tried for years to get Nick to stop using, but his efforts were in vain. Smoking weed was one thing but associating himself with what Nick did was another. The two had gone their separate ways. Jake had turned his passion for skateboarding into a career in California. He had become a professional in the sport with a huge following and A-list sponsors. Nowadays, he had to be careful of his reputation, but Jake also knew he needed to be there for his friend. He escorted

Nick into the bathroom and immersed him in a cold shower—clothes and all.

Downstairs in the living room, Vee lay on the couch coiled in pain. She continued to watch the news on TV. CNN was providing updates on the manhunt every hour on the hour. Even though Vee had experienced Ricky's violent side firsthand, she still held an emotional attachment to him. The man was the father of her only son and was now being hunted as a fugitive by 1,400 members of law enforcement. She watched as New York State Governor Andrew Cuomo held a press conference outside the prison. He was in Dannemora and had just toured the fugitives' escape route. Cuomo had issued a warning to residents statewide and was now answering questions about the elaborate escape. Vee grunted at the TV. She knew Ricky could not be restrained by mere mortals.

Jake had come downstairs and stood in the kitchen. The thick cigarette smoke stench flowing in from the living room made him queasy. He walked to its edge and gazed in sadness at the woman who had raised him for nearly five years. Vee didn't deserve this, he thought. The pain and suffering had exacted a toll, first by Ricky, then her health. The high spirited, robust lady he had known now appeared worn and frail. The change was alarming. Jake approached her through the haze. She glanced up at him with tired eyes. "Take care of Nicky for me, Jake. Take care of my boy." Jake nodded he would. Both heads turned as a rejuvenated Nick made his way downstairs and into the kitchen.

Almost simultaneously, twenty-three-year-old John Triphauser entered the house. "Trip" was Nick's best friend and unofficial member of the household. No knock was needed from him. He checked on Vee daily and often brought her to doctor appointments when Nick was *indisposed*. Trip had just returned from a hunting junket over the weekend and heard the news about the escape. He greeted Jake and asked Nick how he was holding up. "Just peachy," he replied. Nick was standing at the kitchen counter. He had his mom's things set up like an assembly line. Prescriptions, jars of peanut butter and jelly, and bread and coffee from the latest run. Five pills. Six times a day. Augmented by sandwiches and coffee. That was the routine. Nick and Vee had it down pat. A tray was ready with the next installment. Trip offered to take it over to Vee.

After Trip exited the room, Jake motioned Nick toward the door. He had something to say. Nick countered with a preemptive strike. "I gave up dealing, Jake…swear to God. I been shitin' my pants even thinkin' about it, ever since Ricky escaped." Jake sent him a fleeting smile. He had heard it before.

"That's good, Nicky. That's good."

"No, seriously, Jake. Listen, about a year ago, right…this guy I was selling to got arrested. They gave him a stretch in Clinton. The little prick told Ricky everything." Jake glanced at Nick.

"Really?"

"Yeah, really." Nick quipped nervously.

"Your dad's one guy you don't want to piss off, Nicky." Jake had paid for Nick's rehab stints on two occasions. Neither had worked. Maybe his dad's escape would. Fear was a good motivator. "Look, I gotta go. But I'm in town awhile, so call me if you need anything. Okay?"

Nick smiled and said, "Thanks, Jake. You fuckin' killin' it on the circuit, dude."

Jake gave him a strong hug, then grabbed Nick's shoulders so the two were facing each other.

"You remember, I got your back," Jake said firmly. Nick nodded his head. The world-class skater then turned and walked out the door. Nick watched as Jake went through the front yard and disappeared in the maze of media still camped outside the Harris home.

Nick walked into the living room and sat down. Vee and Trip were watching CNN. They were showing decade-old news footage of Ricky dressed in orange prison clothes being escorted by a dozen officers to his sentencing hearing. He appeared defiant, despite being draped in leg irons and handcuffs. Nick sat there livid. Watching his dad being paraded around again in front of the entire world hit him hard. CNN's Jake Tapper began talking via phone with a local Buffalo News reporter who had covered the original trial. Nick grabbed the TV remote and turned up the sound. They were discussing the details of the murder and testimony of Lee Bates. Nick lashed out at the screen. "Lee Bates is a fuckin' liar! ...a little prick only interested in saving his own fat-ass!"

Lee Bates had been Ricky's accomplice during the murder of Bill Rickerson. It was largely due to his testimony Ricky had been convicted. It had never sat well with Nick. Bates had changed his story three times. Nick felt Lee's final testimony had been the prosecutor's bullied version of the events. "I can't listen to any more of this shit!" Nick seethed. He stood up and kissed his mother on the cheek. Then glanced at Trip. "You got her?" Nodding towards Vee. Trip quietly nodded back. Nick entered the kitchen and grabbed a small backpack he had brought down from his room earlier. He made certain it was secure and rushed out the front door.

———— ≖✦≖ ————

The media trucks lined the roads surrounding the house. It was a circus. Whenever Nick stepped out, the cameras turned on and the reporters clamored for an interview. *The son of murderer Ricky Matt!* Nick despised the attention. He was glad the feds kept them away from the house. Nick opened the mail box outside his front door and rummaged through it. There was nothing for him. He shut the box and walked over to his sports car sitting in the driveway. It looked souped-up and ready to go. Nick entered the car and started it. He put it in gear and drove quickly out the front—forcing his way through a sea of vultures. He smiled broadly after he clipped an over aggressive cameraman.

Nick zipped through the country back roads. The car stereo was cranked up high. The music reverberated throughout the cavernous hills. He peered into his rearview mirror. No media vans were following, but there was an unmarked FBI vehicle keeping a healthy distance. He had observed it before. Nick snickered and shifted gears. The car lurched forward. After several winding turns, the lawmen disappeared from view.

Eventually, Nick exited the hills at the edge of town near the lake. He stopped at Tim Horton's to grab a large coffee with three creams and four Splenda. A not-so-subtle craving he shared with his mom. He continued driving down Route 5 along the lake. As he approached Buffalo, he swiftly passed by the old Ford plant. In the distance, he could see the golden dome of the Father Baker Basilica. Nick knew his dad had done time there as a kid in their foster program. He had also heard some bad things had happened.

Thinking about it accelerated his anger. Nick gunned the engine and raced up the Skyway. On the other side, he hopped onto the I-190 which took him through the city of Buffalo towards the Northtowns. Nick cruised along for ten minutes until he came to the exit for the Tonawandas. Tonawanda and its neighbor to the north were both eclectic little towns which sat along the Niagara River where it intersected with the Erie Canal. Nick was familiar with both locales. He exited the off ramp, making his way over a set of railroad tracks and through a series of narrow streets clustered with modest homes. Eventually, he came to a small, quiet neighborhood in a heavily wooded area. Nick parked the car. He had arrived at his destination.

⊷ ≡◆≡ ↤

A two-story, 110-year-old house stared back at him. He stood alone in the driveway with the backpack strapped around his shoulders. He had left his car on a side street around the corner out of sight. Nick gazed at his old house. No one had lived there for years. The outside paint was hewed and streaked with muck. The gutters were filled with old leaves. He started towards the back, walking along the driveway. *Where he had learned how to ride his first bike!* In the backyard, the lawn had gone rogue and was overgrown. The broken down, rusty remnants of his youth still remained; the old swing-set, the rickety slide, even the small merry-go-round. Nick grabbed the rail on the slide and thought about his dad. He didn't really know him well. He had few fond memories. The few he did have, and Nick considered the fondest, were from this spot.

The sound of gravel cracking caught his attention. He peered around the house and saw the unmarked dark sedan pulling into the driveway. Nick let out a grudging laugh. "You FBI boys are dumb, but you ain't stupid." He quickly sprinted off into the woods before they could spot him. It was time to do what he came here to do. The thick brush reached his eye level and looked the same in all directions, but Nick was not bothered. He walked deeper into the forest with purpose and direction. He had made this trek many times before.

Nick had trudged along nearly a quarter mile. He knew he was getting close. He peeled back several branches and took a few more steps forward. He found himself in a small clearing. Nick walked up to an old oak tree. Near its base protruding from the ground was a small makeshift cross made of wood. The writing on the cross read: *Rest in Peace Beau 1975*. Nick dropped to his knees and removed a knife from his backpack. Using the knife and his hands, he began digging a hole in the center of the small grave. After a few minutes, he had tunneled out a sizable two-foot square about a foot deep.

There was an abrupt rustling of trees. A cold chill shot through Nick's veins. He jumped from his knees and wheeled his knife in expectation. Several moments passed. His heart was pounding. He waited. Nothing. No one came. Nick wiped his brow. *Jumpy nerves.* He dropped back down on his knees and returned to work. Nick took a small plastic bag from his backpack. He opened it and counted twenty-four one-hundred-dollar bills. It also contained a cell phone and charger. He resealed the bag and placed it in a sectioned hole in the grave. Next to that, a previously buried plastic bag was bulging out from the dirt.

Nick carefully retrieved it from the ground. It was tightly sealed. Great care had been given to protecting its contents. He brushed off the dirt and placed it in his backpack over his shoulders. He took one final gaze at the wooden cross before he vanished back into the woods.

CHAPTER 4
THE SUBCONSCIOUS'S ARRIVAL

Two days conceded to nights. The TV was now on 24/7. The relentless news coverage of Ricky was exhausting for Nick and Vee, but they could not stop watching. Both had been glued to the couch chain-smoking themselves into oblivion. Nick had even been forced to remove the batteries from the smoke detector in the living room.

The news segments seemed dreamlike, flowing one after another, forming one continuous stream of falsehoods. It was becoming a painful blur to Nick. Governor Cuomo was back on CNN emphasizing the significance of the fugitives' threat. "They are dangerous men. They are killers. They are murderers. There's no reason to believe they wouldn't do it again..." Nick could only glare at the screen. Duane Chapman, a.k.a. Dog the Bounty Hunter, came on as a guest commentator. He was the popular star of a reality show featuring him hunting down bail jumpers. Dog's professional commentary sounded more like over the top smack from a pro wrestler. "They're going to start doing their thing; killing, robbing, and destroying. The first thing they're gonna need is money, drugs, and guns."

Nick shook his head in disbelief. "...clueless dumb piece of shit!"

What tipped the scales again for Nick was Lee Bates. His dad's former accomplice was being interviewed by CNN news host Anderson

Cooper. As video of his dad's incarceration was being shown, Bates described in detail how Ricky had tortured and killed Bill Rickerson. He then added, "If you wanted to take a picture of the devil...that's the face you would see. *Ricky Matt!*" Nick jumped up from the couch. He leapt in the direction of the wall in a fury and shoved his fist through it.

Nick could feel his inner demons wrestling inside him again. He tried to calm down but couldn't. The panic was setting in. He needed to get upstairs. He hastily counted out his mom's pills and set them on the table. He turned towards her. Vee was looking at him with nervous apprehension. "I'm gonna' take care of you, mom... I'm gonna' take care of everything." Nick looked down at his hand; it was shaking. He glanced at the blood on his knuckles. Vee tried to hug her son tightly.

"I'm so sorry you have to go through this, Nicky.

"Don't apologize, Mom. You're not responsible for any of this." Nick made his mom more comfortable on the couch, then hurried upstairs to escape a world which had so callously thrown him and his family under the bus.

Nick retreated to his recliner. He took out a Fentanyl patch and a foil, and lit up. He let himself be taken in by the peaceful haze—riding the dragon back into a world where judgment and pain did not exist. *Like a rapture here on earth.* Half an hour later, Nick was sitting back peaceful and relaxed. He was momentarily transfixed by the white noise on the TV. Its static buzz reverberated in his head. He started to slowly glance around the room. Nick paused on the plastic garbage bag on the nightstand. It was the one he had removed from the grave. He reached over and grabbed it, placing the bag on the table in front of him.

He had left it untouched since bringing it home but tonight felt a sudden impulse of resolve. "Are we ready for this?" he thought. He reached in and pulled out a stack of old letters. They were unopened and still in relatively good shape. He carefully looked them over. They were addressed to Nick with most having a prison address listed in the return label. The sender on each was Richard Matt.

Fear and apprehension filled Nick's eyes. He had hardly known his father. It actually felt more natural for him to call him Ricky than Dad. Dad was a misnomer. He vaguely remembered some things as a child,

18

but for most of his upbringing, Ricky had been in jail or away somewhere else. Essentially out of his life. He spoke to him on the phone a few times but all Ricky seemed to talk about was his many conquests. The calls were brief and far and few between. It was not enough. Ricky seemed to understand that as well. He wished they both had known each other better. He wanted his son to know who he was. He promised to send him letters from time to time. Hopefully they would help explain.

Nick had received Ricky's letters over the years but had never opened them. He simply tossed them into a box and let them accumulate. What was the point of opening them? Perhaps he harbored anger and resentment for a dad who was never there. Maybe he was subconsciously afraid of what he would learn. He didn't know. Still, Nick never threw them out. He did not want to cut the cord completely. Nick felt he could wait for the time when he knew it would be right. Ricky was incarcerated for twenty-five to life, there had been no rush.

But things had changed with the escape. It filled Nick with a sense of urgency—like time was precipitously running out. He felt compelled to read the letters even if it meant facing down his own fears and pain. He wanted *and needed* to understand his dad. Maybe in the process he could understand himself better and remove the self-imposed shackles from his own life. Nick sat back in his chair, preparing himself as if for a voyage. *It was time!* He took a sip of beer and grabbed the first letter in the stack. He opened it and started to read, "Dear, Son. I first came into this world…"

CHAPTER 5
A LITTLE BOY'S JOURNEY

It was June 1968, a tumultuous time in America. The Vietnam War was fully raging, and urban unrest was causing riots in the US cities. The country was still trying to recover from the recent assassination of Dr. Martin Luther King when popular Senator Robert Kennedy met the same ugly fate. People everywhere were fearful, trying to focus their sagging spirits on the upcoming summer to instill some level of hope for the future. The concern was the violence and rising tensions would continue, draining any sense of hope.

On the same day Kennedy was assassinated, life still went on in the small, blue-collar town of Tonawanda, NY. Billowy white clouds cascaded in the blue skies overhead creating a blue-white sheen on the river nearby. On the east edge of town, one of its two main junkyards were getting into full swing with its morning operations.

Joe D, the portly owner of the junkyard, was overseeing the destruction of what had been some of Detroit's finest. The long line of cars had seen better days and were in position to be placed into a large hydraulic press that would compress each one into a five-foot cube of scrap metal for processing. Joe stood in a clearing in the yard, puffing on a Cuban cigar, the hot sun beating off his brow. He watched as a crane operator maneuvered a giant mechanical claw over the next car in line. It clamped down on a beaten-up Chevy Camaro and raised it up. The crane swung the four-thousand-pound heap in the air, then positioned it inside the giant press.

The hydraulic car-crusher revved its engine and began to rumble. The operator started the press, and the walls crept inward slowly. There was a high-pitched squealing sound of grinding metal and breaking glass as the formidable walls began to crush the Camaro. Joe listened to the familiar sounds and groaned in annoyance when he realized his cigar went out. As he tried to relight it, he suddenly stopped and glanced up. He thought he could hear the muffled sound of a child crying. Having four kids of his own, he was tuned into the sound. Straining his ears, he listened again. *It was a child.* The sound was coming from inside the crusher.

Joe sprinted toward the machine as its walls continued to close. He looked up in horror and waved to the machine operator who was blinded by the strong glare of the sun. Joe could hear the metallic mangling sounds continue. Struggling to catch his breath, he climbed the side of the rig and flung his cigar at the window. The operator turned and saw Joe making the kill signal across his neck. He halted the press and exited the side door. "What's wrong, boss?"

Joe waved him over. "Follow me."

Both men climbed inside the press and looked at the partially crushed Camaro. The sound of a child crying was now very clear. It was coming from inside the twisted mess. The two men frantically began prying the twisted metal away with their bare hands. They started to bleed. Joe peeked inside the wreck. He could partly see a little child lying trapped in the back seat. The operator had gotten a crowbar, and both men renewed their efforts. They were able to pull the top of the car back and remove the side door. There was just enough space for Joe to squeeze into the back seat and reach the child. He looked in and saw a frightened, dark-haired little boy dressed in tattered clothing lying on the back seat. He was bawling his eyes out. Pinned to his clothing was a birth certificate. It read: Richard W. Matt Born: 06/25/1966. Joe slowly pulled the boy out of the wreck and held him in his arms to quell the crying. He looked down at him, shaking his head in disbelief. "It's a miracle you're alive kid."

Children's Services scoured the county and state for weeks, but Ricky Matt's biological parents were nowhere to be found. Ricky was placed with Vern and Marcella Owens. He spent the next seven years with them. As an adult, Ricky would later say that his time with the Owens's was functional. He didn't mind it, but he never really felt wanted there. The couple paid more attention to their own two kids and their rental properties than to him or the other foster kids.

On a balmy summer day in August, a sleek black limousine drove slowly down a quiet street on the east side of town. It looked out of place in the working-class neighborhood. The limo continued to the end of the street and stopped in front of a two-story Victorian house on the corner. It turned into the driveway and parked.

Stepping out from the back seat was Johnny Mangano, a local underboss and mob enforcer who had ties to the Gambino crime family in New York City. Johnny was a huge man with a bulky 350-pound frame loosely draped in an expensive black suit. He had been considered handsome back in his day, but that day had passed. As sweat poured through his clothes, Johnny stretched out his huge arms and took a deep breath of the warm summer air. He patiently stood by the back door of the limo and waited.

An attractive woman and two teenage girls exited from the Victorian house. The woman was Elvira Harris. She was wearing a white silk dress that hugged a flawless and sensual figure beneath. It was hard to believe she was almost fifty. The former beauty queen took great care in her appearance, and it showed. She could still turn heads wherever she went, which greatly appeased her vanity. Elvira's young daughters, Anna and Vee, followed closely behind. Both had inherited their mom's good looks and adopted her attention to appearance. Anna was clad in a pretty floral dress which highlighted her dark brown eyes, while her younger sister wore designer jeans and a stylish red blouse. While both girls were pretty, their demeanors were very different; Anna was shy and meek, while Vee was outgoing and feisty.

The three ladies greeted Johnny. The four then entered the back of the limo. They were assisted by Vinnie, Johnny's driver. Johnny's relationship with Elvira had extended way back. The two had known each other from her modeling days in New York City. They were just friends, and Johnny was fine with that. She made him feel good. Only recently they had resumed their friendship after being out of touch. Johnny enjoyed taking Elvira and her kids to their favorite Italian restaurant. Their reservation was always on Wednesday, and always at five o'clock.

As the limo backed out of the driveway, a '57 Chevy pickup pulled in and parked. Elvira's husband stepped out of the truck with his lunchbox in hand. Herb Harris humbly lowered his head. He was aware of the special friendship between Johnny and his wife. It still made him feel a deep sense of shame. *She was with another man!* Herb approached the limo, and the back window crept down. Johnny peered out, a cigar dangling from his lips. "I'm never going to the track again, Johnny," Herb announced. "I promise...or the poker table." Johnny took the cigar out of his mouth.

"Stay away from the game on Saturday, Herbie. It's my last warning. I'm starting to catch a lot of heat from New York on this."

"Sure thing, Johnny. Sure thing." Herb nodded his head. The window went back up, and the limo pulled out of the driveway. It continued on down the street.

Herb stood silently in the driveway and thought about his gambling. It made his shame that much worse. It felt like his heart wanted to burst from his chest! Herb was enamored with the ponies and poker. It had cost him a great deal. He and Elvira had refinanced their home three times to pay off his debts. It still wasn't enough to cover all of his mounting losses. He couldn't stop! Everyone knew it. If not for Johnny, Herb's legs would have been broken long ago. Herb hung his head down, hopeful his family would have a good dinner and return soon.

Discreetly positioned across the street and eyeing the whole exchange was Ricky Matt. The young nine-year-old had been watching since the limo first arrived. He gleaned with excitement. His foster parents house was just two doors down. While playing in their front yard, he had noticed the black limo in the neighborhood a few weeks back. It was not something you see every day. It had stopped by the house on the corner four weeks running, always on the same day and time. His curiosity was on overload. He made it a point to observe each visit. Today was the first time he had seen the big man in the crazy black suit. The gold jewelry around his neck was incredible. It had sparkled in the sun. That was trumped by the young girl in the red top. *She was the prettiest girl he had ever seen!* He could not stop thinking about her.

It was early in the evening when Ricky cautiously made his way towards the house on the corner. The girl had unquestionably stirred his interest. The desire to see her again was so strong he decided to sneak over to the house, maybe he could get a closer look. The homes on that side of the street had dense woods in the back. They extended for miles. He had gone for long walks in there many times. He also found it ideal for hiding.

Ricky walked briskly along the tree line until he reached the backyard of the house. There was a tall metal fence surrounding the yard. He knew there was a dog in back. He had heard it barking on several occasions. As he crept closer to the fence, he could see the doghouse; it was partially illuminated by a backyard light. The sign on the doghouse read BEAU in big letters. Lying at the entrance was a coiled mass of sleeping black fur. Ricky stepped near the fence and accidentally made a noise. Beau came to life, barking up a storm with all his might at the alleged intruder. Ricky tensed up. He called out the dog's name and held out a hard candy through the fence. Beau abruptly stopped barking and came over. His tail wagged as he licked the treat. He was only a pup. Ricky opened the gate and petted him gently.

No one came outside to investigate the barking. Ricky's attention quickly shifted to a first story window in the back of the house. It was the only inside light on. He closed the gate and carefully approached the window. It was too high up. He glanced around and saw a sturdy plastic milk crate on the lawn. He grabbed it and placed it under the window. Ricky stepped on top and was able to easily reach the window ledge. He peered over it and looked inside the room.

It was a bedroom. Ricky could see several colorful scarves hanging from a hook on a small nightstand, and a large vanity mirror atop a desk was filled with brushes. A poster of a beautiful actress adorned the back wall which was painted a pastel pink. Ricky took it all in. As he continued to glance around, the side door next to the bed suddenly opened. Out walked the girl. *His girl!* Her hair was wet, and she was draped in a towel. Ricky's face went flush. She reached for a brush as she sat down at the desk. Ricky stood there mesmerized. She was so beautiful. He could not take his eyes off her!

The impact of a solid right hook suddenly sent Ricky sailing through the air. He crashed to the ground with a hard thud. Although momentarily dazed, he managed to jump to his feet quickly only to be staring down the barrel of a gun pointed at his head. Holding the firearm was a seething Elvira. "Don't move you fucking little pervert!" she screamed. Ricky stood there terrified. The incensed mother shook her head. "I come out here expecting some shylock coming after my Herbie. Instead I find some sneaky-ass little Peeping Tom!"

Ricky was speechless in fear. He blurted out the first thing that came to mind. "I'm sorry, ma'am. I was just looking," he cried.

"Looking?" Elvira exclaimed. "So, did you get a good look at my daughter?" she yelled. Ricky hung his head. "Any reason I shouldn't call the police?" Ricky's head shot back up.

"Please don't, ma'am, I'll never do it again. I promise!"

"Men are always making promises they can't keep," Elvira uttered with a smirk. She lowered the gun.

"I give you my word! I just thought...she was so beautiful." Elvira forced a smile.

"Do you have a name?" she asked.

"Ricky Matt," he answered.

"And where do you live, Ricky Matt?"

Ricky pointed towards the street. "The gray house, a couple houses down. The Owens's."

Elvira's eyebrow shot up. "Marcella and what's his face? You one of their *foster* kids?" She prodded. Ricky nodded with downcast eyes. Elvira could see the embarrassment on his face. "Just a lonely little underfed pecker," she said to herself. He was harmless. "Alright then, I don't want to see you sneakin' around my house again. Do you understand? Or I will call the police. Now git!" Elvira waved him out. Ricky beamed a genuine smile then bolted out the gate as fast as he could and ran towards home. Elvira turned and slowly walked back towards the house. Beau was peeking up at her wagging his tail. She stared down at him with a sneer. "You'll get yours, too, you little bastard." Elvira walked into the house and slammed the door shut. Exasperated.

⇥ ◆ ⇤

Three weeks had passed. Ricky had been grateful the woman had not called the authorities. He still desired to see the girl but thought best to leave it alone for a while. He knew her mom was watching him. He could see her glancing over at his house whenever she came outside. For now, he was content with staying in his own world.

Around noon, Ricky and a friend were standing in a large puddle of water in front of his house. The two boys were taking turns splashing one other and kicking it up in sprays. Earlier in the day, workers had come down the street opening fire hydrants, briefly releasing huge amounts of water into the street. Puddles of ice-cold water were everywhere. It was a windfall for a hot summer day. As the boys played, a large dark-colored car pulled up quietly beside them. They were both uneasy at the sudden appearance of such a menacing looking vehicle. They just stood there frozen. The front window powered down. It was that girl's mom!

Elvira got a sublime thrill sneaking up on the boys in her new Lincoln. It had come courtesy of Johnny. She eyeballed Ricky standing in the puddle. "You wanna make fifty bucks, kid?" She asked holding a fifty-dollar bill up in the air. Ricky stood there thunderstruck. "I know you're dumb. You're not deaf, too, are you?" She added.

Ricky chided back. "No, ma'am." The second boy had scampered away. Elvira opened the passenger side door, and Ricky hopped in. In his mind, he had just hit pay dirt.

That afternoon, Ricky filled his stomach for the first time in weeks. He had gorged himself on three burgers, two orders of fries, and a large shake. Elvira had taken him to a local diner and told him to order whatever he wanted. She insisted. Ricky obliged.

While he ate, they chatted. She told him her name and talked about her family a little. *The daughter's name was Vee!* She also asked some questions about Ricky and his foster family, which he was uncomfortable discussing. When he was done eating, she ordered him a second chocolate milkshake for the ride home.

During the drive, Elvira vaguely mentioned the job without giving details. She would show him what needed to be done when they reached her house. She first had to see if he had the aptitude. When they arrived, Elvira said her husband and daughters would not be back 'till suppertime. She told Ricky to go play in the back. She had to do some things inside first. Ricky went into the backyard and played with Beau. The pup seemed to remember him from before, and they clicked almost immediately. After a while, Elvira emerged from the house wearing work boots and coverall jeans. "Are you ready?" she inquired. The twelve-year-old nodded. She grabbed his hand and led him into the woods.

Around suppertime, the sun was on is way down when Herb arrived home with the kids. Ricky and Elvira were already back. She was in the kitchen making supper. When the others had come in, Elvira introduced him to the family. "This is Ricky Matt, our neighbor from down the street. He was kind enough to help me around the yard today." Ricky had immediately felt awkward and self-conscious being the center of attention, but the three newcomers made him feel right at home.

Meatloaf and mashed potatoes soon steamed off the dinner table. Vee had just finished organizing a plate of food for her new acquaintance. In the kitchen, her mom had whispered to her that Ricky was a foster child so to be nice to him. Ricky could barely touch the food given to him considering how much he had eaten in the afternoon. Vee just attributed it to him being nervous around strangers. Herb had taken an immediate liking to the boy. He had lost his own mother at age seven and had experienced his own difficult upbringing. In this, they felt a mutual kinship.

After dinner, Anna went to her room to read a book. Vee asked her mom if she could take Ricky out back to help feed Beau. She agreed. Elvira knew Vee would take to Ricky like a moth to a flame. She had a penchant for picking up and taking care of animals that were castoffs or strays. This was no different. Ricky fit that bill perfectly. Elvira glanced out the kitchen window and watched the three of them playing happily together in the backyard. A twisted smile was on her lips.

The following Saturday, all was peaceful. The sun was shining, and the leaves on the trees were rustling in the wind. Ricky was staring up into the treetops. They would soon be changing color as fall approached. He stood alone in the backyard of the Harris's house. No one else was there except Beau who was sleeping in the doghouse. Ricky was waiting for Elvira. She was scheduled to meet him there at three o'clock. He felt jumpy. Today was the day he was supposed to earn his fifty bucks. He had been practicing something in secret but did not know to what end. Today he would find out.

He was startled when the Lincoln pulled into the driveway. Elvira got out and walked towards him. "Are you ready to earn your money?" She hissed. Ricky nodded anxiously. Elvira reached into her purse and pulled out a small bundle. Something wrapped in cloth. She handed it to him.

Ricky put into his coat pocket then asked, "What do you want me to do with it?" She leaned in and whispered in his ear. Ricky stepped back in horror. "No!" he bellowed. His eyes wide.

"I'm afraid you'll have to," Elvira declared coldly.

Ricky shouted, "No, I don't!" He began to cry and was met with a quick slap to his face.

"Don't be a little pussy," Elvira barked. "Let me ask you something," she continued. "You've been getting awfully chummy with Vee. You still wanna continue to see her?" Ricky looked at her with tears in his eyes and nodded. "Besides, I've been thinking about that night you trespassed in this very yard and I caught you peeking in my daughter's window. Maybe keeping quiet was not the right thing to do." Ricky could feel his hands starting to shake. "What exactly happens to foster boys who are caught doing bad things? Reform school? You would never see Vee then." With downcast eyes, Ricky gave in.

He simply said, "Okay."

In the early evening, while there was still light, everyone was at home in the Harris household. Herb was sitting in a chair reading the sports page. Anna and Vee were on the living room floor building a new puzzle their mom had bought for them. Elvira was sitting on the sofa watching TV. As she poured herself another cup of hot tea, a faint gunshot rang out in the distance. It was followed by another burst right after that. No one paid much attention—people were often out hunting in the woods. Elvira leaned back and sipped her tea. She was grinning from ear-to-ear.

Later in the evening, Vee went out to feed the dog. She came running back in the house a minute later screaming, "Beau's gone! Beau's gone!" Everyone rushed out to the backyard. Beau was no-where to be found.

"Vee, did you close the side gate when you fed him earlier?"

"I'm sure I did," she yelled.

"I'm sorry, baby, but it's open." The gate was half ajar. Vee looked and started crying. Herb interjected, "He couldn't have gotten far. I'll grab a flashlight and look in the woods."

Elvira hugged Vee to soften the tears. "Your father's right... Beau can't be far. I want you to go in the house and call Ricky at home. Tell him I'll pick him up in the car and drive down the streets in the neigh-borhood. It's better to have two sets of eyes. You and Anna stay here and search around the house in case he's close by." Vee nodded okay and ran into the house to phone Ricky.

A few minutes later, Elvira had the Lincoln in front of Ricky's house. He came outside and climbed into the front passenger seat. The car drove off down the road. Elvira and Ricky sat without saying a word. After turning the corner, Elvira broke the silence. "Everything went well?" she asked.

"Everything's fine," Ricky said stoically. He reached into his pocket and placed the small wrapped bundle next to Elvira. On top, he placed Beau's ID tags. Elvira parked the car along the curb. She grabbed the tags and unwrapped the bundle. Out slid a good-sized handgun. She verified the safety was on then placed it in her purse.

"You follow instructions well. I knew I was right about you." Elvira pulled out a fifty-dollar bill and handed it to Ricky. "You earned it," she said.

Ricky and Vee combed the neighborhood for weeks. They created a small poster that showed Beau's photo, his name, a description, and phone number to call if found. They made dozens of photocopies and stapled them up everywhere. Their efforts were in vain as Ricky knew they would be. Despite this, they became extremely close. She began to take him wherever she went and grew to depend on him. He followed, but it was always with a heavy heart.

During one of their outings, Ricky and Vee sat in a corner booth at a greasy spoon called Bidell's. A familiar waitress glanced over, and Vee raised two fingers. "Two blue plate specials, Alberlado," the waitress yelled back into the kitchen. Both ate their food slowly. Ricky stared at Vee from across the table. Time seemed to stop when he was with her. He had no idea why. When it came time to pay, Ricky put his hand in his pocket and proudly reached for the fifty-dollar bill. He was about to pull it out when he remembered where it came from. A pain shot through his chest. He felt around in his pocket, but all he had left was loose change. Vee stroked his face. She paid the check and smiled. "Thank you for helping me search for Beau, Ricky. I'll never forget that."

Later that night, a storm had come through, and it had started to rain heavily. Ricky stood alone in his backyard. He was drenched. The rain flowed down his face and covered the tears he was crying. Guilt tore at his heart as he thought of Vee. He reached into his pocket and pulled out the fifty-dollar bill. Ricky tore it up and watched the pieces fall to the ground. He fell to his knees and hung his head down in anger and shame. He resolved nothing would separate him from Vee ever again.

CHAPTER 6
GRANDMA DEAREST

"...I didn't kill Beau, Nicky. I walked him deep into the woods to our spot and let him go. Everything else was just show. For a long time after that, I was worried he would suddenly show up and that would be the end of things. He never did. I just hope he found a new home. I still feel awful to this day...ashamed your mother never got to see him after that. I should have punched that bitch Elvira right in the mouth." Nick glanced up from the letter and smiled at the revelation. He *didn't kill Beau!* "Good for you, Ricky," he thought, overwhelmed by a sudden sense of sadness for his dad.

Nick had always been respectful to his late grandmother but now felt a sense of revulsion towards her. "How could she be like that?" he thought, angrily throwing an empty beer can onto the floor. Nick struggled to get off the chair and approached the window. He could still see two unmarked police vehicles dug in across the street along with some media stragglers. Nick shot a look of disdain at the continued news coverage of Ricky on TV. The emotional pain he felt spiraled up as the vilification of his father intensified with each report. At least he had the letters and the courage to read them now. That provided some measure of solace.

Nick knew Ricky was no choirboy, but he was no mass murderer either. He belonged behind bars for poor judgment, not twenty-five to life for murder. The conviction was a sham cooked up by Lee Fucking Bates! Nick glared at the TV. CNN's Don Lemon was on again. "It's been a week, and the escaped convicts could be anywhere by now. Canada, even Mexico. Matt speaks fluent Spanish and knows the terrain down there." Nick snickered.

"Someday, the world's going to learn Ricky's true story." Nick grabbed another beer and sat down in the recliner. He picked up the next letter in the bag. Ricky had titled the first page, *My Seven Years Inside the Foster System*. Nick didn't know what to expect. He had a feeling it would not be pleasant. His mother had told him stories. Despite his apprehension, he felt there was no turning back. He had to know.

The letter started with, "Happy 17th birthday, Nicky. I'm sorry I can't be there. I got another hearing on my appeal next week. But things don't look too promising, my lawyer says. I know your mother won't let you take my calls, or answer any of my letters. I still feel like writing to you anyway. Your letters don't come back to me. So, I'm hoping you're getting mine. Lately, I've been thinking about my time at Father Baker's. Especially that one particular night my life changed forever. I'm not really ashamed about it anymore. I'm not angry either. Well, maybe just a little. Hell, kid, I'm still angry about it a whole fuckin' lot! Anyway, it's the truth, and it needs to be told."

CHAPTER 7
FOSTER CAMP 1978

Our Lady of Victory Basilica in Lackawanna, New York was an impressive building. The outside of the enormous structure was made almost entirely of pure white marble and topped by a gigantic, eye-catching copper dome. It boasted first century Romanesque design that was both ornate and luxurious. Surrounding the basilica, in contrast, were several plain multi-story brick buildings that almost appeared to be military-style barracks.

Among these intimidating buildings, four were constructed with the sole purpose of housing two hundred of western New York's abandoned children, orphans, and youthful offenders. They were the centerpiece of Father Baker's, a certified, level-three foster care facility. Its purpose was to provide higher levels of supervision and structure to the lives of the unfortunate. Albeit the range of emotional and behavioral problems among the kids was wide, the violent offenders and those considered a danger to others or themselves, were normally sent to specialized facilities or even the *Big House* if they were over eighteen.

Father Baker's had an impeccable record for turning around troubled youth. It was strictly run by a cadre of priests and non-clergy alike. While it was not a twenty-four-hour lockdown facility, security was tight, and escapes were rare. The men and women who administered the facility were dedicated to the well-being of their kids. They provided in-house schooling and dispensed their own brand of tough love. As it stood, life did not come easy nor was it trouble-free for a foster or bad child placed there. To instill a feeling of reassurance, the kids were always taught that God would guarantee them comfort should they ever find themselves in a pinch.

⊷ ⚊✦⚊ ⊶

God was nowhere to be found on this night. The soft light of a full moon cascaded over the well-lit compound. The clock had just struck midnight and the doors to the four main buildings were locked for the evening. Most of the kids were fast asleep in their rooms after a long day, enveloped in a comforting silence. In building number three, the quiet stillness was disturbed by a faint sound of laughter coming from a corner room on the second floor.

Inside the room, an older boy kneeling on the floor quickly stood up. The muscular teen reached down and pulled up his shorts and jeans. And zipped up. "I think he enjoyed that a little too much," he said with a smile. A heavyset teen sitting on the bed gave a short laugh. Both teens looked down at a younger boy who was bent over the bed, face down, his knees on the floor. He was stripped of clothing except for a pair of underwear pulled down around his ankles. The heavyset teen held the boy's arms and shoulders down, pinning him to the top of the bed.

After a glance from the other teen, he released his grip, but the young boy remained prostrate, tears streaming from his eyes. The muscular teen stepped behind the boy and bent down close. He ran his hand along the back of the boy's thigh and slowly massaged his butt cheeks. He grabbed the right cheek hard and leaned in so his head was next to the boy's ear. "No more fuck ups. You better have everything on the list tomorrow night. Understand?" The young boy nodded in terror. The muscular teen smiled and let him go. As he stood up, he gave a violent slap to the boy's bare ass with the back of his hand. "Mañana, sweet cheeks!" he exclaimed. Another boy standing lookout near the door gave an all clear signal, and the three intruders walked out of the room.

A shivering twelve-year-old Ricky Matt slowly rolled himself over on to the bed. His face was bruised and his nose bloodied. He reached down and pulled up his underwear, wincing in pain with each movement. Ricky looked up dazedly and stared at the ceiling, reeling in stunned disbelief at what had just happened. Alone with his swirling thoughts, he suddenly felt sick to his stomach. He limped to the bathroom as fast as he could and threw up in the toilet.

Ricky hung his head down, deeply ashamed at what had been done to him and what he had been forced to do. He felt dirty and disgusted. He felt violated. Ricky struggled to get into the shower and turned it on. He desperately tried to scrub off the filth that had been forced upon him. His skin bled from his efforts. Ricky dragged himself from the shower and put on a robe and some clean underwear. He glanced into the mirror. No amount of scrubbing could get rid of what he felt. Ricky shut off the light and crawled into bed, left only with the thoughts of how he had gotten here.

Ricky's troubles started soon after Beau's disappearance. One day at school, he was called upon to recite in front of the class but refused. It wasn't that he didn't want to but that he couldn't. He didn't know how to read. Ricky had always gotten by with his street smarts and a photographic memory. He was too embarrassed to tell the teachers the truth. They just took him as an unruly student who needed to be disciplined. The same scenario played itself out numerous times over the coming months, and Ricky quickly earned a reputation as a troublemaker. He started skipping school on days where reading was required. This escalated to days where he just didn't feel like going in. His increased tardiness became a serious issue. The school gave the Owens's several warnings. After a year and a half and no sign of improvement, the school had finally had enough. The local truant officer arrested Ricky, and he was detained in foster care. Juvenile court deemed him a troubled youth in need of a higher level of supervision. He was removed from the Owens's and placed in the care of Father Baker's until such time that his bad behaviors were corrected.

Staring into the darkness of his room, Ricky could hear the distant rumbling of thunder from an approaching storm. He started to think about his stay at Father Baker's up to that point. His life had become regimented and routine. He also thought the priests were mean. He had seen other kids whacked across the knuckles with a ruler or spanked with a paddle for disobeying the rules. Luckily, it had not happened to him yet. They were teaching him to read after they learned about his illiteracy. He was happy about that. Overall, he was getting used to life there; it just wasn't a home.

His current trouble started when he was assigned to the shopping detail for the week. The facility attendants would go on food runs at local stores and take a few of the kids with them to help. This gave them a chance to be on the outside. Among the kids, it was a desired gig. It was one of the few ways of bringing outside contraband into the facility. Just *shoplift* what you wanted while walking the store aisles.

After Ricky had been chosen, he was approached later in the day by an older, muscular teen named Billy. He had a reputation for violence that was well earned. Most of the other kids were afraid of him. He even had a small clique that followed him around, mostly out of fear. Billy had given Ricky a list of things he wanted lifted from the store. When Ricky initially refused, Billy unleashed a rapid punch to his gut which dropped him to his knees, then violently shoved Ricky to the ground. Billy said he would be back in the evening to collect, one way or another. At the time, Ricky didn't know what he meant, but now he did...*and Billy would be back again tomorrow.* Ricky swore to himself he would never go through this again. There was only one thing for him to do.

— ⊷ ◆ ⊶ —

Ricky rose from the bed and grabbed a small piece of wire from under his mattress. He bent it into a small loop and approached the window. He stuck it into the lock and rotated it until he heard a click. The window opened. Outside, the storm had moved in, and it was raining hard. Ricky stuck his head out and looked down. He was two stories up, but his room was close to a drainpipe that went straight down the outside wall. Ricky grabbed two bed sheets and tied them together. He affixed one end to a small bar near the window and tossed the other end outside.

Without looking back, Ricky climbed out the window into the storm. Rain pelted his face. He slid down the sheets partway and swung himself a short distance to the drainpipe. Despite it being slippery, he managed to shimmy down another fifteen feet. The pipe ended abruptly, so he had to free fall the last six feet. He hit the ground with a thud. Ricky stood up, already soaked to the skin. He was protected from the elements only by his thin robe and a pair of socks. He ran across the compound until he reached the outside fence. The temperature had dropped to the low fifties, and he could feel the chill in his bones, but he didn't care. He had to get away. Ricky quickly climbed the ten-foot-high metal fence. At the top, he glanced back at his *home*. He raised his middle finger and shouted at the top of his lungs, "Fuck all you all!" Ricky descended down the other side and jumped to freedom.

The twelve-year-old ran fast and hard through the night. He didn't know where he was headed just so long as it was far away from Father Baker's. He raced down the two-mile dark, rural road looking for shelter, but there was none to be had. Freezing and exhausted, Ricky staggered into a small ditch and fell into a puddle. The cold water shot through his body like a horde of sharp knives. While the rain had abated, the night air had turned frigid, and he could see his breath. If he remained here, he knew he would freeze to death by morning. His fight was all but gone. In desperation, Ricky crawled out of the ditch and laid on the ground. He even thought about going back. *He couldn't!* Ricky pulled himself back up and started walking. As he did, he saw a phone booth across the road. He dragged himself across the street and grabbed the receiver. There was a dial tone! He began dialing, hoping the person on the other end would accept the charges. He prayed to God Elvira didn't answer.

Ricky sat huddled at the base of the phone booth drifting in and out of sleep. Bitter cold had enveloped his body, and he was losing track of time. He was too tired to move. A pair of headlights far off down the road caught his attention as they turned in his direction. He watched as they quickly grew in size as they approached. He raised his hand to shield his eyes as the brightness became blinding. The lights came to a halt directly in front of him. They were accompanied by the deep rumbling sound of a powerful engine in idle. "Friend or foe?" He laughed to himself. He was too beat to care.

Beyond the glare of the headlights, Ricky could barely make the outline of the vehicle. Two shadowy figures exited the car and approached. As they stepped into the light, Ricky's heart leapt. It was Vee and her dad! He could hear Vee scream "Oh my God!" as she rushed towards him and threw a blanket over his shoulders. Herb went around the other side. "Let's get him on his feet," he said. The two helped Ricky up, his wet robe clinging to his body. Herb carried him to the truck and placed him inside.

Father and daughter both got in. Ricky sat between them in the front seat. He was grateful for the warmth inside the truck. Herb turned on the inside cabin light, and Vee let out a gasp. She was horrified by Ricky's bruised and battered appearance. Vee looked into his eyes and said angrily, "No one is ever gonna do this to you again, Ricky. I promise." She bent down and removed his wet socks, placing his bare feet directly under the floor heater.

After a few minutes, Ricky could slowly feel himself coming back to life. He stared at Vee helplessly as she rubbed his hands to warm them up. Vee glanced back and smiled. She turned towards her dad and said, "We have to bring him home, Dad. He can't go back to that place." Herb hesitated for a moment but saw the look of fear in Ricky's eyes. He knew that look well. "Well...maybe, at least until he's better."

He looked at Ricky and said, "What's the point in going back there anyway? No sense in that, right, son?"

Ricky glanced up at him. "No, sir. No sense in that at all." They both smiled at each other. Ricky leaned back with happiness in his eyes, overwhelmed by a deep sense of relief and gratitude. Vee gave him a comforting hug. Herb shut off the cabin light and checked his mirror. He turned the truck around and headed for home.

<hr />

A few hours later, Ricky laid his head down on a soft pillow in his make-shift bed. The hour was late, and he was alone in the Harris attic. A half-eaten container of food was nearby on the floor courtesy of Mr. Harris who had picked it up for him on the drive back. He had also plugged in a space-heater next to the bed for heat and gave him some old clothes that might fit. A steel garbage pail served as his bathroom, at least for the night. Vee and her dad had snuck Ricky up there in secret, keeping the temporary arrangement from Elvira. With her temperament, they were afraid at what she would do. She was libel to call the authorities. Ricky was happy, at least for the moment. He was amazed at how beautiful Vee had become. Holding this thought in mind and shutting everything else out, the exhausted youth drifted off into a peaceful slumber.

CHAPTER 8
FEELING A MOTHER'S PAIN

A noise awakened Nick. He had fallen asleep on the recliner. His shirt was soaked in perspiration, and he felt tense. There was alarm in his eyes. Something was wrong. He could feel it. Nick set down the letter from his dad and raced downstairs. As he went through the kitchen, he could hear his mom sobbing. She was calling his name.

Nick raced into the living room and approached Vee who was curled up on the couch. He placed his hand gently on her shoulder. "Mom, are you okay?" he offered.

Vee lifted her head and softly cried. "I can't take it anymore, Nicky. I just can't." She opened her clenched fist. Nick could see a handful of pain pills. Alarmed, he slowly removed them from her hand. He stared into his mother's sad eyes and stroked her hair. Tears rolled down her cheeks.

"It's gonna be okay, Mom...it's gonna be okay."

She glanced up at him. "I'm sorry for putting you through this, Nicky...I'm so sorry.""

"Don't worry about a thing," he said. "Just remember, I love you, Mom." He gave her a hug, and Vee returned the affection. "I'll make you something to eat. Watch TV for a little while...but no more news." Nick said with a forced smile. Vee nodded her head.

As Nick went into the kitchen, Vee grabbed the remote and started slowly surfing through the channels. She stopped on an old movie with

Gina Lollobrigida. Her dad used to opine how she looked like the beautiful Italian actress. Vee watched the screen and smiled at the recollection. Her focus shifted to a picture sitting on a shelf near the TV. It was a photo of her and Ricky when they were young and first together. She looked closely at the smiling face of her younger self. She did look like the actress, she thought happily. Her leer quickly faded when she caught a glimpse of her misshapen self in a reflection on a glass frame. Vee changed the channel.

Nick glanced at the overflowing dishes in the sink, then shifted his attention to the cigarette burns on the kitchen floor. His mom would often nod off while standing at the counter. He thought it was a miracle there hadn't been a fire yet. Nick made a sandwich and microwaved a coffee. He placed them on a tray along with his mom's meds and delivered them to the living room. "One Harris special," he said, placing the tray on the coffee table near her. He handed Vee the small plastic cup with her pills. "Take these. You'll feel better in a few minutes." She swallowed all the pills with her coffee.

After about ten minutes, the medications took effect, and she calmed down considerably. Vee ate her sandwich slowly and took sips of her coffee.

"Nicky, please give me a few extra tonight?" she begged. "When they wear off..."

Nick looked at her. "I can't, Mom. You know what the doctor said. It's easy to take too many. You could overdose. It's important to follow the schedule."

Vee rubbed her forehead with her hand. "I'm too tired," she said in resignation. "I can't fight anymore. Maybe it would be better if you just let me go."

"You're not going anywhere, Vee Harris!" Nick said sternly. He sat next to her on the couch and put his arm around her. "You can fight through this, Mom. You were always a fighter."

"I was a fighter," she said wretchedly.

The two sat on the couch and quietly watched TV for a bit. Vee had become more relaxed. Nick had thought it best to stay with her awhile. He had been through these sessions with her before. Once she let out the anxieties, she usually improved. It had been worse today. She had grabbed those extra pain pills. He had put them away but knew she had access to more if she really wanted them. Nick felt terrible for his mom. She was dealing with constant physical pain that followed her nearly every moment of the day. It was an unrelenting burden. He also felt she was being dragged down by deep emotional scars—always struggling with her past. He had often tried to speak to her about it, but she would quickly shut the conversation down. The past was a taboo subject, almost as if she was trying to protect him from it. Maybe the letters would finally open that door. It might also do Vee some good just to talk about it. Maybe he should try.

Nick hesitated at first but then turned towards his mom. "What was it like for you and Ricky growing up?" he asked. Vee ignored him and continued watching the TV. "I need to know, Mom," he continued.

"Never mind about any of that now," she said.

Undaunted, Nick pushed on. "I read some bad things about grandma...and I know about Beau." Vee turned towards him.

"Beau? What do you mean? What kind of things?"

Nick glanced at her nervously. "I have the letters Ricky sent me. I started reading them."

Vee exploded in a rage. "That son of a bitch! He swore he'd never communicate with you ever again!" Her face was consumed with fury as she tried to stand up. She winced in pain and quickly sat back down. She glared over at Nick in anger, but he would not relent. They just stared at each other.

Vee seemed to sense Nick's resolution, and her fight rapidly began to fade. She no longer had the strength. Her anger withdrew, replaced by acceptance and a profound sadness. She started to cry. Nick sat closer and put his arm around her. "I'm sorry, Mom. I didn't mean to cause you more pain. I just need to know why things are the way they are. I need to know the truth."

Vee wiped her eyes and let out a muffled laugh. "The truth?" She grabbed a cigarette from the pack on the table and lit it. She looked at Nick. "You're a good boy, Nicky. You should know the truth," she said. Vee pulled an ashtray closer and mused. "You should know the story of me and Ricky with all the bullshit stripped away."

CHAPTER 9
SENTENCED AT CHILDHOOD

It was just past midnight. The small bedroom on the second floor was pitch black. All the light bulbs had been removed from their sockets. Four-year-old Vee Harris had fought off falling asleep for over two hours, but her exhausted eyes were finally beginning to falter. She had forgotten to wash her hands before dinner and was now serving her sentence. Staying awake in complete darkness until her mother felt she had paid the penalty. Failure was the strap.

Vee lay in bed terrified, thinking about the beating she might receive. She felt her eyelids sinking and pinched herself to stay awake. Vee didn't how much longer she could hold on. Without warning, the door creaked slightly, and her eyes snapped open. She retreated under the covers and peeked through a small opening. The door opened wide. Silhouetted in the low light of the hallway was her mom, Elvira. She stood in the doorway in a short nightgown, a whipping belt securely wrapped around her right hand. Vee clenched the blanket with all her might.

She watched as her mom inched her way forward. Had she lied? Vee thought. Would she still get a beating even if she had stayed awake? Her father and sister were sound asleep in their rooms below. Neither could come to her rescue now. She was alone. Her mom now stood next to the side of the bed. Vee felt the covers slowly being pulled down until her face was exposed. She lay there looking up into the eyes of her mom, who was leaning over her, only inches away. Vee could feel her breath. They stared at each other, and her mom sneered. "I guess you served your penance, you little bitch." Her mom stood up, then added angrily, "I took it when I was your age. No reason you can't as well. And stop whining to your father. That's not going to do you any good." She rubbed the belt slowly against Vee's cheek and walked out of the room. Vee broke down in tears under the covers.

That night, Vee vowed never do anything wrong ever again, but like many times before, the effort would only be short lived. Elvira would always find some excuse to berate or punish her. While Anna would also suffer, Vee seemed to bear the brunt of her mom's anger. She didn't understand how Elvira could be so nice one minute, then so nasty the next. Vee was constantly afraid of tripping that switch. The violent outbursts could come at any time and were frequently the result of something petty. After the fact, her mom often would act as if nothing had happened or would accuse Vee of being at fault. The cycle of abuse became so routine that it embedded itself in their daily life as if it were normal. This persisted through most of Vee's childhood.

⋯ ▰◆▰ ⋯

The abuse in the Harris household reached a crescendo on a crazy summer night six years later. On that night, the kitchen had just been cleaned and tidied. All remnants of the evening meal put away by the girls. They were ready for dessert. Herb was seated at the table enjoying his coffee and a generous slice of chocolate cake. Anna sat down at her place to enjoy her piece. Vee, as she had done so many times before, stood near her father and took a forkful of his dessert. She washed it down with hot chocolate. Herb smiled. He loved both his daughters but seemed to share a special bond with Vee.

While they all enjoyed their cake, Elvira walked into the kitchen. Her stern countenance suggested an underlying rage. They all sensed it, and the room grew silent. Elvira told Vee to sit down at the table and sat across from her. Anna sensed her sister's peril and began to whimper. Herb sat there quietly as Elvira took out a pack of cigarettes from her apron. "I found these under your mattress. Keeping them for a friend, are you?"

Vee glared at her mother. "Those are mine. I took them from daddy."

"Really?" she said. Elvira lit one and handed it to Vee. "Smoke it," she ordered.

The defiant ten-year-old began smoking the cigarette. Herb and Anna remained quiet and watched the intense interplay. After five minutes, Vee finished. Elvira pointed to the dessert dish, and Vee placed the butt in it. Elvira lit another cigarette and handed it to her. "Smoke it." Vee began to smoke the cigarette. As she continued to inhale the warm smoke, it began to leave behind a bad taste. She started to feel sick but was able to keep going until it was finished. Elvira lit a third and handed it to her.

Herb interjected, "Come on Elvira! She's had enough."

Elvira turned towards him and said, "Shut up, Herbie!" She nodded to Vee to continue. Vee continued smoking and started to feel sick to her stomach. She excused herself, ran to the bathroom, and threw up in the toilet. She felt better after a couple of minutes and returned to the table. Elvira was quietly eating a piece of cake. She lit another cigarette and gave it to Vee. Tears welled in the child's eyes, but she resumed smoking. She looked at her dad who only met her with a helpless gaze.

After a few minutes, Vee felt sick again and ran back to the bathroom. This time when she returned, Vee was visibly incensed. Elvira lit up another cigarette and held it out towards her. Instead of taking it, Vee grabbed her fork. She placed a large helping of cake into her mouth from her mother's plate. Then washed it down with Elvira's coffee. "Why you little bitch!" Elvira screamed. She violently extinguished the cigarette on Vee's right hand. Vee shrieked. Herb sprung from his chair and forcefully grabbed Elvira's right wrist.

"That's enough, Elvira!" Elvira stood. Incensed. Herb spun his wife's arm away from Vee. Elvira staggered backwards across the floor and fell against the wall. The back of her head hit hard against a metal radiator, and it started to bleed. A steady flow of blood trickled down her cheek. Herb stood there in disbelief.

An infuriated Elvira sprung up from the floor and grabbed a large knife from the kitchen drawer. She flailed it the air and yelled at Herb. "Come on, you son-of-bitch!"

Herb stepped back. "Calm down, Elvira. This doesn't need to go any further," he said.

"You crossed a line," Elvira screamed.

"I crossed a line—"

"Yeah, look at the blood, Herb!"

"That was an accident," he said.

"Accident my ass!" She howled. Elvira grabbed the wall phone and dialed 911. Herb collapsed in his chair, mortified. He had never raised his hand to Elvira before. It had all happened so fast. She had hurt Vee. Off to the side, Anna and Vee were holding each other, tears pouring down their faces. Herb looked at them with sudden concern. What would happen to his daughters should the police take him away? He put his head in his hands then thought of another problem. What would happen to him when Johnny found out?

A short time later, there was a knock at the front door. Elvira rushed past Herb and opened it. Two uniformed officers entered. Herb could see Elvira talking to them heatedly. She showed them the back of her head. Moments later, Herb was in handcuffs. As he was being escorted out of the kitchen by the officers, he could see the look of terror in Anna and Vee after they realized they were about to be left alone with their mother. Herb started to resist. He called out their names and begged the officers to let him go. They grabbed him, and he started to sob. Herb jerked himself loose. He rushed back towards Elvira and hollered, "If you take me away, she'll hurt my daughter...she'll hurt my little girl!" The two officers were joined by four others now on scene. They overpowered Herb and dragged him out the door kicking and screaming. Anna and Vee stood in stunned silence, listening to their dad wailing in the night while being taken away. They had never seen him act that way. Even Elvira was taken aback by her husband's intensity.

A young officer named David Beamish entered the house and approached the girls. He quickly examined them and noticed the fresh cigarette burn on Vee's right hand. He also observed they were both scared. Probably too afraid to tell the truth about what had happened. They kept glancing over at their mom. Officer Beamish turned to Elvira. "I'll be back to check on the girls tomorrow, Mrs. Harris. That you can count on, ma'am."

"Thank you, officer," she said, looking at him with a scowl. Officer Beamish indeed returned the next day as promised. Then again at other times in the weeks that followed just for a random check. The physical abuse in the Harris household subsequently dropped off for a time for which Vee was very grateful. It was not the case with the verbal onslaught which continued, but that was something Vee had already become adept at handling or could simply tune out.

⸺ ⧫ ⸺

Over the next few years, Elvira kept more to herself, except when she was with Johnny. She loved her outings with him, and the two became very close friends. She and Herb had reconciled after the *incident*, but their relationship was never the same again after that. The days of sleeping in the same bed together or even sharing any intimacy were over. They still remained loyal to one another and even cared for each other in their own way, perhaps finding comfort in their mutual dysfunction. Looking back, Vee had always thought her dad had stayed simply because he feared for her and Anna's safety, but it was much more complex than that. Since he was always boxed in by his debt, an unusual triangle developed between him, Elvira, and Johnny. Each fed off it in different ways and for the wrong reasons. Vee remembered a jarring incident when she was in her early teens that brought the situation to full light. It started with Elvira calling Johnny in a panic—some men were at the house to see Herb.

Johnny's limo pulled into the Harris driveway. It was not a Wednesday nor was it 5 P.M., so it was unusual seeing it there. As the car came to a stop, Herb was escorted off the front porch by two large men in dark suits. They were treating him roughly. One of them discreetly held a handgun pointed at Herb's back. The three men headed toward a black Cadillac parked in the driveway. They stopped when they saw the limo.

Vee unexpectedly sprinted out of the house and ran towards them. Johnny stepped out of the limo and motioned to his driver to stop her. Vinnie quickly intercepted Vee and scooped her up. Johnny threw his cigar to the ground and wobbled toward the three men. One of the black suits stepped forward. His pedigree every bit as tough as Johnny's. They seemed to know each other. Johnny whispered calmly into the man's ear, and the angry mobster nodded his head reluctantly. He put away his weapon and motioned for his partner to follow. Both men got into the Cadillac. The car pulled out of the driveway and disappeared quickly down the street.

Vinnie released Vee, and she ran across the lawn into her father's arms. They gave each other a big hug. "I'm still here, honey," he whispered. Vee smiled through her anguish. She knew her dad loved her more than anything in the world. He had always given her and Anna everything he had. If only he didn't owe so much money to those men, she thought.

"Why can't you just call the police when those bad men come here, Daddy?" she asked.

Herb hung his head down and replied. "It's not that easy, Vee." He glanced over at the limo then back to his daughter. "Go say thanks to Johnny, honey."

The young teen released herself from her father and ran toward Johnny. She leapt into his arms and hugged him tightly. Johnny blushed. "Thank you for helping my dad, Johnny," she said.

"Keep your dad out of trouble, kid," he replied and patted her on the back.

"I'll try." Vee beamed with genuine appreciation. "I promise!" They let each other go, and Vee dashed back to Herb. Elvira stepped out on the porch and waved to Johnny. He nodded in acknowledgment then reentered the back of the limo.

As the car backed out, Johnny glanced out the window. He watched in envy as the kids gleefully gathered around Herb, and Elvira stood nearby. He lowered his head in despair. He wished all this could be his but knew it never would. He led a very different life. The limo hit a bump, and Johnny snapped out of his reverie. He leaned back and grinned. The brawler from Bergen County felt content, almost like a human being. He had just made a young girl's taxing life a little easier to bear.

CHAPTER 10
LOSING ONE'S VIRGINITY

Vee was frightened. She had been out with friends celebrating her fifteenth birthday at Bidell's when the dull pain in her abdomen had become sharp. It had hurt so severely, she almost yelled out. Vee stood up abruptly and told her friends she felt sick. She left the table hurriedly, leaving behind a small group of worried faces. She rushed out the door and headed home, hoping her mom or dad could help.

When she arrived, Vee entered the house hunched over in agony and cried out, "Mom! Dad!" Both quickly stepped into the hallway.

"What's the matter, honey?" Herb asked with concern.

"My stomach! It really hurts."

Elvira put her hand on Vee's forehead. "My God, she's burning up."

Herb interjected, "She might have a stomach virus. There's one going around."

Elvira nodded. "Go get her two Tylenol." Herb said okay and disappeared into the kitchen. Elvira turned to Vee. "And you get straight to bed. I'll be up in a few minutes." Vee rushed up the stairs, moaning.

A short time later, Herb was coming back downstairs after giving Vee the pills. Elvira exited the kitchen carrying a tray with a steaming bowl of hot chicken noodle soup. Herb offered to take it up. "She's my daughter too, Herb. I'm not that heartless...at least not yet," she said with contempt. Herb kissed his wife tenderly and watched her take the tray up the stairs to care for their daughter.

Vee was sitting in bed, her arms tightly wrapped around her knees at the chest. Elvira placed the tray on the table near the bed. She inserted a thermometer in Vee's mouth and took her temperature. Over 102 degrees! "That's an awfully high fever for a stomach virus." Elvira verbalized with concern. "Maybe we should take you to the emergency room." She stood there perplexed. Vee had been waiting to be alone with her mom, too embarrassed to talk in front of her dad.

She glanced up at her and mumbled softly. "The pain's not in my stomach, Mom, it's here." Vee placed her hand on her lower abdomen. "It really burns down there."

Elvira's heart palpitated. Please God, don't let it be what I think it is, she thought to herself. Her concern quickly turning to anger. With a tense fire in her eyes, Elvira asked firmly, "You had sex with a boy, didn't you?"

Shocked, Vee blurted out in a low and raspy voice through her pain. "No, Mother...no, I didn't. I swear to God."

Elvira stood there smugly, already convinced of the truth. "You're lying, you little whore!" She slapped Vee hard across the face. The teenager was in too much pain to fight back. Her mother hit her again.

Elvira moved about the room, building herself into a rage. This was a punishment delivered by God himself. The Harris household had a fornicator on its hands! Oh my God! she said to herself. What would the neighbors say? More importantly, the kids at school? The boy who had violated her daughter would most certainly boast of his conquest to any and all who would listen. Everyone would know. Her daughter was a slut. Elvira placed her head in her hands. Shame filled her eyes.

The deranged woman soon lifted her head determined and rushed into the adjoining bathroom. She stopped at the sink and scoured through the cabinet below. Elvira took out a bottle of liquid Lysol. She turned on the hot water to the bath and emptied the entire bottle of disinfectant into it. "My youngest daughter's a slut!" she cried. "Not anymore! I'll clean that filth right out of you." Elvira went to the bed and grabbed Vee's arm.

"No, Mother," Vee pleaded. Elvira removed her daughter's nightgown and forced the young teen into the boiling cauldron. Vee screamed.

"This is how we took care of the problem in my day," Elvira declared.

The abdominal pain and temperature both subsided. Vee was fine for a couple of days, and Elvira was convinced her treatment had worked. Her daughter was clean. However, the sharp pains soon returned with a vengeance. The agony was so intense, Vee collapsed. Herb finally called for an ambulance.

Vee lay in a hospital gown on the cold examining table. The gynecologist continued with her exam as Elvira sat in a chair against the wall listening intently. "The MRI and X-rays confirm several non-cancerous cysts on your daughter's ovaries. They can be removed with a surgical procedure called a Laparotomy." The doctor went on to explain. "She should be healed just fine inside a week, Mrs. Harris."

"My God, that's a relief," Elvira exclaimed.

"We're done here, Vee," the doctor said. Vee got off the table and put her clothes back on. As she did, the doctor quietly turned to Elvira. "Your daughter told me about the tub and the Lysol, Mrs. Harris. If you ever pursue that course of action again and I hear about it, I will report you to the authorities. Your daughter's hymen was fully intact. You're a nurse. Need I go any further?"

— ✠ —

Two weeks had passed since the incident. Vee had undergone a successful surgery to remove the cysts and was recovering nicely. One thing that had not recovered were her feelings towards her mom. Vee was still outraged her mother hadn't believed her. Elvia had even called her a whore! The anger she felt towards her and everything she'd done had reached a boiling point. Her hands were trembling as she helped Anna in the kitchen clean the afternoon dishes.

Around five o'clock, Herb called to say that a machine had broken down at work. He'd be pulling a double so not to expect him home until late. Elvira put the phone down. She had already been in a foul mood most of the day; this only added fuel to the fire. She took another sip from her glass and continued to polish off a bottle of homemade wine Johnny had dropped off earlier.

Anna and Vee were still working in the kitchen when Elvira staggered in a short time later. She was carrying her glass and wine bottle. They could tell she was drunk and watched her with alarm. Elvira jeered soundly at the two of them. "…Did you know you two little bastards ended my modeling career? That's right." She nodded. "Once you pop out a kid, your days in front of the camera are over." Elvira poured the last of the wine into a glass and threw the bottle in the trash. "My body's best years were wasted while I raised you two. Now, I'm middle aged." Elvira raised her glass towards Anna and Vee. "My ticket back to New York has expired. I thank you both." Elvira drank the wine and violently smashed the glass onto the floor.

Standing close to each other and holding the other's hand, Anna and Vee waited to see what their mother would do next. They had been through these sessions so many times before. Elvira glanced around the room and settled on an open loaf of bread on the counter. "Who did it?" she gasped. "Who did it?" Anna started shaking and began to cry. She had forgotten to close the bread.

"I did," she blurted out.

"You can't seem to do anything without screwing up," Elvira snarled. "Maybe this will help you remember next time." She walked up to Anna and slapped her in the face with the back of her hand. Anna fell to the floor. Elvira raised her hand to hit her again when Vee quickly grabbed Elvira's arm and twisted her away from her sister. Mother and daughter stood face to face. Elvira's initial shock rapidly turned to a psychotic fury. She offered a wry smile and said, "I'm going to give you the worst beating you ever had—you little whore bastard!"

Vee glared at her mom. "You will never hit me or my sister ever again, you son-of-a-bitch!" With that, all of Vee's pent up anger unleashed. She rushed towards her mom and violently pushed her with all her might. Elvira went backwards, tried to regain her footing before going headfirst into the refrigerator. There was a loud thud. Elvira slid down the side of the door and rolled onto the floor. She lay there motionless.

Several moments passed. Vee stood there in disbelief, certain her mother was dead. Her body looked lifeless. Vee could see no breathing. What was she going to do? she thought. Her sister lay huddled in a ball on the floor, crying. She could offer no assistance. Vee's first instinct was to flee. She raced up the stairs and returned a few minutes later with a hastily packed suitcase in hand. Her mind was racing, overrun with dread.

In desperation, Vee dialed her father at work. "Dad, you need to come home right away!... You need to do it right now! I just killed mom... I pushed her!... She was drunk!... She hit Anna!" Vee let out in a rapid, incoherent fashion. "Do you have any extra money lying around the house? I need to leave," she added.

"What?!" Herb shouted back into the phone. "Stay right there, honey! I'll be home in ten minutes." Vee hung up the phone and stepped outside the house to wait.

Standing on the porch, the cold night's drizzle poured down the terrified teen's face. Thoughts of doom raced through her mind. At first, Vee was comforted by the fact her dad would soon be there, but those feelings soon turned to apprehension. He would have to call the police. Vee let out a high-pitched scream then sobbed, not knowing what to do. In a panic, she snatched her luggage and rushed off the porch. She ran through the yard to the back of the house and disappeared into the dark woods.

—◦— ◄✦► —◦—

Despite the foreboding sounds of the nocturnal animals adding to her anxiety, Vee pushed on—driven by more important fears. She struggled through the woods for a good twenty minutes until she was exhausted. Lost in a haze of unfamiliar trees, she dropped to her knees in the soaked mud and rested. The drizzle started to become heavier, and the wind had picked up dramatically. Vee listened to the trees creaking in the wind as their tops swirled with the gusts. Added to this mix was the lonely sound of a train whistle far off in the distance. Vee rose from the mud and walked forward a short distance. She stepped into a wide clearing and glanced up at a set of raised railroad tracks that lead to a large steel trestle. Vee crawled up a steep incline of stones up to the tracks. She was caked in mud, which made the going tough. She made it to the top and saw an old wooden bench which was off to the side.

Vee plopped down on the bench, consumed by despair. What now? she thought. She had killed her mom, and the police would soon be after her. She would go to prison. Tears mixed with sweat rolled off her chin as the wind gusted on the open track blowing her hair around aimlessly. Vee had never felt so low. Maybe it would be better if I were no longer around, she thought. Her sister and dad would be fine. They no longer had mom to worry about. Ricky would be okay without her as well. He was a survivor.

The train whistle erupted again. This time it sounded much closer. Vee looked at the tracks. She stood up and walked towards them, leaving her suitcase next to the bench. Vee stepped in the center of the tracks and started moving in the direction of the whistle. She could hear the steady rumble of the engine. It was not far off. Vee tried to maintain her balance in the dark as she walked along the railroad ties, but it was difficult. The ground was uneven, and the wooden surface of the ties was slippery from the constant drizzle. A strong wind gust knocked her to one knee, but she quickly got back up. The train was getting close. Vee could feel the ground begin to shake beneath her feet from the chugging engine. She watched in nervous fear as the train came around the far bend, its light glaring bright in the center of the track. The teen clenched her fists and persisted forward. The train whistle sounded. As she stepped forward, her shoe got caught between two stones. She pulled her foot out and slipped on one of the ties. A sudden wind gust kept her off balance. As she tried to regain her footing, Vee fell sideways over the rail. She painfully rolled down the stony slope before coming to rest at the bottom of the embankment. As the defeated girl lay on her back, bruised and bloodied, the train roared by overhead. It let off one final whistle as it disappeared down the track into the cold, wet darkness.

Vee let out a wry laugh through the pain. If there was a God, maybe he had just spoken to her or at least showed his sense of humor. She lay there with peaceful resignation in her eyes, staring up into the steady rainfall.

A short time later, Vee was walking along the lower embankment. She had retrieved her suitcase and started following the tracks. In the distance, a pair of headlights turned down the dirt road parallel to the tracks. They quickly headed towards her. As they approached, Vee's face lit up with joy. She could recognize the rumble of her dad's pickup anywhere! She ran towards it. The truck stopped, and her dad jumped out. They ran towards one another and embraced in each other's arms.

"I'm sorry, Dad!" Vee screamed.

"I'm just glad you're alright, honey," he cried. They held each other tight for a minute. Vee raised her head and sadly glanced into her dad's eyes.

"Mom..."

"Your mother's fine...you just knocked her out is all," he said.

"What?" Vee said in surprise.

"She's also very drunk," he added. "I put her to bed. She's fast asleep and fine." A relieved daughter started crying. "Anna told me everything that happened. You're a brave young lady." Herb gave her another hug. "Everything's gonna be fine, honey."

Vee felt like a weight had been lifted off her shoulders, as if she had been given a second chance. She walked back to the truck arm in arm with her dad. Vee turned to him and declared, "I'm going to graduate high school. Then I'm going to nursing school. I'm going to make you the proudest dad ever!"

"You already have, honey. You already have," Herb said with a tear and a smile.

They entered the truck, and Herb fired up the engine. As they rode home, *Hotel California* was playing on the radio. Vee turned up the volume and started singing along, "Plenty of room at the Hotel California. Any time of year, you can find it here…" Vee looked down and noticed she was only wearing one shoe. With a wide smile, she glanced at her dad. He laughed. They both started singing the last part of the song together. "Last thing I remember, I was running for the door. I had to find the passage back to the place I was before. 'Relax,' said the night man. 'We are programmed to receive. You can check out any time you like, but you can never leave…'"

⊷ ⊷ ✦ ⊶ ⊶

Over the next two years, things for Ricky Matt stayed the same. The thin teen was frequently abused by older or bigger boys at Father Baker's. It had become part of his routine. Periodically, he would scale the wall and call Vee from a payphone. Each time he did, Herb would come and get him and hide Ricky in different places in the house. His stays were usually short to avoid detection but, on one occasion, lasted several months. Herb built a concealed, makeshift refuge for Ricky under the porch. It included a small refrigerator, an old army cot, and two space heaters for chilly nights. Elvira discovered the hideout only after investigating the high electric bills and following the extension cord that provided power. She also discovered Ricky and immediately turned him in.

CHAPTER 11
MANIFEST DESTINY

The year was 1981; Ronald Reagan had taken up residence in the White House; fifty-two American hostages had just been released from Iran; the price of gasoline was $1.20 a gallon; and Vee Harris had just turned eighteen. Legally, she was now an adult and free to choose her own path. Vee desperately wanted out of the Harris household and a clean break from Elvira. However, the road to freedom was blocked by financial reality. Vee's paltry salary as a nurses' aid would not allow her to live on her own, and a second job was impossible with her college workload. In haste, she seized upon the only option left.

On a dreary Saturday afternoon not long after her birthday, Vee arrived at the church a good thirty-five minutes late. The small crowd that had gathered looked on in quiet disbelief. The impulsive wedding had been a surprise and a shock. Everything seemed disorganized, including Vee's appearance. Her makeup was aghast, and her dress severely wrinkled. Despite these things, no one intervened, and the ceremony went on. When it was over, Vee was hopeful she had at least made a tolerable choice.

Not long after the wedding, Herb had procured his daughter's twenty-two-year-old husband a job in the maintenance department where he worked. It only lasted a brief period. After two months, *Kevin* thought he was beyond cleaning toilets and quit. With no new job prospects on his horizon or a real desire to work, tension developed between the two newlyweds. Arguments occurred daily and quickly escalated into physical altercations. Vee called 911 twice. She moved out on her third call. During the ensuing months, the determined woman acquired her nursing license and a better position. She moved into a small apartment near her father"s work. In hindsight, Vee realized the marriage was a complete mistake. Her biggest regret was losing her virginity to a man she didn"t love, to a man she barely knew. Her wedding night had been so brutish and filled with such disconnect, Vee felt like she had been violated by a complete stranger.

— ⊨◆⊨ —

On a sweltering night inside the Tonawanda Police Department's Robbery-Homicide division, a hardened Ricky Matt sat across from Detective Dave Beamish. Both knew the game. Beamish looked over the stolen food items atop his desk and glanced up at Ricky. "Filet Mignon, New York Strip...You have excellent taste in meat, Mr. Matt."

"Nothing but the best, right?" the teen said with a proud grin. Beamish smiled as he browsed through the watches next to the beef.

Both knew he would not be prosecuted for the stolen items. Ricky was still a juvie. He would most likely be sent back to Father Baker's or another foster facility. Beamish looked at the fifteen-year-old, he knew the writing was already on the wall. In three years, Ricky would graduate from juvenile to criminal court. He'd probably be sleeping in a jail cell shortly after his eighteenth birthday, cycling in and out of prisons the rest of his life.

Beamish was also a product of the foster care system. He had heard all the cons and been in on a few himself. He knew how to work the system, but he also knew what it could do to a person. Ricky's engaging demeanor had caught the detective off guard. The kid had spunk. He took a liking to him right away. "Paradoxical charm," he mused. Beamish looked at the bruises on the teenager's face. "Where'd you get the beauty marks?" he asked.

"Your mother," Ricky laughed.

Later that evening, Beamish paid a visit to Father Baker's. He felt a genuine concern for the kid. He realized there was only so much he could do, but every little bit helped, especially in a place like Baker's. After doing some checking, Beamish soon found himself in a small room sitting across from the two boys who had administered Ricky's beating. A muscular teen named Billy and a heavy-set kid named Mike. They both sat smugly on their beds. "Hey, man, I ain't eighteen till next year. Come back and visit me then..." Billy taunted. Mike laughed.

Beamish glared at him. "You can go," he stated to Mike. Mike got up and headed out the door.

"Mikey, tell the padre and the nuns I'm gonna be needin' last rites." Billy howled.

Beamish snickered as he shut the door. He grabbed a chair and jammed it under the doorknob, so it couldn't be opened from the outside. An hour later, Beamish emerged from the room unblemished. He walked back to the administrator's office and thanked him for his help. A short while later, a visibly shaken Billy came out of the room. He would never touch Ricky Matt again.

As time passed, Ricky took on a new title in the home, *The Scrounger*. The guy who could get you anything you wanted. Anything that was, for a price. Ricky had a knack for stealing, and he relished the power it gave him. Everyone came to him—including his former abusers. He supplied food, cigarettes, porn...whatever they wanted. *Anything for a price* became his motto. Anything that was, except drugs. Despite their lucrative potential, Ricky held a deep animosity towards them, and anybody who used or pimped them. As a youth, the Owens's had told him his biological parents had been heavy users which played a big part in his abandonment and being left for dead. In their world, little Ricky Matt had become a ball and chain.

Over the next three years, Ricky adopted a "survival of the fittest" men-
tality, building an extensive network of *business* connections to foster his
activity and usurp any rival. His turnkey operation earned him a comfortable living at Father Baker's. Despite his financial independence, he
was never satisfied. Ricky frequently scaled the wall and would go out on
nighttime excursions to rob homes and businesses in the neighborhood.
He would then hurry back to the facility, booty in tow, and be in his room
just before morning roll call. He thrived on the excitement.

During a rare daytime escape, the daredevil managed to steal a car
and drive himself and two fellow juvenile delinquents to Darien Lake.
With stolen money, they spent the day at the amusement park eating
food and going on rides. They were especially proud of having survived
The Viper—screaming with wild abandon at the twists and turns of
their first roller coaster. They didn't even mind their regurgitated hot-
dogs running down their shirts when the ride came to a stop. It merely
put an exclamation point on the experience.

Ricky was arrested for that joyride five days before his seventeenth
birthday. He thought it would be another juvie offense, but at the
judge's discretion, Ricky was charged with 'Felony unauthorized use of
a Vehicle in the Third Degree.' To his further surprise, the charge was
suddenly dropped at the sentencing hearing. The judge struck his gavel
and dismissed the case, nodded to Detective Beamish who was standing
just inside the courtroom door. The would-be felon found out later he
had amassed some good will with the local PD after allowing Beamish
to utilize his local connections and street cred to help bust a large drug
ring in the area. An opportunity he willingly embraced.

On the first Friday after Ricky's return to the facility, the usual
crowd had gathered in his room during the evening to hang out and
shoot the shit. Another juvenile delinquent had joined them named
Jimmy Reyes. He was in the middle of a rambling story talking about
a close friend on the outside who had died after a speedball OD. "...
yeah, and the kid was pissin' his pants, excited you know...he just found
out he had a half-brother here at Father Baker. He was..." Jimmy
stopped midsentence and stared in surprise at Ricky who had just
walked in. "Holy shit!" he said.

"Problem?" Ricky asked as he leaned nonchalantly against the door frame.

Jimmy reached into his shirt pocket and pulled out a picture of his friend. He glanced at it, shook his head. "Dude, this kid looks just like you," he said. He held the photo out. Ricky walked forward and grabbed it. He stared at it, first in amusement, then in disbelief. It did look like him. The other boys watched and nodded in agreement. The curfew lights suddenly blinked, and everyone rushed out of the room mumbling excitedly. Ricky was left standing alone in an emotional tizzy. Could it be true? Could this kid have been his brother? he asked himself. Did it matter anymore? He was dead now. Ricky sat down on his bed and laughed at the perverse nature of the universe.

When Ricky first came to Father Baker's, he had been a happy-go-lucky kid. Things quickly changed during the first few years of his stay. He began to suffer severe bouts of depression where he would remain in his room for days at a time, telling anyone who would listen he wanted to die. Ricky would also experience sudden outbursts of rage that often terrified the other kids. He was diagnosed with general psychosis and the onset of bipolar disorder. The frightened teen was prescribed powerful medications to stabilize his mood and counter depression. His symptoms were kept at bay as long as he took the meds.

Learning about having a possible brother and, then just as quickly, about his sudden death, seemed to trigger another change in Ricky's psyche. He began to experience extreme bouts of paranoia and delusional behavior. Ricky was convinced his brother had been murdered and that the foster facility was trying to kill him by giving him poisoned meds. He secretly began substituting his pills with look-alike placebos to fool the medical staff. By not taking his actual meds, Ricky's original symptoms roared back to life. He experienced wild mood swings and violent outbursts. It culminated in a vicious attack on another boy; Ricky claimed he stole a comic book from his footlocker. He broke the boy's leg and would have done far worse if he had not been restrained. Convinced Ricky's meds were no longer working, staff psychiatrists prescribed electro-shock therapy.

A week later, Ricky was escorted into the dark and musty basement of a local county hospital. In an isolated room, four members of the hospital staff strapped the young teen to a secure gurney. One doctor administered a sedative while another glued electrode to his temples. A protective guard was placed in his mouth so he could not bite his tongue or injure his teeth. As he lay there unable to move, a switch was flipped, and 350 volts sent waves of electric current through Ricky's brain. The procedure induced intense seizures, his body convulsing horribly, and he defecated without control.

However, after the treatment, the results were immediate. Ricky would stay calm for weeks. The brutal sessions became a regular part of his routine. When it was time for another round, Ricky would joke apprehensively that it was time for another trip to the underground electric show.

—⊶⊷—

On June 25, 1984, Ricky Matt walked out of Father Baker's a free man. He officially turned eighteen and was no longer a ward of the state. The emancipated teen stood outside the facility with a footlocker over his shoulder, three hundred dollars in his pocket, and a big smile on his face. It was a beautiful, hot summer day, and he could do as he pleased without having to look over his shoulder. He no longer needed to worry about curfews, strict routines, or punishment for breaking some ridiculous rule.

For Ricky, it felt like he had been released from a prison. But what was next? Where would he go and what would he do? Those were things he had mulled over during the months prior to his release yet still had no answers for. Ricky thought his best option would be to visit his foster parents. He hoped he could stay with them a few months until he came up with a game plan. For job purposes, he had managed to acquire a GED at Father Baker's, but that was it. He was severely lacking in any formal education and real work experience. One area where Ricky wasn't lacking was the looks department. He had grown into a handsome young man. Ricky Matt stood six feet tall and well built. He was strong and wiry with dark hair and a movie star smile. All things he had learned to use to his advantage.

The bus stop was at the corner, a short distance from the facility. Ricky made his way over and waited for the next bus into the city. When it arrived, he got on. It was mostly filled with seniors, students, and a few vagabonds. As he made his way down the aisle, he noticed a beautiful blond teen sitting at a window with an empty seat next to her. As he approached, she glanced up at him and removed her books that were on the seat. Ricky smiled. "Thanks," he said and sat down.

"You have a lot of books. You coming from school?" he inquired. The precocious teen leered at him.

"Bryson Academy. I'm a senior," she said.

Ricky grinned. "Bryson? You're too pretty to go to Bryson." The girl giggled. "Anyway, don't you get summers off?"

"I'm in summer school," she admitted hesitantly.

"Summer school!" Ricky feigned concern. "You only go to summer school if you did something bad. What'd you do? Skip classes? Tell a teacher off?"

"I missed too many math classes," she quietly uttered.

Ricky nodded his head in approval. "I'm beginning to like you already." They both laughed. Within a few minutes, the two were chatting like old friends. It was also obvious they were both attracted to one another. The girl especially seemed to be instantly smitten by Ricky's good looks. Before long they were snuggling close and on the verge of openly making out, much to the chagrin of the two senior ladies sitting across from them.

The young girl leaned into Ricky's ear and whispered, "I get off at the next stop if you'd like to come with me." As the bus slowed to a stop both rose from their seats.

As they exited, Ricky bent down close to the two old ladies and whispered, "You're both welcome to join us." Ricky winked and stepped off the bus, leaving behind two stunned seniors grasping at their handbags.

The two teens walked hand in hand through the swanky neighborhood. Ricky marveled at the large homes, the big yards, and the expensive cars in the circular driveways. He quickly realized he was in a whole different world than he was used to, and this would probably be a one-time visit. The former foster kid felt out of place walking down the affluent street in simple jeans and a black T-shirt, toting a footlocker on his back. The questioning glances from the nosy neighbors added to his discomfort. The girl simply put on a hat and some sunglasses and waved to them as they walked along.

As they reached the end of the street, the girl turned into the driveway of an enormous three-story colonial. Ricky's jaw dropped. "This is your house?" he asked.

She nodded. "My parents are out chasing the American dream. They won't be back until dinner time." Ricky set his footlocker down next to the empty two car garage and shook his head in amazement. The girl escorted him to the utility entrance in back of the house and opened the door with a key. She then urged him on to follow her in a rush up the back stairs to the third floor and her bedroom.

A minute later, the two teenagers were tearing off each other's clothes. They jumped into bed stark naked and spent the entire afternoon having sex in every conceivable position they could think of. At one point, Ricky had thrust himself deep inside her and was pounding her with such brute force, he thought he had knocked her unconsciousness. Her body suddenly went limp. Horrified, he stopped. As soon as he did, she came out of her private trance. "What are you doing? Don't stop now!" she screamed. Ricky happily obliged.

When they were finished, both lay prostrate on top of the bed, their bodies glistening in sweat. Ricky quietly caressed her arm. "I bet they don't teach you that at Bryson Academy." he said. She let out a satisfied sigh and shook her head. Their quiet calm was disturbed by the unexpected sound of a car pulling into the driveway. The girl's eyes snapped open, and she jumped out of bed.

She looked out the window and screamed, "Oh my God, my father's home!" The girl grabbed Ricky's arm and tried to pull him up. "Get up, you idiot! You gotta get out of here right now!" Ricky was now awake. He stood up quickly and glanced out the window. A Mercedes 450SL sat in the driveway out front.

"Oh, fuck!" he said to himself. He started grabbing for his things as the girl hurried him towards the door. "Go down the back stairs! The way we came," she yelled quietly.

Ricky made his way down the stairs carrying his clothes and dressed on the bottom steps. He looked out the side window and could see her father circling his footlocker near the garage. Ricky wasn't about to leave without that. He tucked in his shirt, smoothed his hair, and went out the utility door. Ricky casually strolled to the front of the house. "Hello, sir," he said respectfully.

The father glanced up. "Hello," he responded with a questioning look.

Ricky continued. "I'm from Bryson Academy. I was helping your daughter with her math homework. It's nice to finally meet you, sir." Rick held out his hand, and they shook. "If you don't mind, sir...I need to hurry to catch my bus." Ricky picked up his footlocker and started walking swiftly down the driveway. "Have a nice day now!" he added. The girl's father stood there perplexed waving goodbye.

The moment Ricky got out of sight, he burst out laughing. "The boys back at Father Baker's would never have believed me," he said to himself. He didn't even know her name! The proud peacock strolled through the neighborhood that day feeling on top of the world. Instead of taking the bus, he just felt like walking. Around dusk, he finally hitched a ride to his foster parents' home. There, Ricky's elation quickly turned somber. The Owens's told him he could only stay a week. Two new foster kids were moving in, and they needed his old room. And the subsidies, Ricky bitterly thought to himself.

CHAPTER 12
STAYS IN THE BIG HOUSE

Saddled with no job prospects and dwindling money, Ricky hooked up with an old childhood friend named Joey Michaels. Joey worked for a local roofing company and was able to get Ricky a job with them doing manual labor. He was required to climb a ladder carrying eighty-pound shingles up the side of homes during installations. Ricky wasn't enthusiastic about the job but tried to make an honest go of it. Despite the low pay, he brought in enough money to rent a cheap room and have enough left over to put food on the table every day.

After several months, Ricky became despondent over his *dead-end* situation and began drinking. The troubled teen began putting away two six packs of beer or more per day. He also started to haunt the local strip clubs during his off hours to burn through the time and, in effect, his money. In order to economize, Ricky started rooming with friends for brief periods or shacking up with women he would meet, including regular stints with various dancers from the clubs.

One thing that greatly aggravated Ricky's circumstances was his refusal to deal with his mental illness. Since his release from foster care, he had discarded the shock therapy and medications used for his treatment. As a result, he was often at the mercy of his wild mood swings. One never knew when he was going to go off. During an evening out at one of his frequented clubs, Ricky was sitting at the bar when another patron began ogling his current flame as she danced on stage. Ricky became enraged. Without provocation, he smashed his drinking glass on the bar top and stood up. He picked up the barstool next to him and swung it into the guy's back like a baseball bat. The stunned customer flew forward and crashed to the floor. Ricky tried to hit him again but was restrained by club security until the police arrived. He was arrested and charged with assault.

Ricky was released on bail but lost his job. Desperate for money, he began stealing checks from people he would stay with. He would forge their name and pass the checks off to local stores to pay for food and liquor. He would also use the checks to buy items of value then sell them at a local pawnshop to get hard cash. Ricky tried to keep the dollar amounts from being too high so they would fly under the radar. However, one of his victims discovered the thefts a month later, and Ricky was arrested. Because of the volume of checks forged, Matt was charged with three felonies: forging checks, using a forged instrument, and possession of stolen property. He was sentenced to one year at the Alden Correctional Facility, his first stay at a real prison.

Two months into his stay at Alden, Ricky learned from a fellow inmate that his biological father had sired another son. His name was Wayne Schmidt. Ricky was stunned. He had a half-brother living in Buffalo just twenty miles away! Determined to see his older sibling, inmate 372584 decided to escape. The next day, Ricky scaled the prison's fifteen-foot barbed-wire fence during the morning exercise. He made his way through the rural countryside and snuck on to a local farm where he stole some clothes and a horse. The escaped con rode horseback several miles, quickly traversing the countryside, until he came upon a set of railroad tracks. Ricky ditched the horse and tossed his prison greens in the brush. He waited for the first freight train heading west and hopped on. It took him to Buffalo in less than an hour. Before the train arrived at the city center, Ricky jumped off and made it into the downtown area on foot. He walked through the streets of Buffalo to the address he had been given, arriving at his half-brother's house that evening just in time for dinner.

After questioning fellow inmates, authorities were able to determine Ricky's likely whereabouts. He was subsequently tracked down and picked up a week later without incident. Instead of being returned to Alden, the New York State Department of Corrections transferred Ricky to the Elmira Correctional facility 120 miles away. The maximum-security prison located in the remote and densely wooded Finger Lakes region of New York would now serve as Ricky's home for the remainder of his original sentence and the extra year tagged on for his breakout. He was flagged an escape risk, so extra precautions were taken which placed him under scrutiny at all times. While prison officials were wary of Ricky's reputation, it soared among the other prisoners. His successful exodus from Alden increased the measures afforded him by the inmates at the Elmira facility.

To the surprise of prison officials, the now famed escape artist caused no problems while at Elmira. He quietly served his time, satisfied he had met his brother. During his stay, Ricky taught himself to paint and was a natural. He began painting oil portraits of famous celebrities and other inmates which were widely admired by the surprised prisoners and staff alike. By the end of his sentence, officials were quite pleased with Ricky's exhibition of good behavior. He was released after only serving eighteen months of his three-year stint.

Back on the streets, Ricky quickly blew through the money he had earned in prison. He also had trouble finding a job and soon fell back into old habits. He stole a credit card from an associate and racked up thousands of dollars in charges. He also began canvassing neighborhood mail for checks. He would alter the checks so they were made out to him and cash them. A few weeks after his release, Ricky was arrested for his efforts. He was charged with credit card fraud, possession of stolen property, and washing and cashing fraudulent checks.

Ricky had again amassed multiple felony counts and was sentenced to sixteen to forty-eight months. He headed back to the Elmira Correctional facility, much to the surprise of the warden who was disappointed to see him return so quickly. This time around, Ricky was not thrilled with his confinement and soon began planning an escape. Prison officials got wind of his plans, and he was transferred to the maximum-security facility at Attica. The *fortress*, twenty-five miles east of Buffalo, was unlike anything Ricky had yet experienced. It was a harsh place with an infamous record for keeping order. The imposing facility was surrounded by two-foot thick concrete walls that extended thirty feet high and were mounted by heavily armed guard towers. Daunted by the setup, Ricky accepted his plight and caused no problems. After two years of good behavior, he was released on parole.

Ricky tried in earnest to behave himself this time out. He secured employment and checked in regularly with his parole officer. A year and a half passed without incident. Ricky met a woman at a bar, and they started living together. She soon became pregnant, and they tied the knot. The constraints of married life didn't exactly agree with Ricky. He started drinking more often and would disappear from the apartment for days at a time. Two days before the expected due date of their child, Ricky was arrested on a gun charge. A random parole check of his apartment had turned up the weapon. Ironically, he had been holding it for a friend. Ricky was charged with gun possession and violating his parole. It earned him a two-year stretch back at Attica.

CHAPTER 13
A DECADE OF PERSONAL GROWTH

Fresh off her divorce, Vee Harris was intent on making better choices. She was determined her decisions would no longer be influenced by a mother who had treated her so horribly. It seemed to be a prevailing thought in the Harris household because it precipitated a mass exodus. Emboldened by her sister, Anna left several months later. She fell for a man she barely knew and moved in with him clear across town. He worked as a plumber, was ten years her senior, and the two had little in common. At first, Vee tried to intercede to prevent Anna from making the same mistake she had made, but her efforts were met with resistance. Vee chose to let it be. She knew her sister would have to learn from her own mistakes—a path she too had woefully visited.

With both daughters now out of the nest, Herb decided he no longer needed to live under Elvira's abusive umbrella either. He moved out during the summer and rented an apartment close to work. He still took care of his wife's bills as best he could and helped around the house. He simply could not live under the same roof as her. Elvira had forbidden Anna or Vee from coming over to see him since they had left. In addition, Johnny began stopping by several times a week. It made things awkward and uncomfortable. It was a situation Herb no longer wanted to face.

Vee was proud of her dad for standing up to Elvira. It had taken great courage for him to move out of the house. To celebrate his official liberation and new apartment, she decided to make him a big dinner at his new place. Vee had not been able to see him much since she left home, but now, coincidentally, they lived only a block apart. It would be a new beginning for both with no Elvira to muck up their lives.

In the evening, a proud daughter pulled out all the stops for dinner. She fixed prime rib, mashed potatoes, and all the trimmings. They both ate heartily and enjoyed each other's company. They drank wine and talked unabated like they hadn't done in years. The father and daughter filled in the gaps for each other in both of their lives, mainly from the last two years. Vee radiated joy when telling her dad she had officially become a registered nurse and was making $18.50 an hour. Herb smiled and shook his head, beaming with pride at his daughter. "You did what you said you would do. You should be proud of yourself," he asserted.

After dinner, Vee spent quality time adding a woman's touch to her dad's new apartment. She hung up some fine artwork, put up linen curtains on the windows, and added plants wherever there was an open space. All the little things that make a house a home. Herb was amazed at the transformation. One good thing Vee had inherited from her mom was a refined sense of taste. It was exquisite, and it showed. When Vee had finished, she grabbed her jacket and began to exit. Herb followed her down the steps. At the bottom, she turned and grasped her dad's hand. "I know you stayed all those years for me and Anna," she said.

Herb looked at his daughter and stood there reflecting, a flood of emotion filling his face. "...I'm only sorry...no, I'm disgusted at myself for not ending your anguish sooner, Vee. Or Anna's."

"You did the best you could, Daddy," she pleaded. The father and daughter embraced each other tightly.

—·— ≡◆≡ —·—

The Pontiac cruised down the thruway at 70 mph. The T-tops were down, and Vee's hair flowed vibrantly in the wind. It was Friday night, and she was headed to her favorite dance club. Vee was jubilant, thinking blissfully to herself as she drove; she had a beautiful apartment, a new car, and was earning almost 40k a year. "So, what do you think about me now, world?!" she cried out, laughing. A moment later, night turned to day. The Pontiac was lit up from behind by a bright spotlight from a state police vehicle trailing close behind, its red flashers going. "Oh, shit!" Vee said out loud. "This would have to happen to me." She pulled to the side of the road.

Vee's anxious first thoughts were speeding ticket, followed by sky-rocketing insurance. But she suddenly remembered she had a get out of jail free card, courtesy of Elvira and Johnny. Vee went through her glove compartment and pulled out a small business card. She glanced in her rearview mirror and watched as the trooper exited his car and approached. Vee gazed out the open window and up at the young trooper. "I'm sorry, officer, was I going a little too fast?" Vee grinned.

"You were going 70 mph in a 55-mph zone, ma'am. I'm gonna need to see your license and registration, please," he replied. Vee gave him the two documents along with the business card on top. He took them and glanced at the card. The trooper smirked then looked at Vee. He gave her back the documents. "Just slow it down to the speed limit, okay, ma'am?"

"You have my word," she said.

"One other thing," he added, fumbling through his pocket. He pulled out his card and handed it to Vee.

She inspected it and said, "Why, thank you...Officer Nuncio." She smiled. The trooper smiled back and tipped his hat.

"Ma'am." He walked back to his car. Vee laughed and threw his card in the ashtray filled with cigarette butts. She glanced again at the card she had given him. It was the Buffalo Police Chief's business card with a little note written on it and signed by the chief himself.

<hr />

Uncle Sam's nightclub was the hottest club in town and was *the* place to be on a Friday night in Buffalo. That night was especially popular because it was ladies' night. Although the club was huge and could pack in hundreds of people, it filled up quickly and would close its doors at 9 P.M. because there was no place left to stand. A line would form outside that stretched clear around the block. Would-be party goers waited for hours hoping to gain entrance, but at that point you had to know or be somebody to get into the club.

The crowd was mostly an eclectic mix of young men and women full of high energy eager for a night of drinking, dancing, and carousing. It was not uncommon to see celebrities and professional athletes among them. In particular, hockey and football players from the Buffalo Sabres and Buffalo Bills teams would show up with money to burn on the lookout to score and have a good time. They were often obliged by the abundant ladies available yearning to catch themselves a prized fish. Vee was never into that crowd, she just wanted to get lost in the music and dance the night away. Just like tonight. She walked to the front of the line and waved to the doorman, Bobby. "Looking good, Vee," he said and whisked her right in, much to the dismay of the people next in line.

Inside the club, the crowd was buzzing, and a thumping disco beat reverberated everywhere. The lighted dance floor was packed with men and women awash in a kaleidoscope of color from the over-head spotlights. In the swirling rays, Vee caught brief glimpses of cutoff shirts, spandex tights, and short shorts with high top socks dancing side by side doing the Electric Slide to the beat of the music. The energy was infectious. As Vee walked through the crowd, a tipsy Casanova from the dance floor wearing a silk shirt and holding a drink grabbed Vee's hand and tried to boogie down. She playfully danced a few steps before spotting her two girlfriends seated at one of the tables. She waved him goodbye and quickly joined her friends.

Vee's two friends were nurses from work. They had all decided to meet up for a Friday night bash. As they sat and drank, two good looking charmers came over to say hello. The women took the bait, and soon, expensive drinks were flowing freely at their table. Vee's two friends headed to the dance floor with the men. As Vee watched them dance, she glanced around the club. On the side, near the far wall, were a trio of barber chairs. People were taking turns sitting in them and leaning back, having shots poured in their mouths. In the middle of the crowd, a woman was dancing full throttle four feet above the floor on top of a raised speaker box. At the bar, another sight had caught Vee's eye.

In front of her stood a real lady-killer with long, fiery red hair. The young man was tall and lean with a face filled with spattered freckles. He was wearing ripped jeans and a tattered black T-shirt, holding a Heineken in one hand and a cigarette in the other. Vee called a waitress over and had her bring him another beer. The waitress delivered the beer and pointed to Vee. The man walked over to her table. "Thanks for the beer." He nodded. The smitten nurse smiled back. "I'm Patrick O'Reilly. But my friends call me Taz. I guess it's 'cause I kinda look like the Tasmanian Devil."

Vee laughed at the line. "Let's dance, Taz," she quipped. Taz put his beer on the table, and she snatched his hand, leading him to the dance floor.

They danced with wild abandon under the giant glittering disco ball that hung above the dance floor. Getting lost in the pulsing beat of the music, the two pressed against each other. Their bumping and grinding blending in with the rest of the roisterers in the overcrowded space. By the end of the evening they were both wasted, draped all over one another and making out as if there were no tomorrow. Vee fell hard that evening. They left together, and he spent the night at her apartment.

⊷ ⊷ ⊷

Over the following week, they saw each other almost every day. Taz had lost his job, and Vee asked her dad if he could get something for him where he worked. Herb was able to get him a position in maintenance. He joked with Vee that getting her *men* jobs was becoming a regular thing. Unfortunately, the job didn't last. The national recession had hit the local economy hard, and Herb's company closed its doors. Both he and Taz were now out of work. With his experience, Herb was able to find employment quickly, but Taz was not as fortunate. He was now unemployed, broke, and on the verge of losing his apartment. Seeing the "Save Me" sign on Taz's back, Vee let him move in with her.

Vee spent the next two years in a self-imposed prison. She had strong feelings for Taz and vowed to stand by him until he found work. Unfortunately, steady employment never came. Taz would work in fits and starts and bring in some money, but that was it. He was always waiting for the next big gig, but it never seemed to materialize. At first, Vee didn't mind. Taz was a fun guy, and she enjoyed his company. He helped around the apartment, and she had enough money saved to support them comfortably until he found his thing.

Early on, Taz began borrowing money, which he would always promise to pay back. It started with small amounts that gradually became bigger and bigger over time. He had an addictive cigarette habit, like Vee, but also enjoyed smoking grass daily. Usually his small jobs paid for these vices, but his weed habit started to soar, and he began using coke. Money started disappearing from Vee's bank account. She only noticed it after one of her checks bounced due to insufficient funds. She began falling behind on her bills. One evening, she discovered her expensive jewelry missing from a locked drawer. Taz blamed it on a break-in, but Vee knew better. That had been the final straw; the next day, she kicked Taz to the curb for good. He was just a charming manipulator living off her good graces like a sponge. Worse yet, she had let it happen. Vee couldn't believe she had made such a mistake—again. Herb pointed out there was a silver lining; at least she hadn't married him.

— ✴ —

To get over her doldrums, Vee threw herself into her job. She began hitting the gym five times a week and started eating healthy. Each day after work, she prepared a homecooked meal for her dad and would deliver it to him at his new job. Herb was working second shift, so his meal break came in the early evening. It was often the only time they could see each other because of their conflicting schedules.

One evening, about a month after her breakup, Vee was sitting with her dad in the lunchroom at his work. The two had just finished their meals and were slowly sipping on coffee. Herb was more quiet than usual and sat with downcast eyes. Vee knew something was up. "What's wrong, Dad?" she queried.

Herb glanced up at his daughter. "I miss your mother, Vee. I'll be moving back in next week."

Vee inhaled, shocked by the admission. "Is it money?" she said. "I can help with the apartment."

Herb just shook his head. "You don't deserve the abuse, Daddy. You're better than that!" she said loudly.

Herb winced. "I ain't better than nothing, honey," he said. "It's all set." Vee got up angrily and stormed out.

As she rushed down the hall, Vee thought about her dad bitterly. She was keenly aware his new job didn't pay anywhere near his old one. He probably couldn't keep up paying for the apartment, the house bills, and his gambling debts. He was also filled with too much pride to accept any help, so he just took the path of least resistance. Back to the house and Elvira. It made Vee distraught just to think about it.

— ⚔ —

By her own design, Vee's life turned into a regimented daily grind. *Eat, sleep, and go to work* became her mantra. She did not see much of her dad after he moved back in with Elvira. Nor did she see much of Anna. Even her social life took a backseat to work. Vee devoted herself to her job, often working six days a week and pulling extra shifts when needed. It was no different on this Christmas Eve night.

Vee exited the hospital with a coffee in hand. She had just worked a double and was dead on her feet. It was a holiday, but she was too tired to celebrate. Besides, she had nobody to celebrate with anyway. Vee

83

earned seven hundred dollars for the day which suited her just fine. Now it was time to go home and go to sleep, but first, she had to remember where she parked her car. It had been snowing constantly since she had been outside last, and everything was covered in a blanket of white.

As she walked through the parking lot, a hand suddenly tapped her on the shoulder. "Vee Harris!" a voice cried out. Vee turned around and was met with a big bear hug from Joey Michaels.

"Joey?" she struggled back to say as she tried to recover her breath.

"Whatchu doing here, girl?" he added briskly.

"...I work here now; I'm a nurse," she finally said.

"You work here? Whatchu know about that." Vee looked at the large Band-Aid above his left eye.

"What happened to you?" she asked.

"Oh, I got in a bar fight. Got hit with a bottle...just a few stitches is all. C'mon, gorgeous, get rid of that coffee and let me buy you a fresh one." Joey grabbed Vee's coffee and tossed it into a nearby garbage can, much to her disappointment.

"Joey, I'm really tired..." she said.

"Oh, c'mon...just ten minutes. Just like old times. Besides, how often do we get to see each other?" Vee relented, and the two trudged through the heavy snow to a coffee shop just down the block.

Inside the coffee shop, Vee sat contentedly at a table with her freshly brewed cup of coffee. She watched Joey who was still ordering at the counter. The two had grown up together and often hung out at Bidell's with a small clique. Joey had a thing for her back then, but she never reciprocated. He was a little too high strung for her taste. As Joey sat down at the table, Vee could tell things hadn't changed much. With a bagel in his mouth, he asked, "What are the chances of you and me going out, Vee?"

"About one in a million, Joey," she said dryly.

Not missing a beat, he jumped from his seat and shouted, "Oh, so then I still got a shot?" Vee broke out in disparaging laughter, but that didn't deter Joey.

"Listen...um, hey, whadda' you think about going on a little trip with me tomorrow?" he asked. Vee sent an ice-cold stare through him.

Joey raised his hands in defense. "We'd just be goin' to see my boy Ricky Matt. You remember him, don't you?"

"Of course, I remember him, you idiot. We were best friends long before you met him. I think you got hit on the head a little too hard tonight, Joey." she chided.

"Look, I figured we'd pay him a visit for the holidays. He's had a few bad breaks. Attica's only a half-hour away."

Vee glared at him in disbelief. "Attica! He's in prison?" she burst out. Joey nodded. "You want me to go visit Ricky? In prison? On Christmas Day?"

"Yeah, we'll be back in time for dinner," he replied enthusiastically. "You're fucked up, you know that Joey?" Joey shrugged his shoulders and took another bite out of his bagel.

The waitress came over to their table and set down two plates filled with grilled cheese sandwiches. As Vee took a contemplative bite out of her sandwich, a host of thoughts flooded her mind. She hadn't talked to Ricky in almost ten years. She wondered what he looked like now. It sounded like he was still getting into trouble. He was in Attica for Christ's sake. Vee remembered her vow that she was out of the saving business when it came to men, but this was Ricky, an old friend. She recalled the search for Beau. Ricky had never left her side. Maybe she could return the favor. A simple visit wouldn't hurt. Vee's thoughts turned to tomorrow. She wasn't really doing anything for Christmas. Family dinners were now out with Elvira in the mix. Vee was just going to spend the day at home alone. She didn't even have a pet to keep her company. As she took another bite of her sandwich, she looked at Joey. "You know something...what the hell, why not go, right?"

Joey glanced up and smiled at her change of heart. "That's what I'm talkin' about." He said. "Why the hell not!"

CHAPTER 14
A CHANCE MEETING

It was Christmas Day, and the lake effect snow machine was in high gear. The snow was coming down at an alarming three inches an hour, and the plows could no longer keep up. Snow filled roads and whiteouts from the swirling winds made driving almost impossible. Joey was having a great deal of difficulty maneuvering along the thruway, despite having an SUV with four-wheel drive. The tension on his and Vee's frazzled faces said it all.

"Joey, slow down, I don't want to wind up in the ditch!" Vee yelled.

"We're fine. We're fine. We got this," Joey said nervously as he somehow steered the SUV back onto the road from a wayward slide. Vee anxiously began counting the cars they passed that had slid off the road and were now stuck in a snowbank or in the ditch along the center median.

"This was a bad idea, Joey," she said angrily.

"C'mon, Vee we're more than halfway there. What happened to the tough girl I knew growing up?" Joey playfully chided.

"She gained some common sense. At least enough to know to not go driving in a blizzard," she exclaimed. Then punched Joey in the arm.

As the SUV plodded along, Joey's eyes suddenly lit up. "Take a look at that!" he blared out. The snow had tapered off all of a sudden and stopped. They had passed through the heavy snow band and came out into a patch of clear sky. The sun burst over the clouds and was majestically shinning on the ground. Even a faint rainbow could be seen against the dark gray clouds in the distance. Joey glanced to Vee. "A rainbow! It's gotta be a sign...oh yeah, it's gotta' be a sign," he said with enthusiasm.

"A sign for what?" she sniped back.

"Oh...never mind," Joey mumbled to himself, his face covered with a frown.

The SUV exited the thruway on to the main road. The prison was just a few hundred yards ahead. As they drew nearer, Joey and Vee's focus was immediately drawn to an ornate bell tower atop the main gate. Below it, carved in big bold letters read, "Attica Correctional Facility." It was an intimidating sight, reinforced by the impenetrable concrete walls which staggered thirty feet high and extended a half-mile down Exchange Street. Joey parked the SUV, and both visitors carefully made the short walk across the lot towards the front gate. The guard towers perched atop overlooking everything did little to ease Vee's growing apprehension. She suddenly felt exposed and vulnerable knowing every move she now made was probably being watched.

Inside the facility, Joey and Vee entered the main lobby and went to the visitors' desk. They had to show ID and entered onto the visitor list. Vee also had to fill out a visitor application since she was a first timer. Once it was approved, they were issued passes and assigned a locker to store any items which were not allowed inside the main prison. Vee threw her purse inside the locker and hung up her winter jacket. They both entered the main processing area, passing through a metal detector and got in line at the first inspection checkpoint. Here, each person went through a visual inspection and light pat down for detection of any contraband. Vee watched nervously as the woman ahead of her was asked to step off to the side into a private room for a more intensive search.

Once past the checkpoint, Joey and Vee joined other visitors and proceeded to a heavily gated doorway. It squeaked open, and the group passed into the next section. As soon as they entered, the heavy door shut behind them with a loud clang which made Vee jump. Each individual was examined by drug detection dogs before undergoing a second inspection and pat down. After they were cleared, Joey and Vee were escorted by guards through a series of secure doors to a waiting area and given a number. They sat there until a table became available in the adjacent visiting room. When their number was called, they showed their passes to the guard on the other side of the meshed window and were buzzed in. They entered, and the guard assigned them seats. "Please follow all visiting rules. No physical contact with prisoners," he stated forcefully. Joey and Vee found their seats. Vee sat down heavily and let out a relieved groan.

"Jesus, Joey!" she exclaimed. "Do you have to go through this every time you come here?"

Joey nodded his head in amusement. "Don't worry, you get used to it."

"I would not get used to this," Vee said, shaking her head. The whole experience had been nerve-wracking. The twenty-eight-year-old felt dirty and cheap from all the poking, pat-downs, and constant surveillance. As her nerves settled, Vee leaned back in the chair and looked around the room. It was filled with dozens of large wooden tables and chairs—all bolted to the floor—filled to capacity with inmates and their families meeting up for the holiday. The prisoners were dressed in bright orange jumpsuits with many seemingly desperate to take as many pictures with their loved ones as possible in the short time they had together. Vee teared up as she watched a young boy run to a large, scary looking man with tattoos up and down his arms. The boy launched himself up. The inmate caught him mid-flight, twirled him around, and quickly lowered him to the floor. Both were laughing. Vee felt a profound sadness. Physical contact was not allowed the inmates beyond a brief kiss or embrace. Not even between a father and son.

Vee's attention abruptly shifted toward a tall inmate headed directly toward her. The man had jet black hair and was built like an Adonis. He had tattoos on his arms and walked with an air of rugged confidence. "No, it can't be..." Vee said to herself. "That can't be little Ricky Matt." As he got closer, Vee could see his dark brown eyes which seemed to penetrate right through her. *It was Ricky!* He strolled to their table and offered Vee an infectious grin. He shook hands with Joey. Then reached over to do the same with Vee.

"Joey said he might bring a mystery guest. I had no idea it would be you. How you been, Vee?" he asked softly.

"Oh my God...Ricky?" She let out a girlish laugh. "You look incredible."

Ricky eyed her slender body. "You're looking pretty good yourself."

Ricky sat down at the table across from her, and the two soon became lost in each other's gaze. They started chatting as if they had just seen each other yesterday. "Bet some fries with gravy would go good right about now, huh?" she uttered nervously.

"Anything from Bidell's would go good right about now." Ricky grinned. "You always had my back, Vee. Always. I ain't never gonna' forget that." He gently grabbed her hand. "Did you know that the first time I saw you close up you were coming out of your shower? I snuck up to the back of your house and looked in the window. Your mother almost blew my head off. Pissed my pants right there." He chuckled loudly. "I never told you that one, did I?" Vee shook her head. "I thought you were the most beautiful girl I'd ever seen." Adding, "And now you've grown into the most beautiful woman I've ever seen." Vee blushed.

"And how did you end up ever looking so gorgeous...that's what I wanna know." she asked. Then added, "You were so small and wiry...just a little fucker." Two large men covered in tattoos passed by acknowledging Ricky. "How did a skinny kid like you grow up so handsome and learn to survive in a place like this?"

Ricky's face suddenly became menacing. He squeezed Vee's hand and said in a gritty voice, "I got taller...then I got bigger...then I got sick and tired of people beating on me. I fought back. Now, I'll kill any motherfucker who comes at me, and they know it." Vee was taken aback. But only for a moment. Ricky saw her reaction and immediately relaxed. He continued with a smile. "Besides, if that doesn't work, I kill them with my charm." Ricky waved his hand around like a magician casting a spell. Vee laughed, already captivated by inmate #32537. The two continued their private small talk, elated to forget their own dismal pasts, focusing more on the happy moments they had shared together. As they chatted away, a disappointed Joey sat alone, left out in the cold. This was not what he had expected. Thankfully, a prison guard he had gone to high school with now working in the visitor center came over and kept him company.

An hour into the visit, Vee and Ricky were holding hands under the table. "Stop, Ricky! The guards will see," the giddy girl said nervously.

"No worries, Vee…" he responded confidently. "They're pretty lax. Besides, it's Christmas." The two became entrenched like two high school teens lost in their first love. Vee poured her soul out to Ricky. He, likewise, opened up. Ricky smiled and playfully touched Vee's inner thigh. He slyly handed her a small piece of paper. "It's my prison address," he said.

Vee shook her head and politely declined. "Listen…I had a lot of fun catching up, Ricky. But Joey already told me. You're married, and you have a one-year-old daughter. That's where I draw the line."

Ricky placed the address back into Vee's hand and shouted in a whisper, "That woman hasn't been here to see me in eight months. And we're getting a divorce!"

Vee shot back calmly, "Well, when you two sign the papers, feel free to give me a call." Ricky's nostrils flared. He knew his divorce was six months out at least.

"Fuck that shit, Vee! Listen, I knocked her up by accident when we were both drunk. I felt sorry for her, so I married—it was a big mistake. The bitch is crazy, and I don't wanna have nothin' to do with her." Vee sat there for a long moment. Against her better judgment, she kept Ricky's address. She told him hers.

"I won't forget it." He smiled.

⟶ ⧫ ⟵

The months passed, and winter sailed through spring into summer. Vee made the short trip to Attica each Saturday afternoon for eight straight months. She had adjusted to the rigorous inspections and constant surveillance after all. The visits seemed to fill a void in her life. She was non-judgmental with Ricky, affording him the benefit of the doubt. Despite having growing feelings for him, which seemed to be mutual, she also realized she hadn't seen him in almost ten years. Vee knew very little about how much he was telling her was the truth. Considering her past with men, she wanted some level of reassurance.

Vee befriended the prison guard Joey had met at the visitor center at Christmas. She realized they had all been to the same high school growing up. Vee humorously found out she had actually defended him against a bully in a lunchroom shakedown. He had been smaller and in an earlier grade. They both laughed at the incident, especially now since he stood over six feet tall and was very muscular. During one of their conversations, Vee talked about Ricky. As a favor to his lunchroom protector, the guard tracked down the sign-in sheets for him over the past year and let her have a look. Ricky's wife was not on any of them. Vee sighed when she found out. Ricky had told her the truth.

CHAPTER 15
LOVE IS A MANY SPLENDORED THING

A dozen convicts were dressed in street clothes and filled with a growing exuberance. They were about to become ex-cons. The outer main gate doors at the Attica Correctional Facility opened, and the group exited through them into the cool morning air. Some walked towards the parking lot where a ride awaited them, but most headed towards a waiting bus parked out front. It was their ride back to civilian life and a second chance at freedom.

Two older ex-inmates lagged behind most of the others. They appeared nervous, almost hesitant to leave. The prison had been their home a long time and the thought of being on the outside frightened them. Ricky strolled by the two men happy as a Lark. "C'mon old timers, smile…you're free!" he yelled in passing, patting one of the men on the shoulder. There was no hesitancy with him, the buoyancy in Ricky's voice and spirit was unmistakable. His hair was coiffed. His attire, impeccable. A weathered suitcase swung freely in his right hand. Although the winter day was warmer than usual, it was still chilly. Ricky didn't care, the colder air invigorated him and made him feel alive. He left his overcoat in his suitcase and swaggered toward the bus.

Sitting quietly and unnoticed in the prison parking lot was a dark Pontiac Trans Am. As Ricky drew closer to the bus, the car suddenly gunned its engine and raced quickly through the lot. It came to a screeching halt directly behind the bus, honking its horn wildly, just as Ricky climbed the first step. The repeated shrieks saturated the ears of all aboard. The men glanced out the windows, agitated by the interruption of their smooth exodus.

The noise precipitously stopped. Vee exited the car. She rushed toward the bus entrance and got on. Dressed in tight jeans, a white busty sweater and sporting sculpted hair, she immediately drew the attention of the men on board. Several wolf whistles rang out. Oblivious to the disturbance up front, Ricky made his way to a seat in back. Vee spotted him right away and hollered out. "Ricky Matt!" Ricky turned. Several of the men started calling out "Ricky!" in a high-pitched-voice, mimicking Vee. Ricky smiled at the shenanigans but stood frozen in surprise, staring at Vee. He pushed through the group of ex-cons and reached out for his girl. His big hands grabbed her by the waist and lifted her high into the air. They both looked each other in the eye and smiled. Ricky slowly lowered Vee back down, and the two engaged in a long overdue kiss. The busload of ex-cons erupted in catcalls, clapping and laughter. The reunion was capped off by a congratulatory yell, "You lucky bastard!"

Ricky and Vee drifted off the bus holding hands, confident their new life together would be a fresh start for both. For Vee, Ricky had passed a test. He had said his divorce had come through, but Vee had never actually seen the document. She had a nagging thought in the back of her mind his supposed ex-wife would show up today and claim her property. Vee had waited in the parking lot until the last second to confirm Ricky indeed remained unclaimed. Vee Harris now had her man.

Both got in the car, and Vee drove to an open spot in the back row of the parking lot. Eight months of limited touching and physical affection were suddenly unleashed. Ricky and Vee mauled each other for over an hour inside the Trans Am. Vee was partially unclothed when a correction's officer tapped on the passenger window. They composed themselves, and Ricky rolled down the window. "Don't you think you two should find a motel?" the officer asked amicably."

"You're right, officer. We were just about to leave. Thanks." Ricky said grinning. After the officer left, Vee laughed and handed Ricky a small bag dressed with a bow. He opened it and took out two Snickers bars. A big smile overtook him. He opened one and took a big bite, sharing the rest with Vee.

"Just like old times," she said.

The Trans Am pulled out of the parking lot and took off down the open road. Ricky leaned back in the passenger's seat and stared out the window. It had been a couple years since he had taken in the scenery. His attention soon shifted to the array of instrument gauges on the dashboard. He could feel the power in the engine. Vee glanced over, sensing what Ricky wanted to do next. She knew he loved speed. Vee pulled off to the side of the road and stopped. "Let's switch," she said. Ricky looked at her with a shit-eatin' grin.

"Ohhh, baby," he said excitedly.

The two exited the car and switched positions. Vee glanced at Ricky and tapped on the glove box. "I got some get out of jail free cards so knock yourself out," she said joyfully.

"You sure about this?" he asked.

"It shimmies over a hundred—might be the differential. But you should be good," she chimed back. Ricky howled and put the car in gear. It got up to speed in seconds and disappeared down the road. The hour-long trip to Vee's place took less than thirty-five minutes.

Vee's newly renovated apartment sat on top of an unused garage where the owner allowed her to park her car. It gave the welcoming impression of being a two-story home. Inside, the apartment was beautifully decorated and furnished throughout by Vee's immaculate taste. It had all the amenities. Vee stood in the middle of her living room beaming with pride. "Welcome to your new home," she said to Ricky.

He looked around the room and shook his head in disbelief. "This is incredible, Vee," he said. Adding, "A major step up from where I've been at."

Vee smiled. "Make yourself at home. I'll be in the kitchen making dinner," she said proudly. Vee gave him an affectionate hug and disappeared back into the kitchen with a sprightly jump. Ricky put his suitcase down and sunk into the plush sofa. He leaned back and closed his eyes. He could already smell the mouthwatering aromas of the food starting to cook on the stove.

The early winter dusk had already taken away most of the sunlight outside. Ricky entered the dark hallway after taking a long hot shower. He was dressed only in stonewashed jeans. Where he was standing, Vee could see his chiseled body silhouetted in the contrasting light. He was built like a Greek god, she thought. Ricky stepped forward into the light, exposing the hideous scars that dominated his upper body. A lifetime of beatings, fights, and escapes had taken their toll. Vee's initial shock immediately turned to compassion. Ricky frowned when he realized what she was looking at. "It is what it is, Vee," he declared. "I don't cry over it. What'd be the point?"

She walked over to him and kissed his lips. "We all have scars, Ricky. But I'll always be there for you. That's the point."

Dinner would have to wait; there would be no emotional games tonight. This would be their moment. Vee lit several candles inside the living room. She undressed to her panties and bra and went into the bedroom. Ricky stripped to his briefs and followed her. Soothing music emanated from the stereo as Vee approached Ricky standing by the bed. He motioned to speak but was silenced with a finger placed gently over his lips. Ricky raised Vee in his arms and carefully laid his lover onto the soft sheets. He glanced into her eyes and straddled her sensual body. Ricky slowly removed her panties and began kissing her. Not a word was spoken. Their deep penetrating kisses spoke volumes. They stared into each other's eyes. Their bodies entwined as one. Lost in the sweet moment, Ricky finally made love to his childhood sweetheart and best friend.

—•— ▚◆▚ —•—

Ricky and Vee's bliss continued throughout the holidays and well into the Buffalo winter. Vee's dad had come through again, securing a job for Ricky at a local construction company. The two young lovers even enjoyed regular dinners on Sunday afternoons with Vee's parents at the old house. At first, it had been awkward, considering their past with Elvira, but she had changed somewhat. Ever since Herb had returned home, she seemed more subdued. Elvira was still stern, but she actually tried to be more amenable.

Two months into their new relationship, Vee found out she was pregnant. She and Ricky were both ecstatic, feeling it would only cement their bond. Ricky hoped for a boy this time around. He felt he had been cheated from experiencing fatherhood thus far. Ricky hadn't seen his daughter in quite some time. Not while in prison, nor since his release. His ex-wife had obtained a restraining order which prevented his efforts. Only after a brief legal tussle was he given an opportunity to spend a recent afternoon with his two-year-old, showing her off to his friends at a local bar.

With a new baby now on the way, both having jobs and a nice place to live, the future was looking bright for Ricky and Vee. However, their relationship unexpectedly began to head south. To Vee's surprise, Ricky began acting erratically. He would take his paychecks on Friday afternoon and not return home until Monday morning, reeking of booze. Somehow, he still managed to shower and make it to work on time.

Vee hadn't become aware of it right away. She was working odd hours and pulling doubles on the weekends. She was rarely home except to sleep. Eventually, she noticed the bed wasn't being slept in. To explain his absence, Ricky claimed he was just killing time with some old buddies. He didn't want to be alone. After some checking, Vee learned the whole truth. Ricky had been drinking and playing poker with some of the local riffraff and had amassed a hefty debt. Out of the blue, he had started drinking and gambling his weekends away. Vee was caught off guard. It was a side of Ricky she had never seen.

Ricky knew he was having problems and why. In prison, he had been receiving regular shock therapy treatments throughout his stays. Ricky welcomed his so called mini-electrocutions and consented to them voluntarily. They helped control his wild mood swings, especially the downward spirals. As a side perk, he also discovered they rubbed out some of his long-term memory which was fine with him. Why would he want to remember his childhood anyway? It was a win-win.

Since being released, Ricky no longer received shock therapy or meds to treat his disorders. He also didn't tell Vee or seek out medical treatment. He thought he could fight through any issues that arose on his own. However, the symptoms crept up on him slowly and unawares until they enveloped him. He started to gravitate towards anything that would dull his mind or keep it occupied, just to keep the demons away. Ricky drank excessively, chain smoked, and went out on all-night gambling binges. They all became necessary vices for his survival on the outside.

CHAPTER 16
BONE COLLECTOR

It was St. Patrick's Day, and the drinks were flowing freely at Mulligan's Brick Bar. Ricky had guzzled down a case of beer and six gimlets during an eight-hour poker binge in the back room. Now he sat in the main bar area atop a beer-stained table surrounded by a small group of eager listeners. "...you guys remember the movie *The Great Escape*, right? Well, I did the same thing McQueen did at the Nazi prison camp. Alden's got a blind spot—same as the Kraut guard tower. So, I waited till night and slipped out the window. Made a beeline straight for it." Ricky chuckled. "I actually scaled that motherfuckin' razor sharp fence—look, you can still see the scars." He turned out his arms so the group could see the several faded marks underneath.

"What the fuck did you do next?" somebody asked.

Ricky gave a wry smile and guzzled down another beer. "I stole a Clydesdale from a hick's barn near the prison. The kind they use for parades. Then rode that son-of-bitch bareback to the train station." Ricky lifted his empty shot glass, and the bartender quickly supplied him with another gimlet. He paused a moment and tried to remember what happened next. Ricky continued on with a mischievous grin. "... right. Then at a full gallop, mind you—I jumped off the horse onto the fuckin' caboose of a moving train."

"No shit!" a voice chimed in from the buzzing crowd.

"That ain't what I heard," interrupted an old, wiry stiff standing just in earshot. "You hopped an open box-car on foot...on a slow-moving freight line."

Ricky glared at the man for a moment but then relaxed. "It doesn't matter what the fuck you heard," he said icily. "The point is, I made it." Ricky picked up his gimlet and swallowed it down in one quick gulp.

As Ricky started on another story, a large three-hundred-pound man sitting at the bar downed his fourth double whiskey. He threw his money on the bar to pay his tab and stood up. He was done listening to Ricky's colorful stories. It was time for business. The hulk approached the table, and Ricky glanced up. "Hello, Rocco," he said in a sober moment.

"Ricky," the giant acknowledged. Ricky knew why he was there. And so did his audience as they promptly disbursed. Rocco nodded towards the door and both men exited outside.

They walked around Mulligan's to the cramped alley in the back. It was a dark, dingy space saturated with a rancid smell. A half-dozen steel garbage cans were filled to the brim with rotted foodstuffs. Ricky took off the *Members Only* jacket Vee had purchased for him and placed it gently on top of a garbage can. Rocco did the same. For Ricky, it was either take the beating now or a bullet to the head later. He had lost $2,500 that day on top of what he already owed. Taking his beating now would give him another week to come up with the money.

Ricky stood there stoically with his arms by his side. He was prepared not to fight back and simply take the punishment. Rocco lunged forward and delivered a series of violent blows to Ricky's face. His nose started to bleed, and a gash formed on his chin. The toughened ex-con then staggered back after taking powerful back-to-back punches to the midsection. Ricky paused for a moment, bent over, then stood back up defiantly. Getting angry, Rocco unleashed a barrage of punches to his face and body, but Ricky seemed oblivious to the pain. He refused to go down.

Rocco stood there dumbstruck; he was exhausted and gulping for his next breath. Anyone on the receiving end of that should have been down for the count, he thought to himself. The foul stench of the garbage now forced him to dry heave several times. Ricky stood there callously, eyeing his punisher.

"We done here, Rocco?" He smirked.

Rocco shook his head. From what he could see, the beating hadn't inflicted any significant damage. Ricky almost looked unscathed, despite the ferocity of the attack.

"I got a wife and three kids at home, Ricky," Rocco pleaded.

"And I got Vee, a kid, and one on the way. What's your point?" Ricky asked.

"Angelo hears you walked back into the bar like you just got a bloody nose, I'm a dead man." Rocco removed a blackjack (a piece of leather covering metal) from inside his jacket. "Sorry, I gotta' do this, Ricky."

Seeing this, Ricky took up a defensive position. "That's not in the rules," he said. "I took my punishment for the week. You do this, and it becomes survival of the fittest."

Rocco paid him no heed and lunged forward. He slipped slightly on the wet ground. Ricky bobbed to the side and delivered a solid right hook to Rocco's chin. He got around him and twisted Rocco's arm behind his back. Ricky violently jerked the arm up, breaking it soundly at the elbow. Rocco let out a painful yell, and the blackjack fell to the ground. In a fury, Ricky followed with a series of stern jabs and a savage uppercut to Rocco's chin. It sent the giant man flying into a pile of rubbish.

Rocco lay in a heap of garbage. His face was battered and covered in blood. He was writhing in pain as his cries cascaded into the unwelcoming night. Ricky stood over him angrily. "You shouldn't have done it, Rocco," he said. Ricky bent down and delivered one last powerful blow to the enforcer's jaw, rendering him unconscious. Ricky reached down with his powerful arms and hoisted the huge man over his shoulder. He limped over to the dumpster and threw him in. Sporting a smug grin, Ricky put on his jacket and grabbed Rocco's, tossing it in the dumpster as he stepped out of the alley.

It was a two-hour hike to Vee's apartment. Ricky knew it would be plenty of time to sober up and clear his head. He began the long trek home. With the adrenaline from the fight wearing down, Ricky began to feel sharp, searing pains in his chest every time his lungs filled with air. "That fucker cracked some of my ribs," he said to himself. Ricky just gritted out the pain. He wiped the blood away from his nose and started to smile. Snickered. He didn't care. By tomorrow, everyone would hear about tonight's fight and would know who was king. That suited the former foster kid just fine. Ricky clenched his fists and let out a loud victory roar into the quiet night sky.

⊷⊷ ⊠◆⊠ ⊶⊶

It was 6:30 A.M. The temperature was brisk as dawn started to break. Vee stepped out of her apartment and walked down the steps to the garage below. The front of her Trans Am was facing out, and she stared angrily at the left front fender which had been smashed in. Ricky had gotten into an accident a week earlier after a night of drinking. It made her angry every time she looked at it. Vee checked her watch and entered the car. As it pulled out, Vee abruptly stopped. She sat there simmering in exasperation at the disheveled man that suddenly entered the driveway and slowly approached. Vee rolled down the window. "No sense asking what happened to the other guy," she yelled out in disgust. Ricky just stood there with a downcast face. "Well, at least you're sober," Vee continued. "Your bags are packed, but the locks have been changed. The landlord will let you in this afternoon to pick up your things."

Ricky stood there conquered. He knew his time with Vee was up. "Vee...look, I get to drinking, then the next thing I know, I just can't remember anything," Ricky said remorsefully.

"You remembered where you live, didn't you?" Vee said heatedly.

He glanced up. "Listen, uh...look, I really gotta' take a dump. Could I just use the bathroom? Then I'll go. Please?" Ricky pleaded. Vee scowled and reluctantly handed him her new key through the open window.

"Hurry up. I need to get to work," she said harshly. Ricky headed up the stairs. "Spray the Lysol when you're finished," she yelled after him.

Several minutes later, the upstairs door opened, and Ricky emerged from the apartment. His shirt was off, and his bare arms and chest were covered in blood from several wounds. Vee watched in horror as he staggered down the concrete stairs, falling down hard on the bottom step. Vee grabbed her nursing bag in the back seat and rushed to his aid. She rolled him onto his back and made a quick examination of his wounds. Her initial concern turned hastily to disgust. "If you were trying to bleed out and kill yourself, superficial wounds ain't gonna get it done," she said coldly. "It was a cheap stunt, Ricky," she added angrily. Vee quickly cleaned him up and dressed his wounds. Ricky just lay there with vacant eyes as she worked on him.

When she was done, Vee grabbed the apartment key from Ricky and started to exit. Ricky grabbed her leg. "If I can't have you in my life, then I don't want to live anymore, Vee!" he shouted. Vee stood there a long moment. She was affected by his compassionate plea, but she had had enough.

How much was real and how much was an act? she thought to herself. Vee reached down and kissed him softly on the forehead. "Just pick up your shit this afternoon, okay?" she said. Ricky nodded. He watched helplessly as Vee entered her car and sped off down the street.

Later that afternoon, Joey drove Ricky back to the apartment after work. Both men were caked in dried cement and reeked of alcohol. Ricky was met by the landlord as soon as he arrived. The middle-aged man appeared anxious to get the business over as quickly as possible. "I'll let you in. But I don't want any trouble here, Mr. Matt," he whispered. "Please just retrieve your belongings. Then I need for you to go."

Ricky threw his hands up in the air and shouted, "Fine!" The landlord led Ricky up the stairs then into the apartment.

A short time later, Ricky emerged with two large bags full of clothes and a suitcase. He wanted to make a quick exit, but the landlord was waiting for him at the bottom of the stairs. "Mr. Matt, I mentioned this to Miss Harris this morning. If you folks don't pay your rent today, I'll be forced to file a three-day eviction notice," he exclaimed. "I have bills too, sir."

Ricky waved to Joey standing back at the car. "Be there in a minute, Joey." He then carefully set down his bags and casually walked up to the landlord. "Could you tell me what you said again, please?" he asked politely, but then quickly thrust up his index finger. "Wait...never mind." Without warning, Ricky grabbed the landlord by the shirt collar and twisted him violently to the ground. "I pay the bills around here!" he shouted. "You got a problem, you come to me. Understand?" The landlord nodded in fear. Ricky pulled out a flip knife and pressed it up against the frightened man's neck. "You will not speak to Miss Harris about this again, correct?"

"Correct," the landlord conceded. Ricky released him and grabbed his bags. An unhappy Joey, who had watched the whole thing, now waited nervously for him in the car. As soon as Ricky and the bags were in, the car spun out in an angry cloud of dust.

The following afternoon, Ricky was arrested at his job site. Unable to make bail, he spent the weekend in a holding cell. During his Monday arraignment, his old friend and mentor Detective Beamish showed up in court. They had stayed in touch over the years since Ricky's days at Father Baker. Beamish kept tabs on him and would often try and help when he could. Apparently, Beamish had made some provisions for the arraignment because the judge immediately sentenced Ricky to six weekend months in jail, with the stipulation he report to prison after work on Friday afternoons. It was a sweet deal for a man who had been charged with felony assault with a deadly weapon.

CHAPTER 17
BORN TO BE ALIVE

On the first Friday of his sentence, Ricky showed up at Vee's apartment in a panic. He needed a ride to jail. The repeat felon was taking a chance being there. The landlord had obtained a restraining order, but he was desperate. Vee stood at the door callously. She knew Joey could have given him a lift. She also knew why he was there. Ricky was grasping for another chance.

He looked at her with a somber grin. "Please, Vee, if I'm late one minute, I do six month's straight time," he pleaded. Vee suppressed a groan as she grabbed her purse and flipped him the car keys. Ricky grinned widely. They both walked down to the Trans Am parked below. His deadline was a hard 6 o'clock, and it was already 5:30 P.M. The trip to the Wende Correctional Facility would take twenty-five minutes. Without hesitating, Ricky stepped hard on the accelerator, and the Trans Am fishtailed out of the driveway.

"I know I act like a dick sometimes...but you're my girl, Vee...the only girl I'll ever care about," Ricky announced.

Vee forced a look at him as he drove. When sober and things were good, she thought to herself, he was everything she wanted in a guy. When his switch flipped, he was a different person. In either case, her physical desire for him never waned. She still thought he was the sexiest man she had ever laid eyes on. She was even frightened by the intensity of her desires. Like now. Ricky quickly glanced over at Vee and noticed she was staring at him. "What?" he asked.

Halfway to their destination, they stopped at a traffic light that had turned red. Without uttering a word, Vee moved closer to Ricky. She reached down and undid his belt buckle. Vee jerked his pants down and slid them to his knees. Her head lowered and disappeared between his legs. As Ricky sat there, he glanced over at the car idling next to them. An older lady was looking at him with disgust. He nodded politely. The light turned green, and the Trans Am jumped forward. With his left hand still on the wheel, Ricky reached towards Vee's waist with his right. He undid her jeans and slipped his hand under her panties. They spent the next fifteen minutes pleasuring each other as Ricky maneuvered through traffic. Upon arriving at Wende, Ricky calmly pulled up his pants and exited the car. He strolled into the prison just before the clock struck six wearing a big smile.

Six months passed, and Ricky finished his weekends-only prison stint. He did everything he could to work his way back into Vee's life. He even gave up drinking and gambling. Vee tried to make it work. She caught up on the rent and managed to convince the landlord to give them another chance, despite what had happened. However, being off liquor made Ricky's disruptive outbursts worse. Over the course of a week, two separate arguments escalated into violent fights at the apartment, both requiring police intervention. After that, the landlord had finally had enough, Ricky and Vee were evicted. Vee was incensed, unsure of what to do next. She had credit card bills, a car payment, and a baby on the way that would require 24/7 care.

During dinner one evening at her parent's house, Elvira suggested the expectant mother move back home until she could buy a place of her own. That same offer did not extend to Ricky. The Harris matriarch felt quite differently about his future. "The man's a powder keg, Vee," she said with unease. "Just waiting to explode. And I don't need that. Not at my age. I know we've had our troubles, but what's done is done. You're still my daughter and you're welcome here. But not that uomo cattivo."

"He's not a bad man, Mom," Vee said. "I love him. And he loves me."

Elvira frowned as she took her daughter's hand. "Honey, my time with your father has been a series of broken promises and unfulfilled dreams. What makes you think your life with this jerk is going to be any different? In fact, it'll probably be ten times worse. Herbie was never violent."

"I know Ricky has problems, Mom. But he gave up the drinking and gambling. Just for me and our baby." Vee cried. "Let him stay here. Please? He loves me the best he can, and he is the father of your first grandchild."

Elvira stood up from the table and rubbed her eyes underneath her reading glasses. She had grown up around Ricky's type. The time-tested mom knew her daughter's days could be filled with suffering and danger. She also realized if she didn't allow Ricky to move in, Vee would meekly go with him somewhere else. "Okay, he can move in," she relented. "But one episode and he's out of here. Understand?" Vee smiled and approached Elvira. She was hoping for a hug from her mom but settled for a peck on the cheek.

Over the next two months, things went surprisingly well. Herb had come through and secured Ricky another job. The two men got along well together and spent their evenings after work refurbishing the apartment in the attic at home. Ricky even built a pinewood crib for his child in his free time, spending countless hours in the basement perfecting it. The constant focus on work along with the upcoming birth of his child seemed to have a positive effect on Ricky. It made him less exposed to negative distractions which in turn kept his moods in check. By all appearances, Ricky had turned over a new leaf.

On September 10th, 1991, 6 lb. 5 oz. Nicholas Harris was born. Ricky stood in Vee's hospital room at her bedside overcome with joy. He was passing out expensive cigars to anyone he encountered. For Ricky, this was all new to him. He had been incarcerated during the birth of his first child. Now he was smiling from ear to ear. "We got a boy, Vee! We got a baby boy!" he shouted. "Shit, even you look good to me today, Elvira," he said jokingly. Ricky reached over and warmly kissed his future mother-in-law on the cheek. "Time to bury the hatchet...Mom," he said smiling as he shook her hand. Elvira glanced at her daughter and feigned a smile back at Ricky, wondering where he had stolen the cigars from.

As she sat up in her hospital bed, the first-time mother beamed with happiness. Vee kissed her son, who was nuzzled against her bosom, and carefully tried to hand him to his father. A frightened Ricky stepped back. "Wait a second, guys. Uh...what do I do, Vee? I don't wanna' break'em."

Elvira chuckled. "You're not going to break him, you moron. Just make sure you support the back of his head." Ricky took Nick gingerly into his arms. The boy immediately began to cry. Instinctively, the new father placed the child on his shoulder and began rocking him. He soon quieted down. Tears of joy streaked down Ricky's face. "Things are gonna' be different for you little guy," he said quietly. "I'm your daddy, and I promise you." Vee shed tears of her own as she gazed at Ricky holding his newborn son.

In a gesture of peace, Ricky attempted to hand his son to Elvira. At first, she strangely recoiled. Her face became almost ashen. It was filled with an intense anxiety. Elvira recovered quickly and forced herself to hold her first grandchild. After taking the little boy into her arms, she became lost in thought. Herb placed a loving hand on her shoulder. They glanced at each other with sorrowful faces. Each knowing the reason for their anguished looks.

Almost thirty years earlier, Elvira had been eight and a half months pregnant with their third child. She began experiencing severe abdominal cramps and knew something was wrong. Elvira was rushed to the hospital and gave birth to Herb Jr. To their horror, he had been born dead. The umbilical cord had wrapped around his neck. Elvira had not held a baby boy in her arms since that dreadful day. Not until now. The proud grandmother kissed her grandson with great feeling and gently handed him back to Ricky. She and Herb watched the little boy fall asleep on his father's chest as he sat in a hospital chair.

Two days later, the family brought little Nick home. Vee had taken eight weeks off work, four of which included paid vacation time. They were getting short of money, so Ricky committed himself to doing what needed to be done to pick up the slack. He took extra shifts at work, unloading freight at the local docks. However, the daily toil of unloading 150-pound bags of flour ten hours a day wasn't something he was well-suited for. It was boring work. He knew he was a born hustler and had a knack for it. He could earn five times his weekly pay with one good home invasion. It was always a temptation, but he stayed on the level. For three straight weeks, the devoted father toiled at the docks and returned home every evening to Nick and Vee.

Five weeks after Nick's birth, Vee was invited to a house party with friends from the old neighborhood. She asked Ricky to go, but he declined. "They're your friends," he stated, "not mine." Ricky knew himself to be extremely jealous. If an ex-boyfriend of Vee's showed up at the party, he wasn't sure what he was capable of. Better not to tempt fate, he thought. Vee insisted none of her ex-boyfriends would be there, but it fell on deaf ears. In the end, she went to the party alone. With nothing to do, Ricky decided to treat himself to a local poker game held behind the docks where he worked.

With cash from his sixty-hour work week burning a hole in his pocket, Ricky was gleaming with confidence. He was convinced he could out-hustle the hustlers. He hadn't taken a drink or smoked weed in several weeks. His mind was sharp as a tack. The underground get-together took place behind the company's lakefront warehouse in a small shack. Some of the union workers who organized the game had built, wired, and filled it with nice amenities, including central air and a large fridge. It was nice setup. However, the sharks coming to the game were not there for the refreshments. They stopped by to feed on the new workers like Ricky.

The hour had grown late, and the games were finishing up. Ricky was up $3,500 and sitting pretty. A cigarette dangled from his mouth. A bottle of Coke sat in his lap. Joey entered the shack and quietly approached him. He bent down and whispered in his ear. Ricky's face went cold. He gasped. Someone said, "Call." Ricky laid down a full house. There were several moans at the table followed by a rush of players to the exit. Most of them were broke, wondering what they would tell their wives when they got home.

Ricky didn't care about them or the four thousand dollars in front of him. Joey had seen Vee talking to an ex-boyfriend on the front lawn at the party. They spent the entire evening together being real friendly. Ricky pocketed his winnings and pondered the news. The day before, he had bought the woman he loved an expensive engagement ring, but now all he could think about was her betrayal. He clenched his fist in anger.

Seeing Ricky's growing rage and the card game breaking up, Joey nervously grabbed a sandwich and tried to stop what he had started. "Listen, Ricky," he said, "Maybe they didn't spend the whole evening together. I only caught glimpses of things here and there. Maybe it wasn't even Taz. It's hard to say...I'd been drinking..."

Ricky interrupted. "Fuck that shit, Joey. It is what it is. She lied to me." Ricky took a long swig from an open bottle of scotch sitting nearby and flung a fifty-dollar bill on the table. He angrily rushed out the door and climbed into his used Ford pickup, bought on the cheap at a recent police auction. Ricky cranked over the old engine and sped off into the chilly night, leaving Joey standing in the parking lot with a troubled look.

Ricky stared blankly at the Halloween decorations on each passing house as he drove by, a string of dark thoughts filling his mind. He knew he couldn't live without Vee. That was certain. But now it felt as if she had abandoned him like so many others had before in his life. His imagination raced. He felt intense anger and rage. All directed towards the woman who had been there with him through thick and thin. Ricky tried to force his mind back into neutral. There was a stripper he had befriended a few months earlier when he had been apart from Vee. He still had her number. Maybe he could go there until he cooled down. Ricky took a deep breath and pulled off to the side of the road. The cars seemed to zip by him in one continuous blur.

As he sat alone in silence, Ricky's emotional rage abruptly shifted to profound sadness as he began to sob uncontrollably. He grabbed a sheet of paper and pen from the glovebox and wrote a letter to Vee.

When he was done, he quietly read it back to himself, "Vee, it is now time for us to part ways. Obviously, I think more favorably of myself than you do. So, reflecting on the situation before me, I think it best we say adios. Love, Ricky." He folded the paper and wrote Vee's name on the back.

The Ford got back on the road and headed across town. Ten minutes later, it pulled into the Harris's driveway. Ricky exited the truck and made his way to the front porch. He stood there for an unexpected moment and looked angrily at the quiet house. Everyone inside must have been asleep. Ricky was dead set on ringing the doorbell and waking Vee but then thought better of it because of Nick. He dropped the letter and the house key into the mailbox slot. Ricky reentered his truck. The broken man rubbed his face in his hands. He reached around to his back pocket and felt his stuffed wallet to make sure it was still there. His next stop would be a strip club across the Canadian border. He could lose himself there.

The next afternoon, Vee read Joey the riot act in her driveway. "Why the fuck would you say that Joey! Why?!" she screamed. "Especially to Ricky. You know how he is." Joey looked at the ground shaking his head.

"I don't know, Vee. I...I just fucked up, okay?" He stammered.

"You're goddamn right you fucked up!" she screamed. "Taz wasn't even at the party!"

"I know. I know," Joey said, trying to calm her down. "Listen, Vee... I called Ricky...I told him it was a mistake... The fuckin' lunatic wouldn't believe me."

"What did you expect, for Christ's sake?" she yelled. "What did you expect?" For the first time, Joey stood there openly fearful. Not for himself but for Taz. Ricky had threatened to kill him.

"...I'll just tell Taz to get out of town for a couple days until Ricky cools down, okay?" he said. Vee stood there glaring at him. "What else can I do? ...I mean Jesus, Vee!" Joey yelled out in frustration, throwing up his arms. Vee stormed back in the house.

Later that evening, with Herb away on a fishing trip and Elvira retiring early with the flu, Vee sat alone in the attic apartment getting herself and little Nick ready for bed. Although the apartment was already warm, Vee set the thermostat up a little higher for the sensitive toddler. The protective mother turned down the lights and gently placed her son into the crib by her bed. Intent on rocking him to sleep with a lullaby.

Despite the relative quiet of the house, Vee felt a growing unease. It was making her jittery. An unexpected chill prompted her to go to the window to make sure it was shut. She closed the curtain. Then suddenly gasped. A large figure had darted into the woods. "Oh my God!" she said to herself. Vee stepped back and watched anxiously through the gap in the curtains. Had it been an animal? A man? ...Could she have imagined it? Vee thought. Several minutes passed but nothing appeared. She waited another few minutes, but when nothing showed, Vee was convinced her mind was just playing tricks. She was too wound up about Ricky.

Just to feel safe, she checked the lock on the window, even though it was on the second floor. She lit a cigarette to calm her nerves and grabbed a flashlight. Vee proceeded to make a quick pass through the entire house, making sure every outside door and window was securely locked. When she had finished, she returned to her bedroom. Vee locked the door behind her and angled a wooden chair under the handle to act as a stopper. For added measure, she created a makeshift alarm using string and an old-fashioned alarm clock which would be set off if the door handle was turned from the outside hallway. Now Vee felt more secure. She checked on Nick, slipped into her nightgown, then retreated to her bed where she fell into a deep slumber.

At 2:00 A.M., a sudden noise awakened Vee. The bedroom door was wide open, and a sinister silhouette hovered near her bed in the darkness. It was Ricky. Vee's eyes opened wide in horror. Before she could let out a scream, Ricky lunged forward and pressed his left hand over her mouth. He held the blade of his flip knife against her throat with his right. "Don't say a fuckin' word." He snarled in his gravelly voice. Vee lay there silently.

Ricky wreaked of vodka and quiet rage. He straddled over Vee's body, pinning her to the bed. "You know I'm gonna' have to kill you right, Vee?" he whispered.

"Don't do this, Ricky," she pleaded.

"I told you not to say a fuckin' word!" he replied angrily. Ricky got up on his knees and raised his knife up high so he could end his misery. But before he could strike, Vee freed her left leg and sharply kneed him in the groin. Ricky flinched hard as he rolled over sideways in pain. The knife dropped out of his hand and bounced wildly across the floor. Desperate for survival, Vee grabbed a finger on Ricky's left hand and pulled back with all her might. There was a sharp snap and the finger bent back awkwardly. Ricky stared at the broken extremity. "Look what you did." He chuckled. Ricky turned quickly and threw a violent slap to Vee's face with his other hand, knocking her off the bed.

Vee dove for the knife, but it was wedged solidly between the heater and wall. Ricky grabbed a clump of her hair, brutally pulled her away from it. She spun from his grip with tenacious strength. "Bring it on, Ricky. Bring it on," she shouted. Ricky bull-rushed her into the wall with great force. She fell to the floor hard. He stood over her and began stomping on her chest with his steel-toed boot. The distraught mom writhed in pain but managed to catch his boot and twist his leg so he fell to the floor. She lunged forward, tugging strenuously at his hair and scratching at his eyes with her nails. Ricky jumped to his feet and rushed at Vee again. He pulled her off the floor by her hair and flung her violently on to the bed. Ricky straddled her thin frame and clamped his hands around her neck. He slowly started to squeeze the life out of her.

Unable to move and struggling to breathe, Vee's vision started to blur. She tried to push Ricky off, but her strength was finally giving out. She frantically gasped for air sensing her end was near. In a last act of desperation, Vee stuck out her thumb and shoved it solidly into Ricky's right eye. He let out a groan and fell backwards onto the floor, holding his eye. Vee rolled off the bed taking huge gulps of air. She struggled to walk. Vee picked up a wooden chair on the floor and raced to the window. She sent it crashing through the pane, sending shards of glass everywhere. Vee removed some of the shards that had fallen on her sleeping son. She felt sure Ricky would not hurt the boy. The desperate mother rushed to jump out the shattered window but was intercepted by Ricky. He grabbed her by the waist and threw her to the floor which was covered with pieces of sharp glass. She started to bleed profusely from multiple cuts.

Elvira suddenly appeared in the doorway. She glanced down in horror at her daughter, who was laying on the floor in a pool of blood. Ricky was stomping on her feet with his boot. The Harris matriarch looked at him and bellowed at the top of her lungs. "Get your ass out of here before I call 911, you son-of-a-bitch!"

Ricky stopped and turned towards her. "You want some of this too, *Mom*?" He snickered. Ricky rushed Elvira and grabbed her by the arm. He brutally flung her against the wall. As Ricky moved to hit her, a dazed Vee crawled her way to the top of the stairs. Ricky turned to halt Vee's escape but was stopped by Elvira from behind. She grabbed his hair and tugged back with all her might. In a last-ditch effort, Vee hurled herself forward and slid down fifteen stairs. Ricky released himself from Elvira's dogged grip and slammed her onto the bed. Filled with unbridled rage, he ran down the bloodied stairs toward the mother of his only son.

At the bottom of the landing, lay a semi-conscious Vee. The cord from the wall phone was wrapped around her chest. Although unable to utter a word, she still managed to dial 911. And Ricky knew it. He was greeted with a fuck off and die gesture from Vee despite her state. Covered with blood himself, Ricky stood there motionless. He approached Vee with a savage look in his eyes. In one final gesture, he raised his steel-toe boot and slammed it violently on to Vee's chest. She lay unconscious as Ricky made his way out of the house.

CHAPTER 18
BEATING THE RAP

Late in the afternoon on the following day, a station wagon pulled into the Harris driveway and came to a stop. Herb got out, went around the car, and assisted Vee out from the front passenger seat. She had just been treated and released from the hospital, despite the objections by her physician. Her injuries had not been life threatening, but they were substantial. In addition to the numerous cuts and bruises, she had sustained two black eyes and three broken ribs. The bandages wrapped around her lower chest were visible through her bloodstained shirt. A cast also extended up to the knee on her right leg where Ricky had fractured two bones in her instep. Still, the proud mother persevered and hobbled along on a pair of crutches.

Already waiting in the driveway were two unmarked police cars. The detectives exited their cars when Vee got out of the wagon. One of them offered her assistance into the house, but she politely declined. Vee knew they had come for her statement. A declaration which would imprison the father of her child for a very long time. Ten to twenty years by her estimation. However, deciding Ricky's fate would have to wait. The concerned mom had something more pressing on her mind.

Despite each breath causing severe discomfort, Vee labored to make it into the house. She went into the living room and sank into a large comfortable chair. The anxious mom only waited a few moments before

Elvira entered from the side hallway and handed her Nick. The boy had not been harmed and appeared to be oblivious to what had transpired. The toddler let out a gurgle of joy as he lay in his mother's arms.

Dave Beamish entered the living room with two other officers and calmly took a seat. Elvira followed them in with coffee and snacks. "Thank you, ma'am." Beamish nodded. He grabbed a coffee and helped himself to the cream and sugar. Beamish was now a detective with the North Tonawanda police department. His jurisdiction was in the next town over, but he was tight with the local police captain. He asked if he could stop by to check on the case.

Ricky had recently helped Beamish get three kilos of heroin off the streets. His years of hustling on the street and his prison connections made him a unique source of information. Beamish leveraged Ricky's disdain for drugs into a useful tool to make a dent in the local narcotics traffic. Over the years, his information often led to busts which got drugs out of circulation and saved lives. Those successes also fueled Beamish's rapid rise in the ranks, something Ricky was not unaware of.

When Beamish had heard of the assault, he came to get the facts and determine how much jail time Ricky was looking at. But there was only so much he could do. He had to balance his compassion for the victim with the potential of losing one of his best informants. If Ricky was convicted of all the charges, he would be gone a long time. So far, the corroborating details on the assault were tenuous at best. Elvira hadn't seen Ricky actually assault her daughter so her statement would be hearsay. There was physical evidence of a struggle but that alone was not enough to convict Ricky of the most egregious charges. Everything depended on the statement of Vee Harris. Judging by her battered appearance, Beamish had braced himself for the worst.

However, after nearly two hours and three cups of coffee, Beamish sat dumbfounded by Vee's responses to his questions. "...so, what you're saying now, Miss Harris..." he said, "is that you're not even sure if Ricky even had a knife?" Vee nodded in agreement.

"Maybe I hit my head," she said. "I honestly can't remember a knife even being there. I'm sorry."

"Maybe you're experiencing selective amnesia, hmm?" Beamish smirked.

"Come to think of it, I'm not even 100 percent sure it was Ricky who even attacked me," Vee added. The two locked eyes, and the detective finally relented.

"I see. Well, thank you for your time, Miss Harris."

Beamish and the two other detectives stood up and headed for the door. Before the last detective exited, he turned to Vee and said, "You know, men like Ricky Matt never change, ma'am. Never."

Vee feigned a smile back. "Thank you for stopping by." The detectives returned to their cars and left. Beamish had come there to find holes in Vee's statement so he could reduce Ricky's sentence. Instead, Vee had handed Ricky back his freedom on a silver platter. At most, he would get a couple years. Beamish should have been pleased, but he was angry. Angry at Ricky for brutally beating up a woman and angry at Vee for protecting him. He just shook his head and drove back to the station.

Back at the house, Vee sat down on the couch, wondering if she had done the right thing. When she arrived in the driveway, she was determined to put the final nail in her abuser's coffin. To shut it for good. That son-of-bitch deserved to suffocate in an 8 x 10 cell for the next ten years. However, when the time came to follow through, she couldn't do it. She couldn't let her son be separated from his father for his entire childhood. Vee knew her decision was forcing her to play with fire. She could easily lose her life the next time around.

⁌ ≖◆≖ ⁌

Drunk from an all-day binge of vodka and iced teas, Ricky grabbed an empty beer bottle off the top of the bar. Just for kicks, he threw it at a guy sitting two stools down. Before a full-blown fracas could ensue, two bouncers interceded and escorted Ricky out the door. The revved-up beast entered his truck and headed away from the city. As he drove, Ricky could not stop thinking about Vee and what he had done to her. Earlier in the day, he had tracked down Taz and the two met at Bidell's.

Taz told Ricky he had traveled to Vegas the weekend of the party with his fiancé. The girl even joined them at the diner to corroborate his story. Ricky felt ashamed. In a fit of remorse, he called the Harris household and left a long rambling apology on the answering machine begging Vee to forgive him.

While Ricky was lost in thought, a black and white pulled up behind his truck as it swerved back and forth along the road. The red flashers on the police vehicle lit up. A boozed-up Ricky glanced in the rearview mirror and momentarily thought of fleeing. He wisely pulled over to the side of the road instead. The ex-felon exited the truck and placed his hands on the vehicle. It was just a DWI arrest. Ricky was confident he could likely get it reduced to disturbing the peace in the morning.

Ricky's overnight stint in the local jail unexpectedly turned into a transfer to the Erie County Holding Center. Elvira found the recording he had made on the answering machine. The detailed apology had essentially turned into a confession. She immediately took it to the authorities and an arrest warrant was issued. The district attorney's office finally had enough evidence to charge Ricky for the attack on Vee. His bail was set high at ten thousand dollars. Unable to post it, he would be locked up at the holding center until his trial.

—◦— ≍◊≍ —◦—

Seven weeks into his incarceration, Ricky had easily fallen into a normal jail routine. It was old hat to him. The only difference now was that every night he sat on his lower bunk; he quietly laughed at himself. The con man had conned himself by gift wrapping an audio taped confession. It was so detailed the DA even upped the charge to a Class A Felony: possession of a deadly weapon with intent to harm. Beamish could not help with this one. The former foster kid knew he was fucked.

Ricky's new cellmate was not taking to life behind bars well. The unruly sounds of the cellblock and harsh environment spooked him. He seemed to be in a perpetual state of anguish. His name was David

Tilman, a prominent socialite from Hollywood. The arrogant thirty-four-year-old was indicted for embezzling $1.6 million dollars from his wealthy wife fifteen years his senior. The feds had picked him up as he attempted to flee into Canada at the border crossing in Buffalo.

Because Tilman stood to do hard time if the federal case didn't go his way, the increasingly desperate man decided to take matters into his own hands. One night inside their cell, as he and Ricky lay in their bunks talking, Tilman abruptly jumped down from his top bunk and quietly slid a chair up next to him. In the darkness, he explained his situation. He was married to the granddaughter of a former movie tycoon who had once been president of Warner Brothers. The family was rich and so, too, was his wife. While Tilman managed her assets, technically he did not own any of them. He had signed a prenup. The marriage went sour, and now he felt he was being squeezed out unfairly.

"All the real money belongs to my pain in the ass mother-in-law and my wife," Tilman ranted. "They both just need to be dead." Ricky sunk back in his pillow, uncertain if this was just a dream. A nudge to his shoulder confirmed it wasn't. "I'd be willing to pay quite well for this to happen," he said. "Would you be interested?"

Ricky paused a long moment, then finally said, "I don't know...don't you think you'd be the main suspect if this somehow came about?"

"Not if I'm in jail." Tilman sneered.

"C'mon, Rick, she treats me like shit," he continued. "The little slut is always daring me to file for a divorce. She cheats on me then spits on my pride. I'll give you the $10k you need to spring you out of this den of thieves, then wire another $50k to your account on Monday. What do you say?"

"I say, when the job's completed, you give me another $50k." Ricky laughed.

"$110k total. Done." Tilman agreed without hesitation.

The next morning, Ricky crossed the street in front of the jail free on bail. He couldn't believe it. Holiday decorations adorned the street poles, and Ricky waved to them. Christmas had come one month early. He had a thousand dollars in his pocket and fifty thousand more on the way. Life had finally thrown him a fastball he could hit. The money would buy him his mansion on the lake. Santa had done his job; now it was time for the would-be hitman to do his.

A short time later, Ricky walked up to a payphone on an agreed upon street corner in the city and waited. The phone rang at the expected time. Ricky nervously removed several dimes from his pocket and picked up the phone after ten rings. It was Tilman. He was calling collect. Ricky accepted the charges and inserted some dimes into the slot. "Just confirming the money for the construction job will be in your account Monday morning," a voice said.

"Thank you for your business, sir," Ricky responded. "Have a happy holiday season." He hung up the phone and hailed a cab. A thousand thoughts raced through his mind but first things first. Denise Tilman lived in Los Angeles, California.

Ricky entered the cab and called out a local address to the driver. He leaned back and thought about what he would do with all that money. Especially the fifty thousand dollars set to hit his account first thing Monday morning. Ricky let out a shrill cry and pounded the seat. The Indian cabbie stared into his rearview mirror. "You okay back there, buddy?" he said in a heavy Indian accent.

"Just friggin' drive…you'll get a good tip," Ricky said flippantly.

"You da boss, buddy," the driver replied.

⇥◆⇤

It was 5:30 A.M., and the faint light of dawn was barely detectable in the darkness. A dozen FBI agents stood in frigid temperatures, carefully positioned outside a low-income apartment on Buffalo's east side. Heading the task force was special agent in charge, Frank Maggio. He raised his hand, and the men readied their weapons. The former Green Beret walked up to the front door and knocked loudly. With a commanding voice, he shouted. "This is the FBI. We have a warrant. Please open the door. This is the FBI."

Inside the apartment, a hung-over Ricky and Joey slowly opened their eyes and growled to life. The pounding on the door repeated.

"Oh, fuck, my shit!" Joey exclaimed as his eyes opened wide. Both men realized he had enough cocaine stashed in his mattress for a five-year hitch. Ricky, dressed only in his boxer briefs, peeked through the curtains. He could only see two men in suits. Then suddenly seemed to relax. "What the fuck?" he said. "Those are FBI boys out there, Joey. You're good. It's gotta' be a mistake." Joey nervously disengaged the lock and the other armed agents burst in through the door. Both men were taken to the ground in seconds.

Maggio approached Ricky who was lying face down on the floor. "Are you Richard Matt?" he yelled.

"What's this all about?" Ricky said with agitation. Maggio took a knee.

"It's about a little trip you're thinking of taking out to the west coast," he said.

"I'm not taking any trip out to the west coast, unless you're buying me a ticket," Ricky said sarcastically.

"Get him out of here," Maggio called out to his men angrily.

Ricky spent that morning and all afternoon down at FBI headquarters answering questions about the Tilman murder plot. He snickered when they started treating him like some kind of budding hitman. But on the flipside, he knew murder for hire was serious business. A conviction could get him life. He explained that, when he was released on bail, he phoned Denise Tilman and informed her of the murder plot. She listened intently along with her mother and father-in-law who was a Los Angeles Police Chief. Ricky had agreed to go along with Tilman's scheme just as a ruse.

Through the hours of intense questioning, Ricky had worked his way steadily through a full pack of cigarettes. The small interrogation room at FBI headquarters stunk and started to develop a haze. He took a sip from his third coffee and looked up with a dog-tired face. "I'm a lot of things, Mr. Maggio," Ricky snarled. "But a murderer ain't one of them." He leaned forward and tapped forcefully on the steel table. "I just warned them is all."

"And why would you do that, Ricky?" Maggio asked. Ricky leaned back in his chair while taking a deep puff from his cigarette.

"I don't know, I was, uh…kind of figuring on maybe a little reward…maybe a little somethin', somethin' in the reduced sentence department on the assault charge?"

In the end, Ricky was released. The feds verified the phone conversation with Tilman's wife and that he had indeed warned her. Ricky remained out on bail. Several weeks passed, but no reward came. The only stipend he did receive was a paltry sum from the tabloid show, *A Current Affair*. The producers of the program had tracked him down and flew him to New York City to make an appearance on TV. Dressed in a tuxedo and looking like a million bucks, Ricky was interviewed in front of a live audience so he could describe in detail his role in the bizarre murder-for-hire plot involving one of Hollywood's elite families. It was pure exploitation, but he loved the attention. As interest in the story faded, Ricky went back home. Within a week, he was broke and out of work. Caught in another downward spiral, the former tabloid TV star was accused of sexual assault by a woman he met at a local bar shortly after. He was arrested on a rape charge and sent back to jail.

CHAPTER 19
HOME SWEET HOME

Three months had passed since the brutal attack, and Vee's life was finally getting back to normal. The inside of the house had been repaired by Herb, leaving no souvenirs of that nightmarish evening. Vee had recovered from her injuries and returned to work full time. Even Nick, who had been born with an underdeveloped nervous system, was starting to outgrow the painful condition. It meant he could now be held and clothed like a typical baby, much to Vee's delight. To add to the good news, Ricky had not been in contact since the incident. The Harris household was finally becoming a happy home again.

With the frigid winter temperatures bearing down on everything outside, Elvira prepared dinner in her cozy kitchen as Nick played gleefully in his crib by her side. Vee arrived home in a state of exhaustion, her sixty-hour work week had finally come to an end. She picked up her baby boy and gave him a big hug. Vee set him down and marveled at the cute designer outfit she had bought him from Macy's. She was elated he could finally wear normal clothes.

The mood at the dinner table that evening was peaceful. The Harris family sat around the table content with being in each other's company. Vee, with Nick nearby, felt safe and secure sitting with her parents. It stood in stark contrast with the family dinner table of her youth. Elvira's manner, inherently filled with a biting edge, was tranquil and more somber than usual. She turned to her daughter and placed a hand gently on her shoulder. "I'm sorry, Vee," she said. "I'm sorry for all the things I did to you...sorry for everything."

Vee slowly stood up from the table as the pain of her youth rushed past her in waves. She glanced at her dad who gave her an encouraging nod towards Elvira. Vee approached and took her mother's hand. She gave it a gentle kiss. "I forgive you, Mom," Vee said. The mother and daughter glanced into each other's eyes as they filled with tears. Elvira clasped her daughter's hand with a remorseful smile. She excused herself and quickly disappeared up the stairs, overwhelmed by emotion. Herb walked over to his daughter and gently embraced her.

⊶ ⚔ ⊷

That evening, Vee slowly removed her clothes and turned the hot water on in the tub for a bubble bath. What she needed was a long, hot soak to work out the aches and pains of the week. As the soapy froth filled the tub, she thought pleasantly about how for the first time that she could remember, her family felt complete. Even her sister was doing well. Anna had married a local firefighter whose job came with full benefits and a pension. He was a nice guy to boot. She was set.

Now it was Vee's turn to relax. She grabbed a cigarette and slid into the tub. Vee laid back in the soothing suds and leisurely started going through the days' mail which she had placed on the side. Her attention quickly focused on a letter from the DA's office. She opened it, and her cigarette suddenly dropped from her lips into the water. A grand jury had been convened on her assault case. She had been ordered to appear.

Vee gasped and shook her head in disbelief. She had blocked that night from her mind, banished it off to a deserted island somewhere, but now it had returned to haunt her again. Vee tore up the letter in anger. "You son-of-bitch, Ricky!" She cried out. But there would be nowhere to hide. She had to make a choice. Vee tossed and turned through the night, getting very little sleep. By morning, she decided she simply would not testify. No DA would send her to jail for contempt. She was the victim! Over the following months, Vee ignored two more requests to appear before a grand jury. Eventually, US Marshals showed up at the hospital, and Vee was carted off to jail. Spending two nights behind bars away from Nick had been enough to change her mind. Vee agreed to testify.

⋯ ⋯ ⚬ ⋯ ⋯

It was a balmy day in June at the Erie County Courthouse. Inside the courtroom was standing room only. The attack had gained some notoriety locally. Many had come to hear what Vee had to say about that horrific night. The air conditioning was on the fritz, so the 90 degree-plus temperatures made for an ornery judge and jury. As the prosecutor asked questions about the specifics of the assault, Vee dodged the details and gave vague answers. As the proceedings continued in the same tone, the prosecutor and the jurors were becoming visibly agitated with her evasiveness. Even the crowd had turned on her, but there wasn't anything anyone could do about it.

Johnny Mangano had procured a seasoned defense attorney. He argued Vee hadn't been wearing her glasses that evening. "...nobody wears their eyeglasses to bed at night, folks. Do any of you?" he stated.

When the frustrated prosecutor asked who had attacked her, Vee replied, "...as I was saying, it was pitch dark. And with bad vision in both my eyes, I just can't say for sure who it was that attacked me." As she made that statement, Vee's attention shifted to Ricky seated at the defense table. Her resentful stare said it all. A contrite Ricky could only glance back at her timidly. He knew he had fucked up.

In December of 1993, two-plus years after the assault, Ricky finally took a plea deal. He was given a light sentence of two to four years. A far cry from the twenty years he could have received. Likewise, for the coinciding rape case, the prosecution had no solid evidence against him. It was he-said, she-said. The agreed upon plea deal would cover both cases. Ricky grinned when he signed off on it. With good behavior, he knew he would be out in eighteen months.

CHAPTER 20
GETTING WHAT IS MINE

The sun burst through the morning clouds. Nick had driven five straight hours and was running on fumes. The speed bomb he had ingested to stay awake had finally run its course. The exhausted son of Ricky Matt barely had enough wakefulness to continue his pilgrimage through the winding hills of upstate New York. Up ahead lay his father's home of the last ten years. He had made the journey once before just a few years ago but, for some reason, could not remember the drive up being so grueling.

Nick flipped on his glasses to help his weary eyes. He checked his rearview mirror and could see the feds were still following him a few cars back. It drew a slight chuckle. Nick knew his old man was nowhere in the vicinity. Surely they knew Ricky was too smart to have executed such an escape and not have a getaway plan. He was certain his dad was long gone. It was the one thing "Dog the Bounty Hunter" had proclaimed on TV he had agreed with.

As Nick rounded a long curve, he immediately observed a half-dozen police cruisers blockading the road ahead. State troopers had set up a checkpoint. They thoroughly searched each car that came through from either direction. When Nick's turn came, one officer quickly checked the inside of his car while another inspected the inside of his trunk. A third officer watched Nick. They were all heavily armed. "No luck on locating Ricky Matt yet, officer?" Nick chided.

The officer scowled in agitation. "Move along, sir," he said sternly.

A half-mile of flat road lay ahead. As Nick drove on, he could see dozens of officers fanned out along the countryside. *Did these guys know something I don't?* Nick thought. He quickly dismissed the idea. Nick felt certain his dad had fled the area, perhaps he had exited the country at the border, crossing twenty miles away into Canada. He might have even headed towards home and retrieved the money left in Beau's grave. It was there for him to use. In truth, nobody knew where Ricky was. Nick decided he would stop thinking about his dad's whereabouts; otherwise, it would drive him crazy. He needed to focus. He had traveled almost four hundred miles for another reason, to collect what rightfully belonged to him.

As Nick entered the small town, he passed an old, archaic sign that read: *Welcome to Dannemora POP: 5,000.* His fatigued eyes could already see the tops of the prison guard towers above the trees. Although he had been to the Clinton Correctional Facility before, he hadn't remembered it being so daunting. It seemed to take up half the town. He cautiously drove down the main street which went through the town center. When he drew near the main gate of the prison, he parked in a large lot across from the entrance and exited his vehicle.

Nick hadn't made an appointment but was certain they'd let him in. After all, he was a close relative of the man now headlining every newscast. Nick identified himself and was quickly surrounded by three heavily armed guards. "...I just came by to pick up an oil painting by my dad of me and my mom," he stated calmly. From out of a small side office, a weary Special Agent Maggio approached and showed his badge. He placed a hand on Nick's shoulder and took him off to the side. "A painting, huh?" Maggio said. "Let's go grab some breakfast and have a chat." Nick nodded his head in agreement.

Inside a small diner down the street, Maggio watched Nick as he scoffed down his breakfast. He could not get over the resemblance between him and his dad. It was uncanny. The shrewd veteran took a sip of his black coffee. "They can't let you visit your dad's cell or take any of his personal effects right now...you understand that, right, son?"

Nick glanced up from his breakfast. "I just wanted the painting," he said. "It's all I might ever get...well, that and a pair of Air Jordan's that don't fit."

"I'll see what I can do about the painting. I give you my word," Maggio said. He then added, "Why don't you get some sleep before heading back? We'll cover your hotel."

"No, I'm good." Nick replied. "But thanks, Mr. Maggio. Thanks for all your help." The two stood and shook hands.

Nick felt rejuvenated. The meal and coffee had done their job. That and Maggio's assurance about the painting. He entered his car content. Nick glanced back at the prison, looking at perhaps what might be the last memory of his father. He threw the car into gear and drove off. As he leisurely made his way back through the hills, he turned on some music and took a sip of his coffee. Nick thought about the past. He couldn't help but feel sorry for both his parents. Each of their lives had been filled with such anguish. When they finally got together, their relationship had been a roller coaster. They were happy one minute, and out of control the next. Nick was shocked to learn the details of the assault from his mom. Their lives had all changed after that, including his own. She had filled him in on some of the gaps afterwards, but he could still remember some of it himself. He had lived it.

CHAPTER 21

A FATHER AND SON

Clothed in a soiled diaper, little Nick pushed hard against the attic apartment door, but it would not budge. He was unable to escape the heat no matter what he tried. The weakened toddler was sweating profusely. As he slowly walked back towards his bed, the door swung open. Hit by the sudden outrush of hot air through the doorway, Elvira looked down at her grandson in alarm. "Oh my God," she said as she rushed over to the thermostat. It was set at almost 100 degrees. "How on Earth...?" she said to herself. Elvira lowered the dial and retrieved a damp towel from the bathroom. She wiped the perspiration off Nick's face and puzzled over the thermostat setting. Nick couldn't have reached the thermostat, she thought to herself. He doesn't even know how to use it.

Elvira went over to the window and opened it to release some of the heat. As she returned, Nick sat down and began playing with some of the toys scattered on the floor. Elvira sat on the edge of the bed with a smile as she watched her grandson play. Her pleasant demeanor suddenly turned ice cold. She forcefully snatched a wooden toy soldier from Nick's hand that he had just picked up. Elvira flipped it over to its base. On its underside were carved the initials, H.H. She gently touched the letters and glared at Nick. "Listen, you little spic bastard," she cried. "Do you see your initials on the bottom of this toy? Or any of those others?" Nick sat there frightened but more confused. "Those belong to Herbert Harris Jr.," Elvira continued. "My baby boy never got a chance to play with these and neither should you!" She heatedly picked up the toys and placed them on a high shelf.

"Let's play a little game," Elvira said abruptly. She went to the closet and removed a large suitcase. "Get inside; this will be fun," she uttered. Nick obediently climbed in, and Elvira zipped it closed. She dragged it to the edge of the staircase. "Ready?" she asked and gave it a push. It started to slide down the stairs. Nick's initial laughter changed quickly to cries of pain as the suitcase hit an edge and started bouncing end over end. It crashed with a thud on the landing below. Elvira hurried down the stairway and flipped over the bag. She unzipped it, and Nick stood up dazed and whimpering. "Are you okay, Herbert?" Elvira cried." Are you okay, my little precious?!" She massaged the back of his head and gently took his hand. "Come into the kitchen and help mama cook dinner."

A few days later, Herb had arrived home early from work and was shocked to witness one of Nick's flights down the stairs. The sixty-eight-year-old matriarch had been diagnosed with Alzheimer's a year earlier after exhibiting signs of memory loss and confusion. The symptoms had always been mild, but what he had witnessed with the suitcase and on other recent occasions were on a different level. He knew the time had come when they would not be able to let Elvira be alone with Nick or by herself from that point forward.

The recent break in the bad weather had the residents of North Tonawanda jumping for joy. The entire region had endured a harsh winter even by Buffalo standards. A stretch of days with rising temperatures had quickly melted the snow away and ushered out the winter doldrums. The first day of spring arrived with a balmy temperature of 55 degrees and sunny skies.

The yellow school bus made its way down the street and stopped in front of the Harris home. Nick stepped off the bus carrying a small backpack, proudly donning his blue and white school uniform. The young boy cheerfully ran up the driveway towards his waiting grandparents. He stopped short when he realized they were standing with a man he had never seen before. Next to the man was a nice-looking bike. Nick slowed down and walked cautiously up to the group. The stranger shot a desperate look at his grandparents. He turned to Nick and dropped down on one knee so he could be eye to eye with him. "Hi, Nicky, I'm your dad," he said proudly.

The father and son both beamed at each other. Nick rushed into his father's arms which caught the hardened man off guard. He regained his composure and playfully raised his son high into the air over his head. A grateful father had finally been reunited with his child. Ricky carefully set Nick down and wheeled the bike up to him. "It's all yours, Nicky," he boasted. "And no one is ever gonna take it from ya'. I promise." Nick looked at it in amazement. He had never seen anything so beautiful in his life.

Ricky grinned from ear to ear as he watched his son's joyful exclamations. He had waited long and hard for this moment. Ricky had just been released from prison a couple days earlier after serving thirty months. He had learned while in prison from Vee, his boy wanted a bicycle, so he made a promise to himself to get him one. On his first day out, Ricky bought a top of the line BMX bike with a $750-dollar price tag. He had earned the money on the inside participating in the prison work program and by selling some his paintings to other prisoners. After his release, Ricky had contacted Vee about a visit. She called her parents from work and gave the okay.

During the afternoon, the sun seemed hot despite the mild temperatures. Nick practiced riding the bike, and Ricky ran alongside to keep him balanced. They were both huffing and puffing. The proud father refused to leave his son's side for even a moment. For two treasured hours, Ricky said to himself and the world, "My boy is going to learn how to ride a bike today, and I'm going to be the only one to teach him." As the afternoon became late, Nick finally traveled down the side walk fifty feet on his own.

The excited boy cried out, "I did it, Ricky. I did it!" He continued to ride onto the neighbor's grass and collided head on with a bush. Undaunted, Nick brushed himself off, jumped back on his bike and returned to his dad pedaling fast.

Vee arrived home a half hour early from work and had been watching from the porch. The swelling emotion in her eyes reflected only part of the story. She had forgiven Ricky for what he had done, but she had not forgotten. He was there to see his son which made Vee hopeful. It was a start. Ricky had yet to show responsibility and provide any child support nor had he signed the birth certificate when Nick was born. When it came to his legal rights regarding Nick, he had none. However, she did want Ricky to spend time with his son while he could. Vee had written him in prison that she and Nick would soon be moving to Florida. She was in a serious relationship with a surgeon from the hospital, and they had a daughter together. Her name was Frankie. Their plan was to start a new life together as a family down in Orlando.

After Nick put his bike in the garage, Ricky glimpsed toward Vee. She returned a nodding approval. During their earlier phone conversation, he had asked her if he could show Nick a special place in the woods he used to visit as a child. It would mean a great deal to him. She had agreed. Ricky took hold of Nick's hand and led him into the woods in the back of the house. As they slowly trudged through the rugged terrain, Ricky cut deep notches in the trees every ten yards with his knife. After twenty minutes of twisting turns, they finally reached their destination.

Both stood in small clearing gazing down on a small grave at the base of a tree. "Remember how we got here, Nicky?" Ricky asked. "The trees we marked with the knife show the trail, okay?" The excited boy nodded his head in agreement. It felt like an adventure. "You see this big tree here," Ricky continued. "And the wooden cross on the grave? This will always be our secret little spot, right, son?"

"Yes sir," the boy said humbly. Ricky bent down on one knee, so he was eye level with his son. "I might not see you much in the future, Nicky," he said with a melancholy tone. "But you always remember your daddy loves you very much, okay, buddy?" Nick smiled and jumped into his father's arms. The two hugged each other tightly. Ricky stood up and carefully placed Nick on his shoulders as they headed back. He carried his son through the woods with a great sense of pride, painfully aware it might be their last time together.

CHAPTER 22
A NEW BEGINNING

Vee finished unpacking her good china and glanced out the kitchen window. A large palm tree occupied a small section of her spacious backyard. That was something she would never see back in Buffalo. Her new two-story dwelling had four bedrooms, three baths, and a two-car garage. Most importantly, it contained a husband capable of loving and supporting her, a true partner. Vee stepped out the back door into the bright sunshine of Florida and her new life. She marveled at the luxurious infinity pool and spa installed in her backyard and the granite barbeque pit that extended twenty-five feet to the fence line. It felt like she had stepped into a dream.

Vee's fiancé, Dr. Fig Fanetti, had just finished cooking up hot dogs and hamburgers on the grill as the children stood by watching. Vee could not shake how each of her kids was the spitting image of their dad. Frankie with Dr. Fig and Nick with Ricky. Their temperaments matched as well. Frankie was prim and proper while Nick was impulsive and energetic. The family sat down at a large picnic table and happily dug into their food. Dr. Fig playfully held out his soda can, and the others followed suit. They all clinked in the center and laughed. It was idyllic. Vee sat back trying to hold back tears as she reflected on her new home life. The Taz's and Ricky's of the world were no longer allowed. They had been expelled. Banned from her psyche.

One aspect of her new life Vee had trouble adjusting to was the inherent elitism of her new social network. They now lived in an affluent neighborhood, and many of their neighbors acted with an unpleasant air of superiority and entitlement. Vee's working-class pedigree was the exact opposite, and several of the women picked up on it right away. While they didn't openly exclude her, she could feel their patronizing undercurrent. *She was only there because of Dr. Fig.* It had already stoked her ire on a few occasions. A few days earlier, Vee had signed Nick up for a local modeling contest for kids, simply because some of the ladies had politely told her *not to bother* after she had inquired about it. Their belittling tone towards her son had pushed her over the edge much to the chagrin of Dr. Fig. He had opposed Nick's entry into such a pretentious pageant, but Vee did it anyway. She desperately wanted to show up those pompous snobs.

⋯ ⋙✦⋘ ⋯

On the following Saturday afternoon, the local auditorium was rocking. The modeling contest was already in full swing and playing to a packed house. Disney Studios was next door. It was one of the sponsors of the event, which made it very popular. For the competition, hundreds of contestants were separated by gender into four age brackets to form eight groups. When a group was called, each entrant took their turn to parade across the stage for the judges. Three finalists were selected from each group and one chosen as the winner. Despite all the spectacle and glamour, it was a long show to sit through.

The first ten rows closest to the stage were reserved for the parents of the contestants so they could get a close-up view of their children and root them on. Vee had arrived early and managed to grab a seat in the front row. Her section was filled with many of her haughty neighbors, which suited Vee just fine. She knew her mere presence would annoy them. Although the event was promoted as family-orientated fun, it masked a highly competitive rivalry among the parents who were backstage. Vee's clash with her neighbors was only a microcosm. Many of the stage mothers in attendance lived vicariously off their child's beauty or talent, obsessively traveling from show to show for the prestige or the prize money. It was a cut-throat business, and Vee had walked right into the middle of it.

After patiently watching three groups get paraded and judged, Vee sat up nervously when the Little Mister group was announced. As each boy from the group took his turn in front of the judges, Vee became increasingly anxious. She heard Nick's name called, and he elegantly strutted across the stage in his expensive tux. Vee's built-up tension finally released, and she gushed with pride. Everyone could see her stunning little boy had come dressed to kill. He looks so damn handsome, she boasted to herself.

Shortly after all the boys had gone through, a former top model strutted on stage and read the results of the judges aloud. Nick and two other boys were the finalists! Vee clutched her hands together in anticipation. The two runner-up names were announced, and Nick was left alone on stage. He had won! Vee wept with pride. Nick had beaten all those other kids to claim victory. An event guide escorted Vee up the stairs so she could enjoy the moment on stage with her son. A laurel wreath was placed on Nick's head and hundreds of balloons fell from the rafters, enveloping them. Several photographers rushed the stage to take their picture.

The proud mother and her son stood on the stage for all to see. Happy in their triumph. Vee looked into the jubilant crowd and could see some of her conceited neighbors frowning disappointedly in their seats. "No one is better than you, you hear me, Nicky?!" she yelled loudly so they could hear. "You're more handsome than anybody else here. You remember that!" She stared at her neighbors' faces in defiance and anger.

All Nick could think about at that moment was the amazing six-foot high trophy that sat on the stage in front of him. It stood a good two feet taller than he was. Nick moved toward his first-place prize and playfully tried to climb up the side. It held firm at first but then tumbled onto the stage with a loud crash and broke into several pieces. Nick lay next to it on the stage floor startled by what had happened.

His mother glanced at the shattered trophy in horror. She could hear laughter from the crowd which turned her distress into full-fledged embarrassment. "My God. What did you expect?" she over-heard someone say above the commotion. Nick tried to get up but slipped back down which resulted in another wave of laughter. Vee tried to pick him up by the scruff of the neck, but he wouldn't stay still. As her mother had routinely done to her, Vee, in a burst of sudden anger, gave him several hard whacks to the backside. "Get your ass up!" she yelled at him. Nick began crying. The chuckles in the crowd suddenly turned to jeers and boos. Their shock was followed by disgust. Two guides stepped on stage and hurriedly ushered the mother and son off stage into the wings. The general revulsion in the audience extended to the last row of the auditorium where Dr. Fig looked on in dismay. He could not believe what he had just witnessed. He exited in a hurry.

⊷ ▰◆▰ ⊶

A week later, Vee and the kids waited patiently at the American Airlines gate. Dr. Fig had passed through the checkpoint with them. He was there to say goodbye before they left. Both he and Vee had agreed her returning home to Buffalo with the kids would be best. It was to be a trial separation, but both knew their relationship was over. Vee's violent tirade at the show was still the talk of the town, fueled by the gossipy social circles. It had even made the local news because of the high-profile nature of the event.

Dr. Fig had been humiliated by Vee's behavior. Her abusive action in public had reflected badly on him. For the reserved and genteel doctor, that was unacceptable.

As their parents talked privately, Nick and Frankie stood by a large window hypnotized by the take-offs and landings of all the different planes coming and going. They especially liked the huge rumbling sound made by the big airplanes just before take-off. The two siblings were best friends and got along with the greatest of ease. Nick always watched out for his little sister and hated seeing her so sad. He felt her suffering was Dr. Fig's fault. To help, Nick tried to make Frankie happy as best he could. He had even given her his ice cream cone after she had accidentally dropped hers on the terminal floor, just to keep her smiling.

The anxious looking parents approached their children at the window just as Dr. Fig's beeper went off. "Your daddy has to say goodbye quickly, kids," Vee said.

Dr. Fig stood in front of them and briskly rubbed the top of Nick's head. "Goodbye, Nick," he said. They shook hands firmly but quietly. Dr. Fig turned to Frankie and she started to cry. His beeper sounded a second time as he took a knee beside his little girl. "You'll be back to stay with me the whole summer okay, Frankie?" he said. The little girl nodded sadly. He gave her a quick hug and stood up.

Vee, Nick, and Frankie made their way toward the gate. Frankie glanced back at her dad and yelled out, "Daddy! Daddy!" Dr. Fig tried to look through the maze of people to catch a glimpse of her. Frankie released herself from Vee's grip and raced back towards her dad. She pushed through the onlookers and leapt into his arms with the intention of never letting go. Father and daughter hugged each other tightly as they both became emotional. Dr. Fig handed the reluctant child back to Vee who had returned. Seeing the despair on his sister's face, Nick approached Dr. Fig and kicked him hard in the shin. People standing nearby erupted with laughter. Some even high-fiving Nick as he walked back to his mom. As Dr. Fig hobbled away in embarrassment, Vee looked at him with regret. She knew she had messed up a good thing. Her new life in Florida was over before it had begun. Vee took the kids by the hands and went to board the plane.

CHAPTER 23
RETURN TO SENDER

An abundance of snow had fallen on Buffalo during the month of December. Three feet of the white powder still blanketed the region after the latest storm. Vee drove cautiously through the half-plowed streets in her new SUV, grateful for having four-wheel drive. She was rushing home early from work, hoping to get a glimpse of her children before they had fallen asleep. As she pulled into her driveway, she frowned in disappointment seeing the outside of the house dark. No lights were visible inside through the windows. They must all have gone to bed.

Vee entered the house and flipped on the light switch. She removed her jacket but still felt cold. She checked the thermostat on the wall and saw it was surprisingly low. She turned it up to take the chill out of the air. As she hung up her coat, Vee noticed the light in the kitchen had been left on. She picked up her bags and headed toward the kitchen to turn it off.

Upon entering, Vee saw Elvira sitting at the kitchen table dressed in a flimsy nightgown. Her teeth were chattering. She sat motionless with an eerie blank stare, reminding her daughter of her declining condition. Vee approached cautiously. She glanced down at her mom with heartfelt compassion. "It's me, Mom…it's Vee," she said. Elvira glanced up at her daughter with a masked look.

"Tell your brother I want him in the house now. It's getting late."

"Herbert Jr.'s upstairs in his room asleep, Mom," Vee responded.

"That boy's always getting into some type of tomfoolery," Elvira exclaimed.

Vee sat down at the table. She knew her mom was in the latter stages of Alzheimer's. It was getting worse, and soon she would need round-the-clock professional care. Vee picked up Elvira's brush sitting on the table and stroked her hair. It seemed to comfort the Harris matriarch, almost bringing her back to reality, but the glint in her eye soon died. "Congratulations on winning senior class president, Vee," Elvira said. "Those other kids didn't stand a chance."

Vee smiled back warmly. "Thank you, Momma." Vee carefully escorted Elvira to her room. She decided that the next day she would arrange for a nurses' aide from the hospital to start providing daily home care for her mom.

After putting Elvira to bed, Vee went upstairs to check on the kids. Nick was asleep on the top bunk and Frankie on the bottom. Although the temperature in their room was comfortable, Vee rearranged Frankie's blankets to cover her up just a little more. She kissed her daughter gently on the forehead. At the foot of the bed was Nick's loosely repaired first-place trophy. It stood there and seemed to defiantly stare back at her. She still felt deep remorse for the pain and embarrassment she had inflicted on her son a year earlier. Vee thoughtfully turned towards Nick and instantly found herself transfixed. He had a strange grin on his face as he slept. Vee felt unnerved because she had seen that same expression before on Ricky's face. The resemblance was uncanny. She kissed her son goodnight before exiting the room.

＊＊ ＝◆＝ ＊＊

On Christmas Eve night a few days later, Nick lay in bed crying nonstop. His face was badly swollen, and he was having trouble breathing. From looking at him, Vee knew right away he was having an allergic reaction to something. She didn't know to what, but it was severe. The concerned mother wasn't going to take any chances; if it continued to get worse it could be life threatening. Vee administered a small dose of Benadryl which would help alleviate the reaction until she could get him to the hospital.

Herb stood by the door and said he would watch Frankie as Vee quickly got Nick into his winter jacket and boots. She carried him into the SUV as he continued to cry and buckled him securely into his child seat. Vee started the vehicle to warm it up and brushed the thick layer of snow off the outside. Despite the poor visibility and snow-filled roads, she still made good time to the hospital.

The waiting area in the emergency room was heavily overcrowded. The normally busy hospital was in chaos after a sudden holiday influx of suffering patients and medical emergencies. It was standing room only. Because of his critical condition, Nick was given priority. He was placed on a gurney and immediately wheeled into an examining room with Vee following closely behind. The ER doctor quickly examined him and noted his internal airway was becoming obstructed. If they didn't stop the swelling, they would need to perform an emergency tracheotomy. Vee felt helpless as she could only watch her son struggle for breaths.

Quickly deciding on a non-invasive treatment first, the doctor wanted to try and relax the muscles blocking Nick's airways by giving him an injection of Adrenalin. Vee just hoped there was enough time. A nurse promptly brought a hypodermic needle, and the doctor injected the fluid into Nick's thigh. To everyone's relief, the results were almost immediate. Nick's breathing rapidly returned to normal. Vee put her head in her hands and let out a grateful sigh. "Thank Christ," she said to herself. Vee squeezed her son's hand, and Nick let out a weak smile. She even embraced the young ER doctor who seemed embarrassed by the affectionate gesture.

After an hour, Nick was fast asleep in one of the ER rooms. He would be under observation for the next few hours to make sure he remained stable. Before he had gone to sleep, Vee found out from Nick he had started having problems after eating a peanut butter and jelly sandwich his grandfather had made him. Her son had most likely developed an allergy to peanuts. She could only shake her head in disbelief. As Vee sat by Nick's bedside trying to stay awake, a friend of hers working in the ER stopped by to check in on them. She was glad to hear everything was okay and suggested Vee go grab a coffee in the cafeteria. She would be at the desk and could keep an eye on Nick. Vee, who had been up all night and was dead tired, thankfully accepted the offer.

—— ◄◆► ——

Inside the cafeteria, Vee sat alone at a table quietly drinking a coffee. With a weary gaze, she glanced around the room at the hospital personnel on break. Among them, a young nurse was softly conversing with a lanky resident by the coffee machine while three female nurses sat at a table with two other doctors laughing at some sordid joke. "They ain't what you think, ladies," she said to herself. "Been there and done that." Vee raised her coffee slightly in a mock salute and took a sip. She let out a tired sigh as she closed her eyes.

Vee's tranquility was unexpectedly interrupted by a thunderous crash from inside the ceiling a few tables over. It was followed by what sounded like someone slowly crawling along the inside of the heating duct. Everyone in the cafeteria was glancing up. The large grating on the vent suddenly swung open and a bearded head popped out. The man slowly shimmied his way out and nimbly lowered himself to a tabletop. The utility worker became embarrassed by all the faces staring at him. "Don't mind me," he said as he jumped to the floor.

The self-conscious worker tripped as he turned to exit, slamming into Vee's table and spilling her coffee onto the floor. They both glanced at the mess. "It's not really your night, is it?" Vee said to him.

"No, it is not." The frustrated man laughed. He turned towards Vee and smiled. "I apologize," he said. "Can I buy you another coffee? It's the least I could do for messing up such a pretty lady's night."

Vee nodded yes. "Just don't mess up my life too, okay?" she added. The man looked at her quizzically. "Large with three creams," she said.

Vee watched him as he went to the counter. She thought he was very attractive. He was slim and fit with long brown hair. About the same age as her. More importantly, he wasn't a doctor. He returned shortly with two coffees in hand. "Do you mind if I join you for a sec?" he asked. "I think I need to take a break before I cause any more damage."

Vee took her coffee and laughed. "Sure, why not," she said, then added, "Vee Harris."

He sat down and reached over to shake hands. "Shawn Donald," he replied back.

Two months had passed. Shawn and Vee had been seeing each other two to three times a week since the night they had met in the cafeteria. Shawn thought Vee was the most beautiful and charismatic woman he had ever met. On the flipside, Vee thought Shawn was a good and caring man. She was attracted to him, but he was very different. Shawn was a genuine blue-collared outdoorsman, a good old country boy which for an urbanite like herself took a while getting used to.

For the upcoming weekend, Vee had taken off work and was determined to spend some quality time with her kids. She had originally thought about taking them to Niagara Falls since neither of them had been there and it was only twenty minutes away. However, Shawn had called and convinced her to come out to his place in the country for a cookout. He had two children from a previous marriage and thought a little family barbecue would be a great way for everyone to break the ice.

Before departing in the SUV, Vee checked to see her kids were securely buckled up. She got behind the wheel and sat in the driver seat, briefly lost in reflection. For some reason, Ricky kept creeping back into her thoughts. She knew he had recently been released from jail for some strong-armed robbery. A few days after that, he dropped off a strange video to her dad. It showed Ricky deliberately getting himself shot in the arm with a six-inch blowgun dart. It was bizarre as it was ominous. Vee's reaction after seeing it had also unnerved her, because for some reason, she had become aroused. Vee frowned at herself in the rearview mirror for thinking about it. She did not want to sabotage a good relationship with Shawn. He was a thoughtful man and would be a worthy role model for the kids.

Settling herself down, Vee backed out of the driveway and shifted focus to her driving to avoid any further distractions. For forty minutes, the SUV hugged the shoreline road to Angola, NY. The tranquil beauty of Lake Erie was on the right while a series of immense wooded foothills were on the left. Both vistas extended out in their directions as far as the eye could see. Vee drank up the scenery while Nick and Frankie played video games in the back. They turned inland as they drew nearer to the town. Then followed the country back roads until they arrived at Shawn's log cabin nestled in the hills.

The SUV slowly pulled into the gravel driveway. It came to rest in front of an old, beat-up Ford flatbed parked next to a large cherry tree. Under the tree were two dirt bikes thickly covered in mud. Beyond that stood a small but sturdy built log cabin. The wood used to build it appeared to have been pillaged from the two-acre lot behind the residence. Shawn came from out back when he heard the SUV pull up. He was anxious to show off his modest home to Vee which he had built himself. He was even more eager to introduce her to his two kids playing in the backyard.

Vee released Nick and Frankie from their restraints. The two quickly exited the car. Nick seemed excited for the new adventure. Frankie, not so much. Shawn sensed her shyness too. He walked up to her with a friendly grin. "You must be Frankie," he said. She forced out a sheepish smile as he held out a sucker. "It's a Big Pop, and it's all yours, sweetie." Frankie glanced at her mom and took the candy.

"Thank you, sir," she said timidly. Nick suddenly rushed by them and retrieved his bike from the back of the SUV.

"That's a bad little bike you got there, son," Shawn said, thoroughly impressed. "Where'd you get it from?"

"Ricky bought it for me!" Nick yelled. "Where are all the other kids, mister? I came to play."

Shawn led everyone into the backyard. Toiling next to a huge black-barreled grill were Jesse and Jake Donald. Jesse was a stout twelve-year-old while his younger brother by two years stood wiry and thin. The boys were stomping around in weathered Timberland boots without any socks and dressed in heavily worn jeans paired with unwashed flannel shirts. Their hair was long, oily, and quite disheveled. Their appearance caught the attention of Vee right away who suppressed a comical laugh laced with genuine concern.

Sizzling nicely on the large grill surface appeared to be several pieces of boneless chicken breasts. Their soothing aroma permeated into the spacious backyard. Jesse handed Nick a pair of cooking tongs. "I never cooked chicken on a grill before," Nick said. Jesse leaned close to Nick and whispered in his ear. Nick let out a small laugh then started to turn over the pieces of meat.

Jake approached Vee and held out his hand. "It's nice to meet you, ma'am," he said.

"Do I look that old to you, Jake?" She smiled back shaking his hand.

"Oh, I'm sorry..." he said all flustered.

Vee gently put her hand on his shoulder. "It's all right. It's nice to meet you too," she added.

Vee took Shawn aside. "When was the last time those boys washed their hair?" she asked with a quiet unease.

"They wash it when they take a bath on Sundays, Vee. Today's only Saturday," he said with a casual smile. Vee glanced at the boys. The thought of taking care of three more strays crept into her mind. She did like the idea of Nick having two older boys to play with though. She would have to think things through later.

"Let's eat!" Shawn yelled out as everyone walked towards some patio seats placed around a small fire pit. Jesse came over to Vee and handed her a plate of food. She bit into a piece of the barbecued meat and smiled.

"It's really good, guys. I've never tasted anything quite like this before. What is it?"

Nick chimed in. "It's squirrel, Mommy...it's a squirrel."

Vee glanced at Shawn who was grinning slightly. She spit out her food and flung her plate into the fire. Suddenly incensed, she yelled for

Frankie and Nick and started to rush towards the driveway. "That was a sick joke, Shawn! A sick joke!" she shrieked. Shawn quickly caught up to Vee but was met with a slap in the face by the car door.

"It's not a joke, Vee! It's not a joke!" Shawn pleaded. "It's perfectly healthy. We eat it all the time." Vee tried to slap him again. "Okay, okay, I give up," he said. "I'm sorry. I should have told you." Shawn gestured to calm down and carefully added, "I'd never put you or your kids in harm's way, Vee. My family's been eating squirrel for three generations now. Without incident. I swear." Vee started to calm down.

"Three generations of squirrel eaters?" she said stoically. Shawn nodded.

"You're not in the city anymore, Vee," he said.

"No. I'm not," she replied. Jake and Jesse had joined the small group to see what was happening. Vee put her hand to her cheek and began to smile. "It actually didn't taste half bad," she uttered with a slight smile.

"And they're organic," Jake added. Everyone started to laugh and began returning to the backyard.

CHAPTER 24
A MOVE TO THE COUNTRY

The following summer was a godsend for the Harris family. By the end of August, Vee and the kids along with Elvira had moved in with the Donald's. Shawn's three-bedroom log cabin was too small to accommodate all its new borders, so he began construction on two additional bedrooms, a den, and a second bath. The skillful builder had been on permanent disability for several months from a work-related injury and was able to devote most of his time to its quick completion. His disability checks by themselves weren't enough to cover the added expense, so Vee financed most of the project.

Herb remained behind in the Harris household in North Tonawanda. Unbeknownst to everyone except Vee, he had been diagnosed with advanced Leukemia and given less than a year to live. In the months prior to his diagnosis, Herb had been feeling out of sorts and had brushed it off to old age. When he finally did see a doctor, it was too late. The retired engineer didn't want to be a burden to anyone, so he stayed in his own home. He was still able to get around and did quite nicely by himself. The house was always kept clean and the refrigerator fully stocked. He even traveled out to Shawn's cabin twice a month on weekends to be with the family.

In their new country homestead, the Harris household merged seamlessly with the Donald's. Vee loved Shawn and his boys. They had made the transition easy. Nick especially had developed an immediate kinship with Jesse and Jake. They would take him to their favorite fishing hole in the woods. The three boys would blissfully hang out there all day. Although Nick was new to fishing, he turned out to be a natural. Their regular excursions sparked a healthy rivalry amongst them, particularly Nick and Jake. They were constantly trying to outdo one another in a game of one-upmanship. The competitive group would often catch enough pike and bass to feed everybody for a week.

Late one sunny afternoon as all gathered in the backyard at the cabin for one of their regular feasts, Herb dropped by. Vee was elated. "You look good, Daddy," she said. "Shawn's already cooked a steak on the grill for you. Medium rare. Just the way you like it."

Herb smiled. "I can't wait, honey. I'm starving," he said politely. Herb gingerly sat down next to Elvira at the table, and Vee served him his food. He went through the motions but actually ate very little. Vee noticed it. She knew his appetite had been dwindling in recent weeks. He had told her his stomach could no longer tolerate certain things. It was a strong sign his cancer was progressing. Vee knew his time was getting short and that he was expending a great deal of effort just to keep up appearances. Vee felt helpless, because she was slowly losing her dad and there was nothing she could do about it. For now, she just wanted him to be comfortable and spend as much time with her and the family that he could.

After dinner, Herb let out a chuckle as Jake and Nick rushed around the table and begged their parents to let them try out their new skateboards. Shawn gave Vee the eye.

He was not happy with her recent purchase because the only place to use them was on the main road. Kids have to be allowed to be kids, he thought to himself in the end. Shawn reluctantly nodded his approval. In unison, Jake and Nick let out a jubilant yell and ran up the gravel driveway carrying their skateboards. Vee cried out after them, "You get off the road when a car comes. You hear me?!" The boys waved back obediently.

Jake and Nick hopped on their boards as soon as they exited the driveway, focusing on the long country road ahead. The local section of two-lane blacktop was smooth with a slight incline. It was perfect for skateboarding. Jake took off like he'd been riding for years. He raced along with precision balance and displayed absolutely no fear. He loved speed, and it showed. Nick fought hard to keep up, but the child wasn't in the same class. He fell far behind and even crashed a few times in his pursuit. To his credit, Nick got right back up and never stopped trying.

As the fledgling skateboarders made their way down the road, a rust-laden black Chevy Cavalier speeded toward them. It puffed smoke out of its exhaust as it rumbled along. The car raced by Jake who stepped off to the side of the road to let it pass. The Cavalier sped forward another quarter mile and came to a screeching halt in front of a surprised Nick. The driver's side door opened and out stepped Ricky Matt.

Ricky was dressed to the max in white pants, a black silk shirt and red suspenders. He had recently been released on parole after serving time for violating a previous probation. It was his third time out in two years. Ricky vowed while on the inside things would be different this time 'round, not only for himself, but in his relationship with Nick. To prove to his parole officer and the courts he was on the up and up, he even procured a full-time job at a meat packing company. Now Ricky had come to claim a stake in his son's life.

"You remember your old man, don't you, Nicky?" Ricky asked as he approached. Nick stood there out of breath, quietly looking up at him. He knew who the man was. He was the devoted dad who was never around. Nick answered back with a touch of anger.

"Yeah, you're uh...uh...the man who taught me how to ride my bike." Ricky could sense the hostility and rubbed the top of Nick's head.

"Fair enough, Nicky...fair enough." He smirked. "I'd be mad, too, if I was you." Nick stared at the ground with indignant eyes. Ricky gently placed his hand on Nick's shoulder. "I just wanted to let you know I'll be around more often to see you. Okay?" he offered. Nick looked up slowly and nodded his head. Ricky smiled and reentered the Chevy. "I'll be right back. I have to go say hello to your mom," he yelled as he gunned the engine. Nick watched as the car raced off down the road.

The Cavalier turned into the cabin's driveway and skidded to a halt a few feet from Shawn's truck. Vee saw the car pull in and knew who it was right away. She watched anxiously as Ricky exited the vehicle. He seemed to walk urgently and with purpose as he approached. Vee turned towards Shawn. "Just give me a few minutes with him alone, okay?" she stated quietly.

"Take your time," Shawn said calmly as he retreated to the cooler to grab a beer.

Vee darted toward Ricky and prepared to raise her voice as he got near. "What the hell do you want, Ricky?!" she yelled.

Ricky kissed her on the cheek and seemed genuinely surprised she wasn't the slightest bit interested. "I just came by to visit with my boy and Herb," he said. "Anything wrong with that?"

"Yeah there is!" she said angrily. "You always seem to fuck up every good situation I'm in. That's what's wrong with that."

Ricky pushed by Vee and casually strolled into the backyard. He quickly spotted Herb sitting at the picnic table. He approached the frail man and gave him a hug. He glanced at Elvira who sat next to him. She sat motionless looking straight ahead with a cold stare. Ricky's attention promptly shifted to Shawn, who was busy cooking hot dogs and hamburgers on the grill. He approached and stood next to him—uncomfortably close. Shawn took a step back. The two men glared at each other eye to eye.

Vee and Herb quickly moved to intercede. Shawn grinned and reached into the cooler. He offered his adversary a beer. Ricky took it after a slight hesitation and guzzled it down. "I'm Nick's father, and I'll stop by and see him anytime I want," Ricky said with menace. "You got a problem with that?"

"Nope. No, I don't," Shawn said. "I think every father should see his boy. You're welcome to stop by and see him anytime you'd like." With laidback calmness, Shawn picked up a six-pack from the cooler and handed it to Ricky. "A little something for the trip back. Glad to have finally met you." Ricky stood there speechless as Vee and Herb looked on in quiet surprise.

Ricky groaned and retreated with the six-pack back to his car. He sped out of the driveway, kicking up stones in his wake. The bitter ex-con stepped on the accelerator and drove with a perplexed look on his face. For some reason, he felt like he had just been cheated in a game of poker. He had held his tongue and kept his anger in check, hoping his unannounced visit might rekindle an old flame. Instead, he feared he may have extinguished it for good. Ricky pounded his fist several times on the dashboard in frustration.

Nick and Jake took a break from skateboarding and headed back to the house. Their energy was spent. As they stood on the side of the road and rested, Ricky pulled up in front of the boys and parked. He exited the car. "I told ya' I'd be back," he said to Nick. Palmed in his right hand was a closed switchblade. Ricky flicked it open and suddenly flung the sharp edge into a nearby tree ten feet away. "Before I go, I wanna' teach you how to do that. You kids game?" Both boys nodded their heads nervously.

Ricky retrieved the knife from the tree. "I paid a thousand dollars for this. It's got one of the best blades there is," he boasted. "Now watch me." Ricky repeated the throw several times. When he removed the knife out the last time, the marks on the tree made almost a perfect circle. "Piece of cake," he said smiling. Both kids laughed in admiration. Ricky walked up to them and handed the blade to a captivated Jake. He immediately tried three throws, but not one of them stuck. One of his attempts had even missed the tree completely. Riddled with embarrassment, his enthusiasm waned. He handed the blade to Nick and sped away on his skateboard. "I'm going home!" he yelled back. "I'll let your mom know you're with your dad."

Nick was confident he could stick the knife into the tree, but his first few attempts were as bad as Jake's. Ricky knelt down and showed him how to adjust his arm and wrist motion. Nick kept throwing, and Ricky kept redirecting the boy's efforts. Eventually, Nick hit the tree and let out a burst of joy. Ricky grinned. They continued practicing until Nick could automatically repeat the motion. He nailed five hits in a row. "Like father, like son. Huh, Nicky?" Ricky said proudly. The two laughed and high-fived.

Ricky checked his watch. "Look, kid, I gotta' shove off to work, but I'll be back to see you real soon, okay?" Nick nodded. "Every time I see you, I'm gonna' teach you something new. That's a promise," Ricky said as he gave his son a hug. He stood up and walked back to the car. As he drove off down the road, he glanced into the rearview mirror. Ricky could see Nick standing by the roadside holding on to his skateboard and waving. Sniffling twice, Ricky stuck his arm out the window and waved back.

⚊ ⚌◆⚌ ⚊

Nick glanced at his flip knife sitting on the passenger seat, remembering the image that had taken him back seventeen years. *Standing by the side of the road and watching his dad drive away, waving to him.* It was the last joyful moment he had spent with Ricky outside of prison. Nick shook his head in disgust. He had driven nearly two hundred miles from Dannemora and was only halfway home. Nick had parked at a rest stop on the side of the road to try and catch some sleep, but it would not come.

Trembling from jittery nerves, Nick's emotions felt raw. He glared into the rearview mirror and said out loud, "You taught me how to ride a bike and throw a knife. Thanks for the effort on the father thing, Ricky! I guess giving it your best shot is all any of us can really do." Nick's pent up anger burst forth and suddenly transformed into uncontrollable tears. He dropped his head into his hands. "I know you loved me, Ricky." He sobbed.

After his tears had subsided, Nick glanced around the inside of the car in a haze and took a sip of his coffee. Since trying to sleep was out, he reached into the glove box and pulled out the unopened letters from his dad. Nick opened the next one on the stack and began reading.

Dear Nicky, I hope you and your mom are well. With my upcoming trial only a few weeks away, I wanted you both to know the truth, son. What I did to Bill Rickerson was wrong, and for that, I have to pay. But greed is a capital vice. And the love of money is the root of all evil. Bill was greedy that night, Nicky. He should have given me what I had coming. And I should not have demanded more. Both guilty as charged.

Nick slid the driver seat back so he could be more comfortable. Trying desperately to understand his father, he immersed himself in the letter.

...I'm sitting here in isolation. Staring at these four walls 23 hours a day. Two gang inmates have already tried to kill me with their shanks. I'm not concerned with those wannabes. But I can't fend off everybody. So, in case anything happens to me, Nicky, I want you to know what really happened that night at Bill's. I love you son and only wish I could have been there more for you. Try not to judge me too harshly. It all started when I went over to your Uncle's that night...

CHAPTER 25
GUILTY AS
CHARGED - PERIOD

The dingy, two-bedroom apartment contained ripped leather couches and broken-down folding chairs strewn about the rooms haphazardly. Bed sheets draped over metal rods acted as curtains on the windows while cheap linoleum covered the creaky wooden floor which lay exposed in several spots where the linoleum had worn through. Poorly installed paneling blanketed the walls in a lazy attempt by the landlord to give the place a lift. The ill-kempt rooms were inside an ill-kempt structure located dead center in North Buffalo's low-income housing projects.

Seated at an old wooden table inside the main living area were Ricky, his maternal half-brother, Wayne Schmidt, and their twenty-one-year-old friend, Lee Bates. A half-empty bottle of Grey Goose vodka sat in the center of the table, its contents rapidly dwindling as the three men downed shots at regular intervals. A cuckoo clock mounted off kilter on the wall chimed to indicate the passing hour. The three men took it as a signal to down another round. Ricky stared at the expensive bottle with a mischievous grin. Earlier in the day, he had gone to the liquor store to buy the vodka, but in a spur-of-the-moment decision, he had stolen it instead. Old habits die hard, he thought to himself. Ricky filled his glass and raised it in mock salute. "Fuck all you all in this world." He growled as he swallowed the drink in a quick gulp.

Ricky reached over to Wayne and padded him on the back as he refilled his glass. While the two men were blood relatives, they could not have been more different in appearance and temperament. Ricky was muscular and brash while Wayne was pudgy and meek. In the end, that mattered little to Ricky. Wayne was family and that meant everything. Ricky was glad they had connected after he had been released from prison. He found out Wayne had just settled down with a woman and was about to be married. He also discovered his half-brother was two thousand dollars in debt to a local mobster for gambling. Ricky vowed he would do everything he could to erase that debt.

Across from the two brothers, Lee Bates nervously tapped his empty shot glass on the table. Ricky had met him at a local strip club a few months earlier, and they became part-time drinking buddies. Bates, while not fat, was stout for his six-foot frame with long, sandy brown hair that draped over a pasty complexion covered in acne. He had a submissive personality and still lived with his parents, sleeping in the same bedroom he was raised in as a kid. Ricky thought he was a spineless kiss-ass, okay for hanging out but a little too jittery for what they had to do tonight. However, Ricky conceded to need. He was convinced the kid was the key to the evening's big score. Ricky was also desperate for money. He needed to get Nick's Christmas gift, clear Wayne's debt, and try to rekindle his relationship with Vee. The expected haul would take care of all those things and more.

The multiple waves of vodka shots began going to Ricky's head. He leaned back on his chair and attempted to balance it on its back legs. It started falling back, and he compensated forward. The chair came down with a thud. With an eager restlessness, he glanced around the room filled with junk. Ricky spotted something along the wall and quickly laughed. "Let's have some fun," he grumbled with a sly grin. He stood up from his chair and picked up a blowgun and a dart from a pile along the wall. Items he had pilfered from a home a few weeks earlier. Smiling, Ricky grabbed a video camera off the couch and handed it to Wayne. "Film me," he said.

Both men walked towards the kitchen and Wayne turned on the camera. "We're on," he said. Ricky smiled directly into the lens.

"See, what we're gonna' do," he stammered, "is that we're gonna' dip the tip of this dart in AIDS blood and seal it. Then we patent the son-of-a-bitch and sell it as a deadly weapon. Whadda think? Brilliant, huh?" Ricky held the tip of the dart close to the camera lens sporting a malicious grin.

"You're one sick bastard is what I think," his brother answered back.

Off to the side, Bates stood with a furrowed brow and turned to Wayne. "Is he serious?" he asked nervously.

"The man's just joking, kid," Wayne replied.

"No, I'm not," Ricky blurted out. He handed the loaded blowgun to his brother. "Hammer time," Ricky said. He stiffly held out his arm and slurred. "Shoot it right through the meat of my forearm, Wayne-O."

Wayne glared at him dubiously. "You sure you want me to—"

"Just shoot the fuckin' thing, okay!" Ricky quipped sharply. Wayne placed the camera on a counter and left it on with Ricky in frame. He raised the blow gun and aimed it at his brother's arm. Bates stood frozen, not sure what to think. There was a sudden loud twang, and the projectile nearly went through Ricky's forearm.

"Jesus Christ," Bates muttered. The two brothers laughed.

"King Kong ain't got nothin' on me, motherfuckers!" Ricky boasted. He casually pulled the dart from his arm without so much as a wince.

Ricky grabbed a beer and took a seat. He leaned back in the chair and stared at the ceiling, thinking about the evening ahead. Bill Rickerson, his boss at the meat packing company, owed him a lot of money. Eleven hundred dollars to be exact. Most of it was for roof repairs he had done at the man's home for which he was never paid. Ricky had been hired by the seventy-six-year-old businessman three months earlier after being released on parole. Initially, he felt like things were finally turning around, but right from the start, Bill treated him poorly. The man was a tightwad when it came to his employees yet was always pushing his need for money around the plant. "Gotta' get a thousand for the day," was his mantra. "Yeah, well, how 'bout giving me one of those days, Bill," Ricky said crossly to himself. "You owe me, you fuckin' Jew bastard, and now it's time to collect." He grabbed the bottle of Grey Goose and refilled his glass with purpose.

Ricky swallowed his drink and continued his tirade out loud. "Eight fuckin' bucks an hour...then you fire me 'cause of what Chris said?" He seethed. "What I should do is lock your ass in that walk-in freezer you're always bragging about. Then skin you alive one layer at a time until you give me my fuckin' money." As if on cue, the cuckoo clock chimed in to signal the passing of another hour.

Bates looked at his watch restlessly and turned to Ricky. "Look, I gotta' meet some people later. You gonna' tell us what it is we're supposed to be doing?" he asked.

Ricky stood up from the table and began pacing. "What's the plan, Lee? Is that what you wanna' know?" he said smugly. "Well, here's the fuckin' plan, you little prick. There's ten thousand dollars in cash in Rickerson's house, and we're going over there tonight to get it." Bates looked at him in bewilderment.

"How do you know that?" Wayne interjected. Ricky sat back down, the alcohol now taking a back seat.

"...Okay, six weeks ago, right. I'm in Bill's office," he said, "and his girlfriend calls from the house all frantic and shit. 'Bill, the two cleaning guys are getting close to all the money. What should I do?' she yells over the phone. That Jew bastard turns white as a ghost in front of me...slams down the phone, then rushes home. I'm tellin' you there's ten thousand dollars in there at least. Bill runs an all cash business, and those guys shampooing the carpets were getting very close to it."

Ricky pointed at Bates. "You just knock on the door and get us in. I'll take it from there," he said,

"Why do you need me for that?" Bates asked with a confused look.

"I stopped by his office to collect the money he owed me a few weeks ago," Ricky explained. "There was a minor disagreement, and the motherfucker called the cops. I left before they arrived. Rickerson won't open the door for me, but he would for you. You two are all buddy-buddy now since you did that glass work for him. I think you gave him a hard-on because you fixed it so cheap." Bates frowned nervously as Ricky laughed.

Wayne returned from the bedroom with a pair of batting gloves, packing tape, and an old baseball bat. Bates looked rattled. "What's that for? I thought we were just gonna' get the money?" he inquired.

"This shit is for that bastard in Angola who owes us the one hundred dollars for the vitamins," Ricky replied. "That's stop number two." He approached Wayne and put his hand on his shoulder. "I know you can't come with us, Wayne-O...with the kid on the way and everything. But I still gotcha' covered. Two thousand of this score goes to pay off your debt. We're family, right?" he said. Wayne nodded in appreciation, and the two siblings shook hands. Without any more fanfare, Ricky and Bates put on their winter coats, gathered their things, and walked out the front door.

It was a frigid evening, and the snow was falling heavily. The two men entered Bates' beat-up Chevy Lumina and drove the short distance to Rickerson's in ten minutes. It was 9:30 P.M. when the car pulled up to his house on Harvard Avenue in Tonawanda. There were no parking spots on the snow-covered street, so they turned into the driveway. Bates parked the car behind Bill's old gray station wagon which had a busted front passenger window covered by plastic and secured with duct tape. Ricky grimaced when he saw it.

Without wasting time, Ricky and Bates exited the car and quickly made their way to the front porch of Bill's two-story home. Bates rang the doorbell while Ricky stood off to the side, just out of view. A moment later, the porch light went on, and Bill's gruff face darted through a curtain on the porch window. He seemed to relax when he recognized Bates standing there. There was a sound of the lock being undone and the creaking of the heavy front door as it opened. Bill, looking tired, was dressed in a blue robe with red and white matching pajamas. He yawned. "It's awfully late, Lee. What's up?" he asked. Suddenly, Ricky rushed out from the side. He pushed Lee forward through the front door into Bill who went backwards until all three were in the inside hallway. Ricky grabbed Bill's arm in a vice like grip and looked him in the eye.

"We need to talk, Bill. We gotta' big problem," he said irately.

Ricky forced the old man into the small kitchen. "Sit down," he said as he shoved him into a chair.

"What do you want, Rick?" Bill asked in an annoyed tone.

Flashing an angry scowl, Ricky slapped him across the face. "I want my money is what I want, Bill. Where's that stash you keep in here?" he asked. Composing himself from the sudden blow, Bill calmly uttered.

"I don't know what you're talking about." Ricky grabbed a banana from a bowl on the table and began peeling it.

"Oh, yes you do." He snickered. He bit off a large chunk and, in a quick flurry, delivered three brutally hard slaps to Bill's face. "You know what I'm talkin' about. C'mon now, Billy."

Bates approached. His nerves were on edge. "You didn't say nothing about this, Ricky," he said. Bates turned to a stunned Bill in a pleading voice. "Please just give him the money, okay, Bill? If you don't, I don't know what he'll do to you."

Ricky grabbed Bates by the shoulder and dragged him into the hallway. "Go wait in the fuckin' car, you little pussy!" he yelled. Bates fled out the door as Ricky returned to the kitchen.

Bill's nose was dripping with blood. "You could have called 911, Bill. Why didn't you?" Ricky asked.

Bill sat there and smirked. "No need to," he said smugly. Ricky bent down close so they were face to face.

"Look, all I want is the $1,100 you owe me...plus whatever else you got in here for telling people I broke into your vehicle. No one will hire me now."

"Are you deaf?" Bill shot back. "I told you there's no money in here. Besides, what about all the meat you stole from me? I figure we're even now."

Ricky grabbed Bill's collar with a violent tug and shouted. "I gotta little boy! Christmas comes for him, too, you Jew cocksucker!" He angrily snatched Bill's toupee off his head and stuffed it into his coat pocket.

The spirited old man glared at him, then spit in his face. "Get out of my house you, white gutter trash!" Bill growled.

Ricky wiped off his face and, in a violent outburst, sent a devastating punch to the center of Bill's chest. The blow sent Bill and the chair crashing to the floor. Their momentum carried them backwards, and both men tumbled down a half-dozen stairs leading into a sunken dining room. Bills' face bounced hard off the floor as he rolled to a stop on his side. The old man groaned as he struggled to one knee. Ricky rushed down the stairs and tried to help Bill to his feet. "Just please give me the money, okay, Bill?" Ricky said in a pleading tone.

The dazed old man cried out. "There's no money in here, you Italian cocksucker!" His breath suddenly became labored and the color in his face, ghost-like. Ricky watched in horror as Bill struggled to breath, then dropped to the floor. He was no longer breathing.

Ricky dropped to his knees and rolled Bill onto his back. He began doing chest compressions, trying to remember what he had learned in the CPR class he had taken in prison. After ten minutes of desperately attempting to revive the old man, Ricky collapsed on the floor in exhaustion. He lay on his back next to Bill looking up at the ceiling in despair "Oh, fuck me," he said to himself. In nervous agitation, he put his hands to his forehead. "Fuck!" he screamed out. Ricky turned his head towards the lifeless corpse. "Why didn't you just give me the money you owed me, you cheap fuck?" he yelled. Ricky sat up and tried to think. Accident or not, he was probably facing a second-degree murder rap.

There was a sudden loud knock on the back door. Ricky glanced up in fright. "What the fuck?" he said to himself. "It couldn't be Lee. He was out front, that pussy wouldn't pound like that anyway." The loud knock repeated. Did he get the cops?! he thought nervously. ...No fuckin' way. Of that he felt sure. Ricky grabbed a steel poker from the fireplace and quietly waited on the steps to the kitchen. The pounding stopped, and the sound of slowly retreating footsteps crunching through the snow could be heard from outside. Ricky glanced out the back window. He could see a figure walking towards a large snowplow truck which had pulled into the end of the driveway on the left side. Its engine was still running and its lights were on. The person entered the truck and started backing out. Ricky rushed through the hallway and peered through the front porch window. He watched the truck go by Bill's station wagon and the Lumina. It backed out the driveway and disappeared down the street.

A few minutes later, Ricky emerged from the house, moving with a controlled sense of urgency. Bill's body was draped over his right shoulder and covered by a garbage bag. Bates' silhouette popped up in the Lumina. The driver's side window quickly rolled down. "Jesus Christ, Bill's head is sticking out of the garbage bag, Ricky!" he screamed in horror.

"Open the trunk, you fuckin' idiot," Ricky blared out. Bates frantically jumped out of the car and opened the trunk.

"What the fuck happened?" he yelled.

"What the fuck happened was that Bill had a heart attack and died. That's what the fuck happened!" Ricky said as he dumped the body into the trunk. It made a loud thud as it bounced off the spare tire. He shut the trunk hard, hoping it would end his fright. It didn't. Both men got in the front seat, Bates behind the wheel. He quickly backed the car out of the driveway and stepped hard on the gas. The wheels spun in the thick snow as the back end of the car slid from side to side. It ping-ponged off several parked cars before it made its way forward down the street into the worsening blizzard.

They drove to a house Ricky had been staying at a few miles away. Ricky jumped out of the vehicle and ran into the snowy night towards the garage in the back. He returned a few moments later with a shovel. Ricky threw it in the back seat and hopped back in the front. A bewildered Bates turned towards him. "I'm late for a birthday party, Ricky. My friends are waiting for me. Do you think I could go?" he asked nervously.

Ricky let out a forced laugh. "What the fuck are you talking about?" he exclaimed. "We got a dead body in the trunk. We're facing twenty-five to life here, Lee. That's a lot of birthdays with you being fucked in the ass."

"Okay. Okay," Bates blurted out.

"Let's take care of business first," Ricky said heatedly. "Take I-290 to the I-190 and head to the Southtowns. We'll bury the fucker in the Angola tunnels. Without a body, there ain't no crime." Ricky smirked at Bates in expectation. He tapped on the dashboard, then pointed forward. Bates relented and started driving down the street. As they made their way along, Ricky lit a cigarette and slowly exhaled a big puff of smoke in an attempt to calm down. He glanced at Bates and shook his head. "Birthday party, huh?" he said out loud. "Maybe you could let Bill tag along and let him warm up."

Several minutes later, the car edged its way onto the congested thruway and immediately hit traffic. The relentless snowfall was creating havoc for drivers. Three lanes had been reduced to two. The cars were lined up bumper to bumper creating a long trail of red taillights. While they weren't at a dead stop, they were moving at a snail's pace. The normal five-minute trip to the Buffalo skyway took a half-hour. The slow going intensified both men's jittery nerves. Bates turned on some music to try and distract them from the deafening quiet.

When they finally made it to the Skyway, a sign at the entrance flashed its amber lights, warning of high winds ahead. Bates cautiously drove forward, inching his way up the on ramp to the tall structure. A large rental truck was pinned against the six-foot embankment wall, blocking the outside lane. A state trooper's vehicle was parked behind it with its lights flashing. An officer stood at the front of the truck waving cars through individually in the one open lane. Bates and Ricky looked at him with nervous apprehension as they slowly approached. Both men breathed a sigh of relief when he waved them through.

The Chevy crawled its way across the bridge without issue but struggled on the downside. Some spots were almost pure ice, and the car began sliding. Bates fought to maintain control as the back end kept shifting back and forth, almost slamming into the guardrail multiple times. Ricky shot Bates a look. "Slow the fuck down, Lee!" he yelled. "We got one dead guy in here already."

"I got it! I got it!" Bates yelled back.

"Your back tires are bald. They got no fuckin' grip," Ricky scolded him.

To their relief, they made it off the treacherous downgrade and continued on to Rt-5. They saw a Tim Horton's up ahead and pulled into the drive-thru to get some coffee. Bates hit the steering wheel in frustration when he couldn't roll down the window because it had frozen shut. He opened the door a few inches and screamed his order into the intercom. Then rolled the car ahead to the service window. There was just enough room in the tight space to open the car door, so he could squeeze his hand out of the window to pay for and grab the coffees. "This night couldn't get any worse," he said out loud.

The winter storm soon intensified. Heavy snows were coming off the lake in waves and pummeling the area. Bates and Ricky got back onto the main road, hugging Rt-5 along the lake. Traffic moved slowly. Both men were becoming restless. They entered a small hamlet and came to rest at its only stop light. As they sat in silence sipping on their coffees, the car was jolted forward by a sudden impact from behind. A car had slid into them. Both men looked at each other. Bates glanced in the rearview mirror and could see the trunk had popped open from the collision. "Oh, fuck!" he yelled. Ricky looked out the back window. "Take care of it, Lee," he said. Bates quickly exited the car and slammed the trunk closed. He peered through the falling snow into the other car and noticed an older lady preparing to get out. Bates knocked on the hood to get her attention. She looked up. He pointed to the bumper and shook his head, making a forget-about-it gesture. Before the lady could open her door, he rushed back into the Lumina and sped off.

After slowly heading south for thirty more minutes, a sign showed the village of Angola was less than a mile away. They turned inland towards the tunnels. Bates and Ricky worked their way through the hills to their destination and spent the next hour scouring the area for a suitable place to covertly bury the body. However, the snow had made it impossible. Many of the smaller access roads were buried and hard to detect in the dark. To add to their worries, the normally empty back roads were filled with local traffic which only happened when the main roads along the lakefront were closed. A frustrated Ricky slammed his fist in the dashboard. "Can't do it, Lee! It's like a fuckin' parade in here!" he screamed. "Just keep headin' south!"

Six hours had passed, and each man had taken their turn at the wheel. The strong stench of cigarette smoke filled the car and permeated every pore of their bodies. The two men had traveled hundreds of miles and even ventured inside the Ohio and Pennsylvania borders. They had stopped at numerous locations but could find no place to bury the body. The ground everywhere was too hard; it was like frozen tundra. As the sun rose in the early morning, Ricky stopped at a hardware store just outside Cleveland to purchase an eighty-dollar digging tool. It was supposed to make it easy to cut through solid ground. Ricky tried it a few times and the effort required was still too backbreaking and took too long.

Exhausted and finally out of patience, both men gave up looking for a spot and decided to head for home. It was late afternoon, and they were 225 miles from Buffalo. They stopped at a diner to get something to eat. Both were not looking forward to their arduous journey back. The snow was still coming down across the region, so the going was slow, the normal four-hour route took almost seven hours. The snow-encrusted car finally arrived back in Tonawanda at 11 P.M., twenty-four hours after they had originally departed.

As rational thought took a back seat to desperation, Ricky came up with a last-ditch idea to hide the body. At least temporarily. He told Bates to head to Tonawanda Island. It was a small track of land in the middle of the Niagara River only accessible by a fifty-foot wooden bridge. Much of it was covered by empty lots and vacant buildings. Ricky had lived only a mile away as a kid and had explored it often. He knew the island well. There was a remote area near an abandoned warehouse he used to play in that would fit their needs perfectly.

The two men drove across the wooden bridge onto the small island. They made their way a few hundred yards inland and slowly crept in back of an old warehouse that was still standing. Bates extinguished the headlights. Then parked the car. Both men were spent. Ricky looked around with exhausted eyes. The trees in the lot were bigger and there was more clutter, but it was just as he remembered as a kid. Just covered by snow.

Ricky told Bates to open the trunk and went to the back of the car. The trunk popped open. Ricky looked at Bill's head which was still sticking out of the garbage bag. In sudden anger, he punched the side of the car which made a large dent. "Why couldn't you just give me the money, you cheap fuck?" he cried out. Ricky reached for a cigarette. He chuckled and shook his head. "Fuck all you all motherfuckers. I'm having a cigarette!" Ricky sat down on a log and puffed away as if he didn't have a care in the world. He looked up and let the gently falling snow hit his face. It felt refreshing.

After finishing a second cigarette, Ricky returned to the car and tried to lift Bill's frozen body from the trunk. He struggled mightily but still managed to hoist the stiff corpse over his shoulder. To him, it felt like he was carrying a heavy mannequin. Ricky headed off to the thick brush while Bates retreated back to the car. He refused to touch the dead body and just kept hoping the nightmare would end.

Trudging through the deep snow, Ricky maneuvered through garbage and several large pieces of driftwood which had been piled on the grounds over the years. He found a small alcove next to an old Sycamore tree and placed the body in it. Ricky pushed it in so it was snug and partially hidden. He glanced around to make sure he was not being watched. The coast clear, he spied a large piece of rigid tarp amongst the junk. He pulled it out and used it to cover Bill. Ricky placed two heavy railroad ties on top of the tarp along with several pieces of scattered wood and branches. He covered it all with snow for good measure. Ricky was confident the body would not be discovered.

The car headed back towards town. Ricky felt better now that they had discarded the body. The steady flow of caffeine he'd been drinking coupled with his pumped-up adrenaline had made him wide awake despite the lack of sleep. He and Bates went back to the house he was staying at to shower and get a change of clothes. Ricky told Bates he needed to loosen up and was going to the club in Canada. Bates was happily on board with that.

With Ricky behind the wheel of the Lumina, the two men crossed the border into Canada. They went through customs and drove the short distance to their favorite strip club. Glowing pink neon lighting spelled out *Pure Platinum* above the sexy silhouette of a naked female across the facade. Despite the frigid temps, a long line of patrons stood under the awning outside waiting to get into the club. Ricky pulled the car close to the entrance and pounded on the car horn several times. He rolled down the window and waved to the bouncer at the front door. "Hey, Tony!" he yelled. The man waved back, then disappeared inside.

Less than a minute later, a young woman emerged from the club. She had long, sexy legs and curly brown hair. She was scantily clad in a G-string and short fur jacket she had thrown on for her brief excursion outside. She slithered enticingly towards the car. "Heyyy, Corina," Ricky said. "You gotta be cold wearin' just that." She kissed him seductively through the open car window and reached inside her jacket. As she pulled out a key, her perky young breasts popped out. A man standing in line let out an explicit whistle. Corina jiggled her butt cheeks and gave the man a wink. Ricky looked at her with a furrowed brow.

Corina mouthed to her jealous lover in a seductive Spanish accent. " Mía jugos es fluido. Ju best be ready." She rubbed her breasts with the motel key and handed it to Ricky.

"Later with that shit, okay," he said. "I need to talk to you, pronto."

Hearing his urgency, she responded in kind. "Dos horas, Ricardo... dos horas?"

"Two hours?" Ricky shot back in irritation.

"Solo apurate, comprende?" Corina nodded and strutted back into the club.

Ricky and Corina had been seeing each other for a little over a year. She claimed she wanted to get married, but Ricky knew it was only to secure her Green Card. Honestly, he didn't really care. She was a sexy woman in bed and a nice distraction from his trouble filled life. They hooked up later that night at the same motel they always had. This time Bates was with them, so they slipped into the bathroom for some privacy. Instead of their usual night of sex and games, Ricky felt more like talking. He felt a deep need to confess or at least talk to someone about what had happened. He was desperate to give his side of the story. Corina was the closest thing he had to an intimate friend.

When the two lonely hearts went into the bathroom, Bates sat alone in the living room at a small table drinking beers from a six-pack. They had left the bathroom door ajar so Bates kept glancing through the crack hoping he could catch some of the action in the mirror. He soon realized they were just talking. "The made' con spit in my face, and I just...perdio' eso." He could hear Ricky say. The talk was a combination of Spanish and English, but Bates quickly got the gist of the conversation. Ricky was spilling his guts out about what had happened, to a stripper, in a bathroom at a seedy motel room. "You gotta' be fuckin' kidding me," Bates said under his breath.

CHAPTER 26
DIA' DE NAVIDAD 1997

It was Christmas Day, and presents lay in abundance under the decorated tree. At the dining room table, the Harris and Donald families were finishing up a holiday feast of turkey, mashed potatoes, stuffing, and gravy. Vee had made it all from scratch. The only person missing from the celebration was Herb who had not been feeling well and elected to stay home. Vee took solace in knowing she and the kids would visit him later in the afternoon. However, at the moment there were presents to open, and judging by all the eager faces, that was priority number one.

At his home in Tonawanda, a frail Herb glanced down at the turkey dinner on the table in front of him. The small banquet looked tasty, complete with all the trimmings. He just hoped his stomach would allow him to eat some of it. Ricky entered the kitchen with a warm grin. He had just finished folding a load of laundry and was excited to have dinner with his old friend and the grandfather of his son.

Ricky had been secretly taking care of Herb over the past few months. When the remorseful ex-con was released from prison, he paid Herb a visit to apologize in person for what he had done. Ricky swore he would never lay a hand on his wife or daughter ever again. The two reconciled. Since then, Ricky began visiting on a regular basis. As Herb's health declined, he started doing his food shopping and helping with basic chores around the house like the laundry and washing dishes. Ricky loved the man who had never judged him. He was glad to be able to help or just sit down with him and share a holiday meal.

A week later on New Year's Day, while most people were busy watching the Rose Bowl football game on TV or recovering from their previous evening's celebration, Ricky was on his way back to Tonawanda Island. He had decided to retrieve Rickerson's body and dispose of it permanently. He was starting to feel paranoid about its possible discovery. Ricky found out a missing person's report had been filed by Rickerson's family the Monday following his disappearance. Since then, there had been a lot of scuttlebutt around town about what may or may not have happened. He heard the police had been questioning neighbors and employees down at the plant.

Although he and Bates had laid low, the increased talk was making him jumpy. The local weather forecasters had also predicted a temperature rise into the forties later in the week, so the snow would begin to thaw. The idea of someone accidentally stumbling on to the body, however unlikely, only added to his paranoia. Ricky decided to get rid of the problem once and for all. The basic plan was to cut the body up and dump the smaller, more manageable pieces in different locations throughout the area. They would be almost impossible to discover or identify.

Ricky drove onto the island and pulled up to the abandoned warehouse, parking on the side so his car was out of sight. He retrieved a shovel out of the back seat and headed into the back brush. Ricky made his way directly to the old Sycamore tree and straightaway went to work at its base. He cleared out the snow, the debris, and the two heavy railroad ties. Ricky grabbed the rigid tarp and yanked it out of the alcove, exposing Bill's body. It was frozen to the ground, so he used the shovel to pry it loose.

Once it was free, Ricky pulled it out and set it flat on the ground. He ripped the garbage bag off and looked at the body. The cold had kept it well preserved, clothes and all. The sweat poured off Ricky's body, and he felt a little nauseous knowing what he had to do next. He pulled a small hacksaw from his jacket and dropped to his knees adjacent to the body. Ricky tugged on one of the rigid arms so it extended out away from the body and balanced it atop a piece of wood so it was raised above the ground. He held the arm firmly and began sawing at the wrist.

Thirty minutes later, Ricky sat on a log wiping his mouth with a rag. He had vomited in the snow when he cut off Bill's head and was still trying to get over the nausea. He put his face in his hands and let out a deep breath. Ricky grimaced as he looked at the head laying on the ground amid all the other body parts. Tired of looking at the grisly scene, he got up and threw the head in a large black plastic bag. He grabbed a stack of the bags and began filling them with the gruesome pieces: the hands and feet, sections of the arms and legs, and the two halves of the trunk. In the end, he had filled a total of seven bags.

When he was finished, Ricky gathered up all the bags and carried them back to the car. He placed them in the trunk and drove off. Knowing the area, Ricky canvassed a couple of the local docks along the shoreline which were isolated and seldom used in winter. He weighed down two of the bigger bags and dumped them into the river in spots still free of ice. Ricky took the remaining bags and randomly placed them in dumpsters around town where they would eventually become part of some garbage dump. A fitting end to a cheap prick, Ricky thought as he drove back home.

The next day, Ricky met with Bates on the island. As they sat in the car, Ricky told him everything he had done. Bates turned towards him with a startled look. "Jesus Christ, you cut him up?" he said with disgust.

Ricky smirked. "It was the easiest way to get rid of the body," he said matter-of-factly. "Now we don't have to worry about it anymore." As he said it, Ricky pulled out a .45 caliber pistol from inside his jacket. He forced it into Bates' mouth and pulled back the hammer. A shocked Bates looked at him in terror. "If you ever tell anyone, you're dead,

Lee," Ricky said with menace. "And if I can't do it, someone else will. Do you understand?" Bates nodded fearfully, and Ricky slowly removed the gun.

Bates breathed a sigh of relief and glared at Ricky. "Do you think I wanna' go to prison?" Bates exclaimed. "I won't say a fuckin' word to anyone!" He was tempted to ask about the stripper in Canada or anyone else Ricky had blabbed to but couldn't. He was too scared.

Two days later, a tip was received by the North Tonawanda Police Department implicating Bates in the Rickerson disappearance. Police contacted him on a Friday and setup an interview for the following Monday under the guise of routine questioning of Bill's former employees and contract workers. Over the weekend a human torso was pulled from the Niagara River by a local fisherman. Although it could not be confirmed, police had reason to believe it belonged to Bill Rickerson. The missing person case had suddenly escalated into a possible murder investigation.

On Monday, a panicky Bates showed up at the station. He was escorted through the busy squad room and seated in a chair at one of the desks. Detective Ralph Singer thanked him for coming in. He offered up some ginger ale and coffee from which Bates chose the latter. They both sat down with some small talk before beginning the interview. Singer said the questioning was just routine. They needed to follow-up on any connections Bill had that might develop into promising leads. Rickerson's family was very worried. Bates nodded in understanding.

The veteran detective asked Bates to verify his personal information for their records. Afterwards, he subtly shifted to a series of questions relating to Bill: What was his association with Bill? Did Bill have any enemies? When was the last time he had seen him? And, 'Did he notice anything unusual in the days prior to the disappearance? They went through each question in great detail as Singer took notes. Bates answered everything and even felt at ease with the generic nature of the questions. In fact, the whole interview process had been much more relaxed than he expected, almost cordial.

The squad room was beginning to fill up with people as the usual afternoon rush rolled in. The noise went up proportionally. "Do you mind if we go in the backroom, Lee?" Singer asked. "It's a little quieter in there. Can't hear yourself think here."

Bates shrugged his shoulders. "Sure, why not," he said. Both men stood up, and the detective escorted him down a side hallway to the interrogation room in back.

"It'll be much cozier in here," Singer said as they entered. "Can I get you another coffee?" he added. Bates nodded.

When he returned, Singer placed a coffee in front of Bates who was sitting at a table in the center of the room. The detective sat across from him and placed his pad and paper on the tabletop. He glanced through his notes, looked up, and smiled. "So, let's go through this one more time to make sure I have everything," he said. Bates frowned in expectation of the tedious effort. They spent the next hour reviewing everything Bates had told him in the squad room. When they finished, Bates started to get up, but Singer motioned for him to wait a minute. "Just a couple more things Lee," he said. "Do you mind?" Bates voluntarily sat back down. He glanced at his watch with a sense of apprehension, he had been at the station approaching four hours now.

"So, Lee, can you tell me where you were on the night Bill disappeared?" Singer asked. Bates looked at him in surprise. "Just routine," Singer assured him, noting the surprise. "The more people we can check off our list now, the easier it is for our investigation later." Bates smiled uncomfortably.

"I don't even know what day that was," he said. "After six o'clock on Friday, the twenty-first of last month," Singer replied. "There was a big snowstorm."

"Jeez," Bates replied. "If it was a Friday night, I'm usually at a bar or a club. If it was snowing, I might've stayed home. Honestly, I don't remember."

"That's okay," Singer replied. "If it comes to mind, let me know."

Bates watched nervously as the detective flipped through his notes again. "I understand you're friends with a Richard Matt?" he asked casually. Bates face tensed up in genuine worry.

"Ricky...yeah, sure, I know him," he responded nervously.

"He's quite a character," Singer said.

"That's one way of saying it," Bates replied with a short laugh.

"What can you tell me about him?" The detective pressed further. Bates looked at him anxiously.

"We met about eight months ago in Canada," he explained. "At a strip club. Found out we both lived in North Tonawanda. We go out drinking once in a while, maybe a club. That's all."

"I see," Singer uttered. "Could you provide a list of places you both frequented?"

Bates suddenly stopped talking. He realized he was no longer being asked routine questions. *He was being interrogated like a suspect!* They had tied him to Ricky. Fucking great! he thought to himself. He also realized they didn't have anything on him, or they would have arrested him. If he wanted to, he could just get up and leave. But that would make him appear guilty. Bates figured the best strategy was to sit tight and not say anything. *He would not say another fucking word!*

"I'm sorry Detective Singer, but I'm not going to answer any more questions," Bates said. "It feels like you're treating me like I'm a suspect or something." At that moment the door swung open and a gruff looking man in a gray suit rushed in and slammed his fist on the table. "That's right, you dumb, little dipshit. You are a suspect!" Bates squirmed back in his seat. He looked up at the ornery, silver-haired man who now sat on the edge of the table peering down at him.

"This is Detective Gregory, Lee," Singer added. "He's with Robbery/Homicide."

"Homicide?" Bates stuttered.

"So, tell me, Lee," Gregory stated. "What happened to Rickerson?"

"How the hell should I know?" he exclaimed as he looked at Singer in confusion.

"Lee, I'm not going to lie to you," the calm detective said. "You've been implicated in Bill Rickerson's disappearance."

"What?" Bates cried out in shock.

"I'll ask you again," Gregory interjected. "What happened to Bill Rickerson?"

"I don't know!" Bates yelled out.

"Was there an accident?" Gregory continued. "Accidents happen all the time. Just this morning we fished a human body out of the Niagara River. It didn't have any arms or legs though. Or a head for that matter." Bates face went pale.

The two detectives grilled Bates relentlessly. Gregory asked the questions as Singer poked holes in the details. A bewildered Bates soon lost track of time and sat there in a daze, faltering under the non-stop assault. He didn't know if he was coming or going. Through the haze, Bates thought he had tried to request a lawyer a couple times, but they ignored him or heard them mumble under their breath that he wasn't actually under arrest. He didn't need one. Bates just sat there in confusion as they continued to ask the same questions, over and over.

At about 1 A.M., almost ten hours since he had arrived at the station, an emotionally fatigued Bates bolted upright from his chair. "Okay, I'll tell you what you want to know!" he screamed.

"Damn right you will, you little bastard." Gregory growled. "And what I want to know is the truth." Bates sat back down in his chair. Broken.

Singer placed a pad of blank paper in front of him with a pen. "Write down everything, Lee. Don't leave anything out," he said. Bates wrote down everything he could remember as it had happened, from first going to Rickerson's house, Ricky coming out with the body, driving around in the snow, going to Tonawanda Island, and Ricky telling him he had cut up the body.

Thirty minutes later, an emotionally distraught and teary eyed Bates finally signed off on his statement. Gregory grabbed the papers. "... And if you're lying to us, Lee, all bets are off. It's twenty-five years to life. A man's been murdered."

"I'm not lying, sir," Bates whimpered. "I've told you the truth. That's everything."

Seven weeks later, Bates dejectedly sat in his cell, no closer to making bond. He had been jailed as a participant in a crime that had resulted in a murder. To his horror, he was listed as a joint principal! If convicted, he really could go to jail for twenty-five to life. Gregory had not been kidding. So far, Bates had held firm to his story, but the prosecutor wasn't interested in any plea deal. He had implicated himself by admitting he was at the scene and an active participant. However, the law had nothing that would stick on Ricky. Plus, he wasn't talking. Bates hadn't actually seen him commit any crime. If he wanted any kind of a deal, he'd have to start singing a different tune.

CHAPTER 27
SAYING GOODBYE TO FRIENDS

Ricky looked like a million bucks dressed in his black, hand-tailored wool suit. He was standing in front of a full-length mirror inside the local tailor shop of Silvio Petroni. Silvio was a personal friend of Elvira's who, as a favor, had asked him to get Ricky quickly fitted for a suit. No expense spared. He had done a masterful job. Ricky stood in front of a mirror admiring the work and his appearance.

The suit was for Herb's funeral. The patriarch of the Harris family had finally succumbed to cancer three days earlier. Before his death, Elvira and Vee had learned from Herb that Ricky had been taking care of him for the last several months. It had struck a deep chord with both of them. Despite Elvira's mental decline from Alzheimer's, the emotional pain of her husband's death seemed to bring increased moments of lucidity. In one of those stretches, she had procured the suit for Ricky as a goodwill gesture, and to honor her husband who had seen fit to reconcile with the man who was the father of their grandson.

As Ricky prepared to leave, Shawn walked into the shop. He had come to Silvio's the day before on Vee's recommendation and pre-selected a suit off the rack. It was the only way he could afford one. As he walked to the counter, Ricky approached him. Shawn offered his hand. Ricky obliged awkwardly. "A sad day," Shawn said.

"It is," Ricky replied with a subdued voice. "How's everyone taking it?"

"It's tough, but they're holding up okay," Shawn responded. "Vee and Elvira are taking it the hardest."

Ricky's face turned glum at the thought and shook his head. "Listen, I gotta get going..." he said quickly. "I'll see you at the wake this afternoon." Shawn raised his hand in farewell as Ricky walked out the door.

In the late afternoon, Ricky showed up at the funeral parlor an hour before the first viewing. The troubled owner was reticent to let him in. He strongly stated that additional preparations still needed to be done, but Ricky would not leave. "Listen, the man in there is the grandfather of my little boy," he said forcefully. "I just want to spend some time alone with him to pay my last respects before everyone gets here. Understand?" Rattled by his intimidating manner, the mortician reluctantly yielded.

"Ten minutes," he said. "We need to finish our prep." The owner escorted him into the visitation room and left Ricky to his privacy.

Herb lay in repose in a beautiful walnut coffin. He was dressed handsomely in a black suit and almost appeared to be sleeping. Ricky took a knee at the casket, softly stroked the dead man's brow. "You were a good man," he said quietly. "Never judged anyone. Closest thing I ever had to an actual father." He hung his head down in silent reflection.

After a couple minutes, a teary-eyed Ricky raised his head. He scanned the room to make sure it was clear from prying eyes. "I apologize, old buddy, but I need your help one last time," he said quietly. Ricky fumbled through his jacket, removing a foot-long object, partially draped in cloth from the inside pocket. It was a small hacksaw with a severely bent blade. He gently lifted Herb's legs and placed the wrapped saw under the padding in the bottom of the casket. He carefully repositioned the legs back to their original spot. Ricky stood up and looked at Herb one final time. "Rest in peace, my friend," he said solemnly. As if on cue, a determined knock resounded from the entrance door, indicating Ricky's time alone with the deceased had ended.

An hour later, the viewing room was saturated with mourners. Elvira was seated in the front row with Nick and Anna. Shawn and his boys were in the aisle behind them. The remainder of the seats had quickly filled with other family members and friends. Many of whom had come to pay their respects not only to Herb but to Elvira. Vee, dressed in a black silk dress and crying off and on, had searched Ricky out in the crowded room and found him alone in the back. He had refused to enter any further. They found a small alcove near a window in the back for some privacy and sat down to talk. They talked cordially for a good ten minutes. It seemed like old times. Vee still could not shake the idea of Ricky caring for her father the way that he did. She felt deeply grateful.

As they sat in a moment of quiet, Vee peered into the eyes of the man sitting next to her. She could still see the frightened twelve-year-old boy her father had picked up at the phone booth so many years earlier. Ricky slid his arms around her waist and held her tightly. "You were always the only one for me, Vee. Always," he whispered. Vee trembled with emotion. Ricky gently released his hold. "I should be going," he said anxiously. "Let you get back to your mom and the kids." The two stood up and looked at each other, almost with a sense of finality. They hugged tightly, and Ricky gave her a passionate kiss goodbye. Without saying another word, he swiftly exited out the front door into the cold winter night.

⊷—⊨♦≡—↦

Later that evening, the Tim Horton's in Tonawanda was unusually crowded considering the time. It was inundated with a mob of high school kids and vagrants all trying to escape the extreme cold outside. In their midst in a corner booth, Ricky sat across from Dave Beamish. Earlier in the day, the detective had informed Ricky that he was a person of interest in the Rickerson murder. It was no longer considered a missing person's case. He had asked Ricky if he would meet up with him at the police station to hear what he had to say. Ricky nixed the police station idea but did agree to meet him privately at the coffee shop. Beamish had given Ricky his assurance that he would not be arrested and that their conversation would be strictly off the record.

Now dressed in a winter parka and jeans, Ricky sat with his hands around the warm coffee cup appearing as jittery as he felt. His anxiety was crawling out of his skin. "...Dave, we're talking about a homicide here," he exclaimed. "We're not talking about some little shit burglary."

"I'm aware of what we're talking about," Beamish responded calmly. Ricky suddenly lurched forward and reached inside the detective's jacket feeling his chest. Beamish instinctively grabbed Ricky's wrist and pushed him back across the table. "Don't ever do that again, Ricky," he warned as he readjusted the Beretta holstered inside his shoulder harness. "I'm not wired. You'll just have to take my word for it."

Ricky sat back and sipped from his coffee. "Fair enough." He grunted. "Fair enough."

As the two men sat across from each other sizing each other up, a homeless man walked up to them looking for a handout. Ricky pulled out a stack of bills from his pocket and gave the man a crisp new five. "Poker gods change sides?" Beamish remarked.

"The money's legit, Dave. You'll just have to take *my* word for it." Ricky chuckled. Beamish gave him a disbelieving look. Ricky scowled in response. "The grandfather of my kid passed away," he said. "It's my inheritance." The detective frowned at him with heavy eyebrows. "Look it up if you want," Ricky continued. "He's in today's paper. Herb Harris."

Beamish shook his head. "That's not why I'm here. You want to tell me what happened to Bill Rickerson?" he asked firmly. Unsure what to do next, Ricky took another sip of coffee.

"Off the record." Beamish nodded in response. "Okay, okay," Ricky said hesitantly. Then carefully added, "Rickerson owed me and Lee Bates a lot of money for work we did. Only he wouldn't pay. Anyways...so, Lee hounds me for weeks telling me we should go collect. Right? So, we do. We go to Rickerson's house and ask for our money. He refuses, so we search his house. Nothing," Ricky said throwing up his hands.

"And what happened to Rickerson?" Beamish asked again.

"Well, after realizing Bill didn't have any money in the house, Lee got really pissed off. Things got out of hand...one thing led to another..."

"And?" Beamish tapped on the table. "And Lee went berserk. He bashed Bill's head in with a tire iron." Ricky said flatly.

Beamish scowled and took a sip from his coffee. "I talked to Lee Bates at length. He doesn't exactly fit the profile of a guy that would go berserk and bash someone's head in with a tire iron." Ricky sulked in his chair, sensing Beamish knew he was lying. The detective stood up and slipped on his jacket. "I came here in good faith with the expectation that you would tell me the truth off the record," he said. "Then I might be able to help you. If you're going to feed me a bunch of bullshit, you're just wasting my time." Beamish zipped up his jacket and turned to leave.

"Hold on! Wait!" Ricky yelled out nervously as he got up. Beamish spun back towards him. "Let's just say for a second Bill's death was an accident," Ricky whispered. "I'm just sayin'...you know, hypothetically speaking. You hear me on that?"

"I hear you fine," Beamish replied.

"Okay, so, let's just say...well, when we're in the house. I get into an altercation with Bill...but only after that bastard spits on me. So, I lose it...and punch him in the chest—just like anyone else would. Then the fucker decides to drop dead of a heart attack on the spot." The veteran detective sighed and glared at Ricky in disappointment.

"What kind of sentence you think I'd get for accidentally killing Bill?" Ricky asked nervously.

"That all depends on where the evidence leads," Beamish said. "The evidence leads to first degree manslaughter. That's where it leads."

Ricky exclaimed, "A ten spot I could do."

"Then why not just turn yourself in?" The detective asked. "If what you're saying is true, an autopsy could easily verify that. Just tell me where the body is." Ricky's face went flush.

"Oh, fuck!" he cried under his breath.

"What?" Beamish asked with curiosity. Ricky shook his head as if to say forget it. He glanced up from his befuddled state and looked at his longtime mentor. "Give me twenty-four hours to think about it, Dave. I'll come in and make a statement."

Beamish shook his hand and said, "Fair enough."

By the following afternoon, Ricky knew what he had to do. First, ho-wever, he wanted to attend to his grooming needs. "A man should al-ways look his best when doing something big," Ricky kept saying to himself. Since money was no object, he had made an appointment at Vito's, one of the best barber shops in town. Ricky drove to the city in a stolen pickup truck and abandoned it on one of the side streets near the shop. An hour later, he stepped out of Vito's with perfectly groomed hair and sporting a big grin.

Ricky walked down the street feeling rejuvenated. He hailed a cab and had it take him to the projects in Buffalo's dilapidated North Side. The cab stopped near one of the older tenements and he got out. Ricky paid the driver and walked the block to his brother's apartment. Once inside, he told him everything that happened that night at Rickerson's and what had followed. "I can do eight to ten years," Ricky said nerv-ously, "but not twenty-five to life."

"Are you still going to the cops?" Wayne asked.

"Fuck no!" Ricky yelled. "I don't have any proof anymore. I really fucked myself over this time."

"What are you gonna' do?" his brother stuttered.

"That's where you come in Wayne-O," Ricky replied. "I need to borrow your van 'cause I'm going to Mexico."

"What?!" Wayne yelped in a flustered voice.

"...I'll get a duplicate key made, so you'll still have the original," Ricky explained. "That way you're not an accomplice...you just call the cops and say somebody stole your van. I'll drive it down to Texas, then leave it at the border. I'll leave you some money so you can take a bus down to get it. Whadda think?"

"Jesus, Ricky!" his brother cried out. "I can't let you take my van. I'll lose my job." Wayne raised his hands in an imploring gesture but knew it was useless. "C'mon man, I can't afford that with a kid on the way."

Ricky shook his head in disappointment as he visibly seethed with anger. In a flash, he lunged towards his brother and grabbed him by the neck. Ricky drove Wayne back violently and pinned him against the wall. He angrily glared into his brother's eyes. Then started to squeeze his neck. "You're my brother. You're blood," he said tensely. "I love you, but I will kill you!" Wayne looked at his brother in terror as he futilely tried to squirm out of his powerful grasp.

"Okay, Ricky. Okay," he gasped. "I'll do it." Ricky slowly released him.

"I'll be back in a half hour with a duplicate key," he said. "When I take the van later, give me twenty-four hours before you report it stolen." Wayne nodded grimly.

Ten days passed at the North Tonawanda Police Department, and there was still no sign of Ricky Matt. It appeared he would not be coming in voluntarily. An arrest warrant had not been issued because of a lack of evidence. Even if he had been apprehended and charged with second-degree murder, it would have been virtually impossible to make it stick. In this light, prosecutors decided to solidify their case against the man they did have in custody, Lee Bates.

Bates sat alone in the interrogation room. He was hunched over with his forehead resting uncomfortably on the steel table. His life had become a nightmare. The twenty-one-year-old's dignity had been slowly stripped away after spending the last month in isolation at the county jail. The DA's office had hounded him daily until he no longer had the will to fight. Unless Bates provided more evidence against Ricky, he would now be bearing the brunt of the punishment for Rickerson's murder. That was a twenty-five to life sentence with no guarantee of parole.

The door creaked opened, and a small group of men entered. Bates' public defender sat next to him while two detectives and the district attorney sat on the opposite side of the table. The DA opened his briefcase and placed a document in front of Bates. "I reviewed your new statement, Mr. Bates, which I find satisfactory," he said. "But just to be clear, you are recanting your original statement in place of this new document?"

Bates looked at his public defender who nodded. "Yes," Bates whimpered. "The first one was not the complete truth about what happened that night. I made up some of the details to protect Ricky Matt, sir."

"Before you sign the new statement," the DA said coldly. "I want you to review it carefully. Verify every detail is a factual retelling of what happened the night Bill Rickerson was murdered. You will have to restate it at trial under oath. Do you understand?" Bates nodded glumly.

The public defender briefly glanced at it before giving it to Bates. He anxiously started browsing through the main details. The statement summarily read that he and Ricky had entered the Rickerson home. That both men had participated in the attack and abduction of Bill Rickerson. Bates had witnessed Ricky and Bill fight over the money, and that during the confrontation, Ricky had stabbed Bill in the ear with a knife sharpening rod. Bates had objected to Bill's cruel treatment. Ricky responded by smashing his knee with the butt end of a shotgun. A weapon which he had carried into the house under his jacket. Ricky began drinking from a bottle of wine and poured most of its contents over Bill's head, calling him a "cheap Jew cocksucker."

Bates further stated that Ricky then tied Bill's hands and feet with packing tape before searching the home for money. Ricky returned from the basement in a rage after coming up empty handed. He hoisted Bill over his shoulder, and the three men went outside in the blizzard. Ricky dumped a still conscious Bill inside the trunk of the Chevy Lumina. Bates described their long driving excursion through the snowstorm looking for a place to eventually bury Bill's body. Ricky said he would have to kill him. As they drove, Ricky forced Bates to pull over several times and open the trunk. Ricky repeatedly tried to elicit from Bill where he hid the money. When Bill wouldn't comply, Ricky would torture him. Then they made a stop just outside Cleveland, and Ricky went to talk to Bill again. The old man said something to Ricky who flew into a sudden rage. Bates watched Ricky violently grab Bill's head and snap his neck. After this, the remainder of the document followed the narrative of the original statement.

The DA looked at Bates who had finished reading. "If you're done and everything is correct, then sign it," he said. Bates stared at the document in a brain fog as sweat ran down his forehead. If he didn't sign, it was twenty-five to life. If he did sign, he would be taking the plea deal, sixteen and a half years with a good chance for early parole. With a tense brow, Bates thought of what Ricky might do to him against the possibility of spending the rest of his natural life behind bars. He slowly picked up the pen and let out a piercing, almost-painful sound. Bates signed the statement. The DA simply smiled. He could now put out an arrest warrant for Richard Matt.

⊶⊷ ⇌◆⇌ ⊶⊷

Three weeks later, Texas rangers recovered Wayne's van a few hundred feet from the Rio Grande. US Marshals suspected Ricky had fled on foot into Mexico to escape his warrant. They had been correct. He had covered the short distance to Matamoros, a small town just across the Mexican border. The jubilant fugitive had made it to freedom, but it was short-lived. Within a week of arriving, Ricky got into a violent altercation at a local strip club and viciously stabbed an American businessman to death in the men's bathroom. Ricky claimed to Mexican authorities that the man had propositioned him in the bathroom and tried to touch him inappropriately which made Ricky snap. However, a witness indicated Ricky had tried to rob the man and stabbed him repeatedly after the man had fought back.

Ricky was immediately arrested by federal police. To his surprise, there was no trial and he never went before a judge. While being held in jail, Ricky received a notice that he had been convicted of murder and sentenced to twenty-three years in prison. Ricky was stunned. Shortly afterwards, he was transferred to the notorious penal complex in Matamoros. Even to a seasoned con like Ricky, the place was bar-

baric. It was home to many hardened members of rival drug gangs and cartels. Even Ricky did not believe he would survive there long. In desperation, Ricky called collect to a surprised Detective Beamish asking him for help. He begged for bribe money just so he could have a bed or pay for protection. He even told the detective exactly where he had dumped the plastic bags containing Rickerson's body parts to leverage support. However, when the searches revealed nothing, Beamish's interest and connection soon faded. Ricky was on his own.

CHAPTER 28
OUT OF SIGHT, OUT OF MIND

Nick beat the car dashboard and screamed. "Those sons-of-bitches! Those sons-of-bitches!" He gnashed his teeth and pounded repeatedly on the steering wheel as he unleashed his anger. His strength quickly ebbed, and he began to calm down. Nick hung his head down in exhaustion. "Oh, fuck." He groaned to himself. Nick put his hands to his head and sobbed. Through his tears, he slowly folded the letter from his dad and placed it back in the glove box.

When his head started to clear, Nick got back onto the road but only drove a short distance. He stopped at a small diner to grab a coffee. The tired teen walked in looking frazzled with disheveled hair and dried tears on his cheeks. An alarmed older female worker looked at him with concern and asked him if he was all right. She offered him a cup of water. Nick waved her off politely and nodded he was fine. He ordered a coffee, then plopped down in a booth. Someone had left behind a daily paper on the tabletop. He opened it to the front page. Nick grimaced as he gazed at another article about the prison escape and his *monster-like* father on the loose, roaming the countryside. He flung the paper off the table in exasperation.

Nick took a sip of his coffee and thought back about the time he had first learned Ricky had fled to Mexico. He had been seven years old. Up until then, Nick had known very little about his dad, let alone remember anything about him leaving. Looking back, he now realized Vee had been protecting him from his dad's reputation and the bad publicity surrounding his name. Since Nick's last name was Harris and not Matt, Vee had also hoped his young classmates would never find out. It was so much different compared to today where the news media seemed to know everything and scrutinize the family's every move, broadcasting it continuously. Sometimes it felt like the whole world was watching.

Still, it had not been easy back then either. At the time, Nick loved his teachers and his new friends at school. He also loved living with Shawn, Jesse, and Jake. For the first time in his life, he felt like he belonged. However, it felt like his world was threatened by the shadow of his father. He had seen the news. Heard the gossip. *Local murder suspect jailed in Mexico!* Ricky would not be back to play with him ever again. His mom had told him that he was the son of a troubled man who had done very bad things. He was mortified people would find out. Nick's anxiety was made worse when the TV news began mentioning the Harris name in connection with Ricky as local family members.

Nick remembered how his fears had come to manifest one day at school during his second-grade writing class. He had been busy at his desk working on a writing exercise along with the other students. Their English teacher, Miss Phyllis, was walking up and down the aisles glancing at the papers as the students worked diligently. She was checking for proper handwriting and penmanship, for which she had always been a stickler.

Miss Phyllis stopped next to Nick who had finished the exercise early. She smiled affectionately at him and perused through his paper. The veteran educator nodded approvingly and patted Nick on the head. "Well done, Nicky," she said. She began to put Nick's paper down when she suddenly paused. He had signed Donald as his last name instead of Harris. Miss Phyllis looked at the signature in surprise and turned towards Nick. "Nicky, why didn't you sign your paper correctly? You're going to need to erase that last name and sign it properly, okay?"

"That is my last name, Miss Phyllis," Nick responded anxiously. "I have a new dad now."

"Oh, I didn't know," she said in surprise. "But we haven't been notified," she continued, "and until we are, you have to sign your old name. Rules are rules."

Miss Phyllis handed Nick his paper, but he just looked at it with dismay. She asked again politely but was met by the same response. She then insisted, but Nick still refused. Frustrated by his behavior, she ordered him to the principal's office. Red with embarrassment as the other kids stared and laughed, Nick howled and bolted from his chair. He sprinted out the classroom's back door into the hallway. Nick raced down the hall until he was confronted by the school guard who was sitting at his desk watching a small TV. The old timer would not allow Nick to go any further. The former cop sat him down in a chair by his desk and looked at him with curiosity. "Aren't you the Harris boy?" he asked. Nick hung his head in shame.

Fortunately for Nick and the rest of the family, the uproar surrounding Ricky died down quickly. His arrest in Mexico would keep him in prison there for the next twenty years. He was essentially out of their lives. Along with Ricky being exiled for good, the next two years proved to be transformational for the family in many ways. Elvira had passed in her sleep after a long battle with Alzheimer's. She had been followed by Johnny Mangano, her long-time friend and confidant, who strangely died from a heart attack two days later. Vee and Shawn had also begun growing apart. Vee felt she was financially supporting the family herself while he sat at home and did nothing, not even housework. The strained relationship finally cracked when the distraught breadwinner believed he had been seeing another woman on the side.

In the summer of 2000, Vee decided to leave Shawn's log cabin and purchase her own property, a move that would give the thirty-eight-year-old her first real taste of independence. The new, two-story rustic house occupied a beautiful corner lot on the outskirts of Angola. Its location sat beside a lonely junction between two intersecting country roads lined with fields and trees. An above ground pool took up half of the front yard while a convenient two-car garage stood waiting to receive in the back.

On the official move-in day, Vee pulled into the driveway in her new SUV and came to a stop. She, Frankie, and Nick exited the vehicle and took in the picturesque view of their new home. There were smiles all around. In unison, the kids let out a shout of joy and ran towards the front door. Vee smiled as they quickly disappeared inside. She knew they would like what they found. She had been working long hours at the hospital and was pulling in good money as an RN. She had spared no expense with the interior furnishings.

Inside, two enormous couches and a large recliner made with the finest Hillsboro leather sat in the living room while a classic wood table and chairs from Thomasville filled the dining area. It was beautiful and stylish. Upstairs, Frankie and Nick both had their own rooms. As a centerpiece, each contained a TV, a DVD player, and a large recliner positioned in front of an entertainment center filled to the brim with the latest video games and movies. A kid's dream! Of the two, Nicks' room was larger and almost seemed designed for an adult. However, the bunk bed with the superhero covers belied the age of its new occupant.

—•— ⚎ —•—

A wide-eyed Nick stood in the center of the room, soaking in his good fortune. He walked to the entertainment center and grabbed his favorite DVD, an old animated version of Robin Hood. Nick inserted it in the player and turned on the TV. He grinned smugly as he sat back in his chair and opened the door to a small refrigerator on his right. Nick grabbed a can of Coke from inside and opened it awkwardly, spilling a good portion on the leather chair. He hastily used his shirt sleeve to try and clean it up.

Vee was standing in the doorway with a creased brow, staring at the mess. She walked up to Nick and threw a towel at him. "Clean it up!" she scolded him. As Nick worked frantically to wipe up the spill, Vee removed a pack of cigarettes from her pocket. She tried to take out a cigarette but had trouble. She lifted the pack up and could see that only half were left. Vee heatedly glanced at Nick. "Nicky, have you been at my cigarettes again?" she shrieked. "How many times have I told you, you're a kid, my kid...and you ain't smoking." Nick hung his head in silence.

An irate Vee had had enough. "You know what, forget what I said. Since you like them so much," she continued. "I figured we'd kick back and watch *Robin Hood*. Maybe finish off the pack. You good with that?" Nick was unsure what to say. He didn't want to lie but was afraid to tell the truth. Vee lit a cigarette and took a long puff. She handed it to Nick who took it reluctantly. "Smoke it," she said. Nick fumbled with it for several seconds. Vee shoved his chin roughly with her fingers. "Smoke it!" she yelled. Nick started smoking it and finished after several minutes. "Not too strong, are they?" Vee asked sarcastically. She lit another and handed it over to Nick. He smoked it through. They sat for fifteen minutes watching *Robin Hood* as Vee kept feeding him cigarettes. After the fourth one, Nick began to feel sick to his stomach and began to dry heave. He ran into the bathroom and threw up in the toilet.

Vee followed him in and turned on the faucet. She lifted up Nick's head and gave him several mouthfuls of water. He took several deep breaths to try and get the taste out of his mouth. Nick started to walk towards the door, but Vee snatched him by the arm and dragged him to the sink. She placed his right hand firmly on the porcelain top and, in a fury, extinguished a lit cigarette on the top of his hand. Nick felt the pain surge through him but stood motionless and did not utter a word. His cold visceral stare spooked Vee. He almost looked like Ricky as a youth, with the same sardonic grin.

The bewildered mother gasped. "I've been through this before... so, don't fuck with me, Nicky," she said. Tears began to well in Nick's eyes. Vee looked at him in horror as she was suddenly overcome by emotion. Her anger changed to sadness. "Oh my God," she whispered to herself. "What am I doing? I'm just like my mom." Vee began crying. "I'm so sorry, Nicky," she said. A sobbing Nick rushed to his mom and hugged her tightly.

"I love you, Mom!" he cried out. "I promise I won't ever smoke again."

Vee stood immobile, filled with dread. "I love you too, Nicky," she said in a frightened voice as she glanced at the burn mark on his hand.

A half hour later, Nick plopped into his chair happy as a lark. His mom had carefully bandaged his hand and said she loved him. He was now alone in his room with a big smile on his face, drinking his Coke. Nick heard a loud cry from outside and ran to his bedroom window. Standing in the driveway, suitcase in hand, was Jesse Donald. Nick raced down the stairs to let his big brother inside. Jesse unhappily said Jake would not be joining them. He had decided to stay with his dad. They gave each other a hug and were soon joined by Frankie. As the three laughed and rushed back up to his room, Nick yelled out at the top of the stairs. "Mom! Jesse is here!" A few minutes later, Vee stood in the doorway and watched in delight as the three kids sat playing video games.

CHAPTER 29
TEENAGER IN LOVE

A half dozen friends from Nick's freshman class were knocking each other down with enormous inflatable boxing gloves in the adult bounce house on the Harris front lawn. Another group of teens was splashing and swimming in the above ground pool. Nick stood in the pool's center in water up to his chest. Atop his shoulders sat Wendy Masterson, a spirited, fourteen-year-old beauty who was lean and lithe with radiant brown hair and eyes to match. She was considered something of a rebel by her classmates and often very outspoken. Wendy and Nick had gravitated towards one another from the first moment they had met at school.

Across from them in the water and ready to face off was another teen couple in an identical pose. Someone standing on the lawn outside the pool suddenly yelled out, "One, two, three, go!" The two human totem poles rushed towards each other. After several seconds of flailing arms and fun-filled screams, their latest opponents went crashing into the water. Wendy and Nick raised their arms in mock triumph before falling into the water themselves in howls of laughter. Their reign as king and queen of the pool continued as rousing cheers burst from the spectators.

Everyone loved Nick. His easy-going charm and good looks made him very popular in school. They also loved the parties his mom threw. For a parent, Vee was considered pretty cool by the other kids. She would often allow a beer or two to be consumed by the underage teens at her get-togethers. "Better they do it here than somewhere else un-supervised," she would say. Her parties were always fun and kept light. The teenage girls were also drawn to her because, unlike their own parents, she would actually listen to their problems and offer non-judgmental advice when asked. It was like having a second mom.

It was still daylight as the early evening rolled around, the party-goers gathered around a large ice cream cake atop a picnic table to sing Nick "Happy Birthday." He was officially crowned fourteen. Nick smiled and blew out the candles to a wave of cheers. He pointed to his mom across the table and exclaimed loudly, "I just wanna' say that I got the greatest mom in the world, and I love her." Vee came over to give him a big hug. Afterwards, two girls stood in line to give Nick a kiss. He laughed warmly. "Wendy's first, guys...Wendy's first," he said to their disappointment. Wendy approached. They embraced tenderly and kissed to a round of loud cheers. The two separated and stared into each other's eyes smiling. It was obvious to anyone watching they were both in love.

Breaking up the reverie, Jake Donald tapped Nick on the shoulder. Nick turned and let out a big grin. The two gave each other a hug. In three short years, Jake had hit the big time in California. The eighteen-year-old was now a world-class skateboarder with his own line of skateboards and sneakers but he never forgot his roots. Jake stepped to the side revealing two large presents. Nick rushed over and ripped the wrapping off the longer of the two. "Holy shit!" he yelled as he removed two skateboards from the box.

"Happy birthday, bro," Jake said. Nick took one of the boards and handed it to Jake.

"Let's break 'em in," Nick hollered. "First one to the creek wins."

Jake shook his head. "No, Nicky...thanks, man...I got a sore ankle," he said. However, after Nick's eager persistence and a persistent crowd, Jake reluctantly agreed.

The two teens headed out onto the long county road. As he walked by, Jake offered a *not-to-worry* wink to a nervous Vee, who had fought through the large group of teens to grab a front row seat. A young boy emerged from the crowd carrying a long stick with his t-shirt tied loosely to the end, serving as a flag. Nick and Jake both leaned in on their boards, at the ready. The flag dropped and the racers rode off. Jake shot out quickly and grabbed the lead over his younger counterpart. After a dozen yards, he seemed to slow down a bit and Nick started to catch up. The young boy turned on the afterburners and started to leave Jake behind.

That seemed to awaken the top ranked competitor's spirit as he suddenly jumped into another gear, much to the delight of the crowd. He quickly caught up to Nick, and they both raced side by side for several yards. They approached a steep decline in the road at a high rate of speed. While they both zipped down the hill rapidly, Jake used his experience to gain extra momentum from the rapid descent and propel himself forward. He shot out in front of Nick leaving him in the dust. He arrived at the creek fifty feet ahead of Nick, waving his arms. Nick followed with an exhilarated smile on his face, just happy he was able to give the champ a decent run. The brothers slowly skated back to the house together just like old times at the cabin. When they arrived, Jake and Nick were mobbed by the jubilant crowd. Everyone felt like a winner that day.

⇥✦⇤

Over the course of the next year, things ran fairly smoothly for the Harris family. The kids both did exceptionally well in their classes and actively participated in competitive sports after school, Nick taking up ice hockey and Frankie, lacrosse. On the personal side, Nick's relationship with Wendy took a step forward as she became an everyday staple in his life. The two became inseparable. Heading in the opposite direction was Frankie's relationship with her dad. Dr. Fig had married a young nurse in Florida a few years back and were already on their third child. By this time, Frankie had become an afterthought in his life, but she didn't care. She had Nick and her mom. The only bad incident for the family during this time was when Nick was caught smoking pot at school. He received a one-week suspension from school administrators and a verbal dressing down from Vee. Nick swore to his mom he would never do it again.

Not long after Nick's fifteenth birthday the following summer, Vee purchased a fully equipped RV. She gathered the courage to take off two weeks from work for the first time in her life. Vee took the kids, along with Trip and Jesse, on a memorable ten-day holiday to Myrtle Beach. The experience had given the forty-four-year-old a taste of what she had been missing out on all those years working endless doubles and mandatory overtimes. In an effort to change things up, Vee took a part-time job with the state evaluating the performances of nursing homes in the local area. It soon grew into a full-time supervisory position. The money was fantastic and included a car and expenses. It was a straight forty-hour work week, and compared to RN work, virtually stress free. Vee could not believe her good fortune. She was grateful for the increased free time to enjoy her life and her family under the umbrella of financial comfort.

CHAPTER 30
CALLING JOHNNY LAW

The Boeing 707 was on its last leg from Tijuana, Mexico to Houston, Texas. Air-traffic controllers had given the jet's pilots special permission, as prearranged by the state department, to enter US airspace as soon as it had taken off. The flight, and all communication with it, was done under a veil of extreme secrecy and closely monitored by US Marshals. On board, fifty-six heavily armed Mexican federal agents were carefully guarding twenty-seven inmates from Mexican prisons being extradited to the United States. The prisoners, most of whom were high-ranking members of the Gulf and Arellano-Felix drug cartels, were all considered violent and extremely dangerous.

Felipe Calderon, Mexico's president, had vowed to bring down the drug cartels ravaging his country. He had backed up his promise by launching an all-out offensive against them. The ensuing raids had resulted in massive arrests and surging prison populations. In an effort to quell the overcrowding and break the corrupt influence of the cartels in the prisons, Calderon had implemented a new extradition policy with the United States. He would send to his northern neighbor all inmates with outstanding federal warrants in the US, principally Mexican nationals with cartel affiliations. The top-secret flight was the first prisoner transfer under the new policy.

The convicts were considered *the worst of the worst* and were treated accordingly. Each prisoner wore a white jumpsuit for easy identification and was restrained by handcuffs that were attached to a belly chain around the waist. Leg irons were secured around the ankles, reducing any movement to a short shuffling walk. The jet's interior cabin had been specially refitted for the transfer to add further restraint and security. Individual rows consisted of two seats on either side of the center aisle with each enclosed in a steel reinforced cage which was locked during transport. The caged rows extended to the back of the plane. Prisoners were seated in pairs and firmly secured in their individual seats. In the front of the cabin, a cadre of sixteen Mexican agents sat facing the prisoners while another group sat in the rear. Each wore camouflage fatigues and had their head shrouded in a black helmet and ski mask. All were fully armed and ready to strike on a moment's notice should trouble occur.

Sitting in the front row with a wry smile and staring back at the men in ski masks, mainly the AK-15 assault rifles, was Osiel Cardenas. The brutal drug lord was the former head of the Gulf Cartel and one of the most feared men in Northern Mexico. Four years earlier he had been captured by the Mexican military during a government crackdown and had been imprisoned in La Palma and later Matamoros. It was presumed Cardenas bribed prison guards and government officials to enjoy special perks during his incarceration. He was allowed conjugal visits from women, received catered meals, and was able to play soccer on the prison field each day. With such a pampered life behind bars, many believed Cardenas still ran the Gulf cartel from his cozy cell. In the US, he had outstanding warrants for drug trafficking, money laundering, and threatening to murder two FBI agents. When the new government policy went into effect, Osiel Cardenas was one of the first names to be brought up for extradition.

Sitting next to Cardenas on the plane was Ricky Matt. Ricky had served nine of his twenty-three-year stretch. Twenty-four hours earlier, he had been peacefully asleep in his cell at Matamoros when he was abruptly wakened by guards in the middle of the night and told to pack his things. Ricky was immediately placed in a secure transfer vehicle along with other inmates and driven to an airport where they were marched onto the heavily guarded plane. The cabin windows had been permanently covered which only added to the mystery.

When the plane took off, Ricky had no idea where he was being taken or why he was grouped together with two dozen drug lords. He figured he would find out soon enough. With a resigned smirk, Ricky turned towards Cardenas. "Eres mi amigo para toda la vida, El Patróne," he said in well-spoken Spanish.

"And you are also my friend, Mr. Matt," Cardenas replied back in broken English.

"Silencio!" one of the masked agents yelled. The two prisoners laughed quietly in their chains. They had shared a cell together the last three years and had become close friends. Cardenas also thought of Ricky as something of a good luck charm. He was convinced God had miraculously intervened and saved Ricky's life after a failed prison break a few years earlier.

On that hot summer night, he and Ricky had both snuck out of their cell and made it to the roof at Matamoros determined to escape. Cardenas stayed in the shadows of an exit door as Ricky made his way silently across the roof first. Just as he was about to clamber down the outer wall, gunfire erupted from one of the guard towers. Searchlights went on and zeroed in on a helpless Ricky who went down in a hail of bullets. Cardenas himself had witnessed Ricky get hit several times. He quickly retreated back to his cell, convinced his cellmate was dead. Shockingly, Ricky returned to his cell two weeks later. None the worse for wear. The nine rounds that had struck him had all missed vital organs. Even the doctors who had worked on him considered it a miracle.

Before being taken under Cardenas's protection, Ricky's time at Matamoros had been a grueling hell on Earth. He was harassed incessantly, often starved, and forced to sleep on a concrete floor. Ricky was physically tortured and beaten by both guards and prisoners alike simply because he was an American. He would regularly be hung from a wooden beam by his hands or feet and cut with razors or beaten until he had passed out. During one attack, he had been forcibly pinned to a table by guards while a prisoner tattooed *MEXICO FOREVER* on his back. The abuse had been relentless, and Ricky did not believe he would live to see the end of his sentence. Cardenas had changed all that, making his last three years in the prison more tolerable. Ricky spoke fluent

Spanish, and the two conversed daily in their cell. Cardenas was even more comforted when he found out Ricky's biological mother was half Mexican. It made him easier to accept as a trustworthy compadre.

The Boeing 707 landed at an old military airfield located in an isolated desert area just outside of Houston. Dozens of heavily armed US federal agents took over the transfer of the prisoners. Ricky shuffled off the plane first in advance of Cardenas and was shocked to find himself back in the US. The rest of the prisoners followed in pairs. When they were all off the plane, the group was whisked away to a heavily guarded detention area for processing.

By early evening, the only detainee left in the intake center was Ricky. Prison authorities had no paperwork on him and were at a loss as to who he was. They felt certain he wasn't a cartel member but were confused as to why he had been included on a flight with their most dangerous criminals. Authorities questioned Ricky endlessly, but he was deliberately evasive, just to bide time. Three days later, his prints came back with a positive match from the national database. Realizing the game was over, Ricky confirmed his identity. He was summarily extradited back to Buffalo for an outstanding murder warrant.

◄═◆═►

The snow fell steadily outside the windows of the sophomore English class. Seated by one of the windows with his arms folded and a smug look was Nick. He had just finished his English exam and felt pretty confident about the results. The fifteen-year-old had aced two tests earlier in the day and had also found out he had made the regional travel team for hockey. Things were going well. Nick turned to his left and looked at Wendy with a smile. She was in the seat next to him, still working diligently on the exam. A knock on the door disturbed the quiet of the room. Everyone looked up in curiosity. Interrupting a midterm exam was not a typical occurrence. The concerned teacher walked over to the door and stepped out into the hallway.

The teacher quickly returned to his desk at the front. "No cause for alarm," he said. "Everybody go back to finishing your exams." The teacher turned toward Nick. "Nick, I see you're already done. Could you step out into the hallway for a minute?" A surprised Nick stood up. He glanced at Sky and met her questioning gaze with a quick shrug. Nick began walking up the center aisle and could see the principal with his mom standing in the hallway through the window in the door.

"Oh, fuck!" he mouthed to himself. His stomach dropped. Nick knew he was in trouble. He and a friend had recently burned down an abandoned farmhouse in Silver Creek just for kicks. It was dilapidated and sitting in a large deserted lot in the middle of nowhere. Apparently, somebody cared about it. Nick felt certain he would be spending the evening at the police station. All eyes in the room remained focused on their classmate as he was escorted out the door.

In the hallway, Nick was met by his mom and the principal. Vee's frantic stare spoke volumes. "Let's go, Nicky," she said nervously. "They'll be waiting for us."

"What?" Nick replied with a perplexing glance.

"It's better if you go with your mom, Nick," the principal added. Without uttering another word, Vee grabbed Nick by the arm and guided him down the hallway. They exited the school quickly. Nick watched his mom glancing from side to side as if she was on the lookout for someone.

"Mom. What's goin' on?" he said.

"Shut up, Nicky, and get in the car," Vee yelled. The two entered the car. Nick anxiously looked on as his mom stepped on the accelerator hard and fled out of the parking lot.

— ⚞◆⚟ —

Ricky Matt had returned to Buffalo that afternoon. He appeared thin but in good spirits. Ricky walked through the airport in handcuffs wearing a long-sleeve sweatshirt with the word "Shady" printed on the front. He was escorted by a US Marshal and six New York State Troopers. The entire group was surrounded by a flock of reporters. A private exit at the airport had been available for Ricky's transfer, but authorities had decided to parade the fugitive for all the world to see. A large number of law enforcement officials greeted Ricky's arrival outside the terminal, superseded only by the number of news reporters. The ensuing media frenzy would soon captivate Buffalo and the entire region. MURDER SUSPECT RETURNS TO BUFFALO!

— ⚝ —

Inside Tim Horton's, Vee and Nick sat at a center table in the back. Vee took a sip of her coffee and looked at her son with apprehension. "You gonna tell me what's goin' on?" Nick asked.

She reached out and grabbed Nick's hand. "Your father was brought back from Mexico today, Nicky," she said. "They brought him back to face the murder charge from ten years ago. I didn't want you to find out from some dumb ass reporter nosing around at school. This is gonna be all over the news."

Nick sat there stunned. His thoughts began to race, filled with visions of doom. Confusion gave way to panic. Nick stood up in the booth, grabbed his coffee, and began pacing. "What will happen when my friends found out my dad was a murderer?" Nick asked himself. Ricky had already been tried, convicted, and sentenced in the court of public opinion once before. The same thing would happen again. Would he be hated like his father? Labeled the son of a killer? More importantly, how would Wendy look at him now? Sweat poured from Nick's brow, and he began hyperventilating. Vee reached for a paper bag and placed it over his nose and mouth. He breathed into it deeply and began circling the table wildly. Alarmed by Nick's odd behavior, customers stood up and stepped back as members of the staff looked on in bewilderment. Nick glanced up and saw everyone staring at him. "Would you please just stop looking at me?" he pleaded.

CHAPTER 31
KING KONG AIN'T GOT NOTHIN' ON ME

The visiting area in the Niagara County Holding Center appeared cold and antiseptic. Bland colors seemed to saturate every corner of the large room. White fluorescent lights beamed down on a concrete floor populated by stainless steel tables and benches, all firmly bolted down. Dozens of inmates, either awaiting trial or for transfer to the state penitentiary, sat and conversed with family and friends.

In the corner of the room, sitting on top of one of the tables, was Nick. Vee was huddled beside him on a bench looking nervous. No one sat near them. Initially, the two of them thought it was strange but then heard Ricky's name whispered a few times amongst the other tables. His reputation had preceded him. Not hard when it was being blasted all over the news. Word had gotten out, the grisly killer who had survived a brutal Mexican prison for nearly ten years would be making an appearance. He was now among Niagara County Correction's most famous. The man and his family were given a wide berth, out of respect or maybe fear.

The chatter in the room seemed to rise when Ricky finally strutted in. He came out from the back-holding area escorted by two guards. Dressed in prison greens, the forty-one-year-old looked sharp but quietly menacing. Nick saw him as soon as he stepped forward. He watched Ricky scouring the room and appear disappointed not finding his two visitors. Nick jumped down from the table and quickly made a beeline for his dad, a man he had only seen twice in his lifetime.

Ricky saw Nick's approach and started walking towards him. The father and son met and embraced in a big bear hug. The two stepped back and stared at each other, amazed at their striking resemblance. "You ain't no kid anymore," Ricky said with a grin. "You been studying hard and gettin' good grades, Nicky?" The teenager happily nodded yes. Ricky's grin turned into a genuine smile as he patted his son on the back.

Ricky glanced over Nick's shoulder and saw Vee stand up from the table. In a flash, his smile turned into an angry scowl. Ricky pushed Nick aside and rushed towards Vee until the two stood face to face. His eyes were filled with intense fury. "Where the fuck were you when I was in Mexico, Vee?!" Ricky yelled.

"Where the fuck were you while I was working two jobs and taking care of nine people, you asshole?!" Vee shouted right back.

"You wanna' know where I was?!" he said. "I'll show you where the fuck I was." Ricky violently stripped off his shirt so it hung down at his waist, exposing his upper body. The quieted crowd watched the fracas as several guards rushed forward. "You see these holes...you see these holes?!" Ricky shouted. He began counting the odd indented marks on his chest and midsection from the bullets he had received during his escape attempt. "... four, five, six...," Switching to his back, he continued, "...seven, eight, and motherfuckin' nine. See'em, Vee? And all these other scars. You wanna know where I was? I was in fuckin' hell!"

In a fit, Ricky hopped onto one of the tables. He looked down at Vee. Then at everyone in the room staring up at him. As if issuing a defiant challenge to anyone listening, he growled out in rage. "They couldn't kill me then, and they can't kill me now...!" The guards began encircling the table with their batons at the ready. Ricky saw them and made a calming motion with his hands. He slowly stepped down and sat at the table. Ricky crossed his arms and turned towards Vee with a sullen expression. "...Don't you see, Vee, I'm already dead," he whispered in a pained voice. "They killed me thirty years ago."

Vee shook her head in despair. "I can't go through this again, Ricky," she said, and fled the room.

Nick stood there mesmerized by his father's rant and his parents intense clash. He wanted to rush after his mom, but he also wanted to talk to his dad. He might not get another chance. Nick sat down quietly at the table next to Ricky looking at the myriad of scars. Was his dad indestructible? he wondered. Ricky looked at him with a resigned grin. "They do bad things to you in prison sometimes, Nicky. Those bastards hung me upside down...then beat me for hours with a rubber hose. Broke four ribs one time...but they never broke me, son. Not once." Nick sat in enamored silence. Ricky pointed to a scar from a bullet that had just missed his heart. "Anybody else gets shot here, they're dead... not me," he boasted.

Next to the scar, Ricky ran his finger over a small tattoo of a man's face with long hair and a beard. Underneath it read *Jesus is my Friend*. "I got this to keep a buddy of mine happy," he said thoughtfully. Ricky twisted his shoulder forward so Nick could see his back. On it was displayed a large tattoo that said *MEXICO FOREVER*. "See that? It's all about man's desire to survive, Nicky. You do what you gotta do to guarantee that survival. You hear me?" Nick nodded his head.

Ricky reached up and grabbed his front teeth. He abruptly yanked them out, and Nick gasped. "Steel-plate dentures." Ricky chuckled with a raspy lisp. "Faggot Mexican guard wanted to suck my dick. When I wouldn't let him, he kicked my teeth in." Ricky gummed his mouth and snapped the teeth back into place. "Don't ever lose your self-respect," he said sternly. "Which reminds me..." Ricky leaned forward and menacingly pointed his finger at Nick. "If I ever hear you're doing or selling drugs, I will hunt you down and kill you with my bare hands. You got that?"

"Yes, sir," Nick said with genuine fear.

Vee returned to the table in a calmer state and sat across from Ricky. She asked Nick to slide down the bench to give them some privacy. Vee and Ricky began talking about the impending case and what he should do. "Tommy said you need to plea it down. With no eyewitness or weapon involved, it's voluntary manslaughter at best. Any competent lawyer should be able to rip Bates' story to shreds." Ricky just kept looking at Vee, nodding his head as she talked. He suddenly snapped.

"A hundred fuckin' dollars is all I needed for my own bed, Vee! A hundred fuckin' dollars! I had to sleep on a concrete floor. Then piss and shit in the center of the room's drain. Where the fuck were you?!"

Vee sighed in resignation. "You made your own bed, Ricky; you had to lie in it," she said. Vee stood up, ignoring Ricky's angry stare. "C'mon, Nicky. We're leaving now. Let's go."

As Vee walked away from the table, Nick noticed his dad staring at his mom's butt. Ricky noticed that he noticed. "I haven't been with a woman in a long time, son," he said grinning. "Sometimes lookin' and dreamin' is all you got. You got a girlfriend?" Nick blushed. Two large guards approached Ricky at the table.

"Time to go back," one of them said.

Ricky held up a finger to wait and turned towards Nick. "Always remember three things, kid," he said. "Work hard, pay your dues, and always respect women. But in the end, remember this: Family's all you got." Nick smiled through his gloomy feelings. There was so much he wanted to talk to him about and ask, but all he blurted out was, "I'll see you, Ricky." The two hugged, and Nick caught up to his mom. As Ricky watched both walk away, his attention briefly shifted back to Vee's assets one last time.

CHAPTER 32
BROAD STREET BULLY

The rink attendance for the heated hockey rivalry was standing room only. The hometown Angels were beating the Devils 4 – 0. Despite the lopsided score, the home crowd was anything but jubilant. The game had been a physical contest from the start with both sides providing an ample supply of penalty filled hockey. As the score had become difficult to control, so did the cheap shots and rough play, especially from the visitors. With two minutes remaining in the contest, the tense atmosphere felt like a powder keg ready to explode.

Locked in the penalty box sat an enraged Nick. Upset at his team's imminent defeat, he stood up and started pounding on the penalty box door with his broken stick to invigorate his teammates and antagonize the fiery crowd. Nick's play resembled that of his on-ice hero, Dave "The Hammer" Shultz, the once feared enforcer of the *Broad Street Bullies* in Philly who was famous for his aggressively rough play. He always made sure the other team paid a physical price for each game, especially in a loss. Nick liked to take that philosophy one step further.

As play resumed, Nick's penalty expired, and the gatekeeper released him onto the ice. Armed with a surplus of anger and a feeling of indestructability, Nick made a beeline for Mahoney, the Angels' biggest player who had been raising hell all night. Without so much as a warning, Nick body-slammed the big teen headfirst into the ice, knocking his helmet off. He threw off his gloves and started pummeling the defenseless player in the face. Several Angels players went after Nick but were intercepted by his teammates. Both teams quickly cleared their benches and joined the melee. An out of control brawl ensued with opposing players squaring off against each other. Even Trip, Nick's normally even-tempered line mate, got caught up in the moment and skated over to guard Nick's back, tackling a player.

Almost immediately, two uniformed police officers, the coaching staffs from both teams, and a mob of parents rushed onto the ice to help the refs stop the violent fracas. The on-ice battle came to an end after several minutes. Nick, having beaten his man into a bloody stupor, raised his hands in triumph and offered up a loud proclamation to anyone in earshot. "I'm the son of Ricky "Hacksaw" Matt! Play against me and the Devils at your own risk!" The grinning teen was crudely grabbed by the two police officers and promptly escorted off the ice.

Vee noticed a big change in Nick's behavior after their visit with Ricky at the Niagara County lockup. He had become more combative, with a devil-may-care attitude and was, at times, downright nasty. It only seemed to get worse in the following weeks. The hockey brawl was only one example. At the end of the month, Vee was shocked to discover her skyrocketing phone bill. She studied the charges and saw numerous collect calls from the holding center. Ricky had been calling the house while she was at work and talking to Nick behind her back. They would chat several times a week for hours. Vee could only shake her head in frustration, trying to imagine the bullshit Ricky was filling Nick's head with.

It was true. Ricky had spewed a lifetime of horrific exploits to his son. Yakking about living in the human jungle, survival of the fittest, and working the streets. About conning, grifting, and not trusting anyone—except for family. Ricky also tried to build himself up in his son's eyes. Portraying himself *as an indestructible God with incredible strength and being impossible to kill. He had the scars to prove it. During their last conversation, he had told Nick he was a human chimera, essentially possessing two sets of DNA. Ricky boasted he had proof after beating a rape charge. A swab taken from inside his mouth did not match the DNA sample retrieved from the woman's panties. Besides, the sex between the two had been consensual. "She wanted it, Nicky...and when I gave it to her..." The phone suddenly went dead. Vee had secretly listened in on the conversation. She had heard enough and hung up. After that, no more collect calls would be accepted. Vee had the telephone number changed and forbade Nick to give it to his father.*

Two weeks after the hockey brawl, Nick procured his first paying job on the nearby Cattaraugus Indian Reservation. *The Rez* was close to home and contained numerous gas stations which were always busy because their gas was tax free. People would come in droves to fill their tanks and stick it to the government. Nick figured it was a quick way to pick up some money. His friend Trip drove the eager job seeker to all the closest service stations until they found one with a job opening.

Nick started off work that summer strong, pumping gas day and night with a vengeance. He worked his normal forty hours and picked up some overtime on the weekends. The teen was soon raking in cash hand over fist. He occasionally brought home close to eight hundred dollars a week. Even Vee was impressed. Nick felt like he was living large and spent proportionately. He bought new skateboards, the latest designer clothes, and a barrage of gifts for Wendy and her friends. Nick even purchased a new car stereo system for his mom. Money left over that didn't go to his weed and cigarette habits was hidden in a small crawlspace in the attic.

During the winter, Nick abruptly quit his job. The weather had turned bitterly cold, and everyone assumed standing outside eight hours a day in the freezing temps no longer appealed to the sixteen-year-old. However, Nick had been stealing money from the station. At first, he had pocketed small cash sales but then discovered a way to hide larger thefts by charging or skimming the amounts onto credit cards. Over the course of six months, he had brought home almost ten thousand dollars. He figured it was only a matter of time before the reservation police would have paid him a visit. Even if they did, Nick didn't care. He was still only a juvie.

CHAPTER 33
PROSECUTORIAL
MISCONDUCT

Dressed in an elegantly tailored, dark blue suit and black leather shoes, Ricky looked like a million bucks. Even the leg shackles and handcuffs could not sway onlookers from the movie star good looks of the alleged murderer as he was escorted into the courthouse to stand trial. Flanked by a host of law enforcement officers, Ricky took his position at the defense table and was seated. Each day, his handcuffs were removed so their appearance would not prejudice the jury. However, underneath his suit, Ricky always wore a taser belt around his waist. If he became unruly at any point during the trial, he could be instantly stunned into submission by fifty thousand volts of electricity by a remote-control device held by one of the officers.

The wooden benches behind the defense and prosecution tables extended twenty rows back on both sides of the aisle. They were filled to capacity each day with spectators drawn like a magnet to catch a glimpse of the man described as an inhumane monster and gruesome killer. His mere presence seemed to evoke extreme feelings of both awe and disgust. One female groupie, who had become obsessed with Ricky, had obtained his measurements and provided him with a half dozen well-cut designer suits for the trial. She would be there in the front row in support almost every day.

Bill Rickerson's family also maintained a regular presence near the front on the prosecutions side. Ricky would not glance in their direction and ignored their contemptuous stares. Nick would attend the court-room sessions sporadically. He would be seated in the back row, silently supporting his dad. Wendy had given him some dark, horn-rimmed glasses and an authentic looking mustache from her makeup class at school to alter his appearance just enough to avoid being identified. The last thing he wanted was to be hounded by reporters and be the subject of their scrutiny. Vee avoided the proceedings altogether until the end. It was too much of a circus. In the weeks prior to trial, she had been secretly visiting Ricky in jail trying to aid his defense team con-sisting of a public defender and co-counsel. Vee was concerned the father of her son might be sent away for life. Her instincts told her the visits were wrong, but deep down, part of her still loved him, and there wasn't a damn thing she could do to alter that.

As the trial started, the prosecution wasted little time showing their hand, painting Ricky as a master manipulator who was also a violent and sadistic killer. He was *evil incarnate*. Over the course of the next four weeks, they paraded over thirty witnesses supporting this descrip-tion, giving a comprehensive view of Ricky's character, his guilty ac-tions, and his own self-incriminating babblings. Witnesses included, Corina, Ricky's Cuban girlfriend from Canada, many of his frequent bar buddies, and his former mentor, Detective Dave Beamish. On the day of the aging detective's testimony, he approached Ricky at the de-fense table before court began. The two men cordially shook hands. Ricky had read the discovery evidence and knew Beamish would be tes-tifying about their history and private communications. Ricky said there would be no hard feelings, just do what he had to do.

Despite the vast number of supportive witnesses, the crux of the prosecution's case rested on the precarious shoulders of Lee Bates. The last and the most vital witness at the trial. The thirty-one-year old in-mate was on loan from his incarceration downstate, already having served nine years of his sixteen-year plea deal for his part in the Rick-erson murder. When Bates was escorted to the witness stand, it was the first time the two former associates had seen each other in person in over a decade. It was also the first time since the trial began that the usually stoic Ricky appeared visibly agitated. He watched his old partner in crime like a hawk. Bates appeared nervous and jittery. The man had ballooned to 275 pounds over the years and looked uncomfortable and slipshod in an ill-fitted, wrinkled suit. The hot seat on a witness stand appeared to be the last place he wanted to be.

A packed house watched Bates testify and recount his official version of what happened that night in 1997. "...uh, uh, like I said, I went into the old man's house with Ricky. Bill and him started arguing right away about the money. Then Ricky smacked him in the face."

"Then what happened, Mr. Bates?" the prosecutor asked forcefully.

Bates made a quick glance at Ricky and lowered his head. "...Uh, uh, then I remember Bill spit at Ricky. And the next thing I know, Ricky goes nuts and sticks a pointed knife sharpener in the old man's ear. I tried to stop him, but Rick busted up my knee pretty good with the end of his shotgun."

Bates continued his story, describing how he had helplessly watched Ricky tie up Mr. Rickerson with duct tape, viciously torture him, then throw the squirming victim into the trunk of Bates' car. He further asserted that the two men drove the old man through three states looking for a place to bury him. Ricky would force him to stop the car and he would open the trunk to interrogate and torture Bill some more. Somewhere outside Cleveland, Ricky snapped Bill Rickerson's neck in a violent rage after the old man had said something to upset him.

The prosecution team spent the remainder of the day and the next going over that night again and the days that followed with the disposal of Rickerson's body. This time, they forced Bates to go over each horrific moment in great detail so that the grisly nature of the crime was etched in the mind of every juror. While the jury members had focused hard on the testimony, some taking extensive notes, many appeared visibly shaken and upset by the gruesome details. Two women on the jury and several spectators in the courtroom glared in contempt at Ricky, who sat aloof, staring nonchalantly at the witness on the stand. Nick, who had listened to all of Bates' testimony, sat in the back writhing in anger at the lies.

On Bates' third day of testimony, the public defender, Michael Roberts, finally got a shot at him on cross examination. The young lawyer started with defense exhibit one. Bates' original signed statement he had given to the police on January 6, 1998. "…and you signed this first statement, Mr. Bates? The one that asserts that you were not present when Mr. Matt allegedly accosted Mr. Rickerson?"

"Yes, sir, but that's not what happened…" Bates feebly answered.

"It's not, Mr. Bates? You signed this statement of your own free will, is that correct?" Roberts fired back.

"Yes, sir," Bates replied.

"So, then this is the truth of what happened that night…" the lawyer continued. "That you weren't actually there, and you only saw Mr. Matt carry Mr. Rickerson out of the home after the fact, right?"

"Yes… uh, no. That's not what I mean! That's not what happened," Bates said in bewilderment.

Roberts threw his hands up in exasperation. "Then what did happen, Mr. Bates?"

Bates sat in confusion, sweating profusely in his own turmoil. His breathing had become labored, and he began shaking. The judge asked a courtroom EMT to take a look at him, but Bates waved him off. In a huff, he finally exploded. "I told them what they wanted to hear so I could get out of there that night! I was hungry and scared! But that's not what happened."

"It's not?" Roberts queried. Before adding. "Then the second statement you gave on February twenty-fourth, 1998 with the prosecutor, the police, and your defense attorney present. That is the one you're now claiming is the truth?"

"Yes, sir," Bates said with a quiver in his lip.

Roberts continued with his skillful cross examination, the jury and the crowd hanging on every word. "So…the second statement you gave in the comfort of the prosecution team and your lawyers turned out to be pretty convenient for you, wouldn't you say, Mr. Bates?" he said.

Bates looked up in frustration. "That statement was the truth and got me sixteen and a half years in prison."

The opportunistic lawyer lunged forward and got right into Bates' face, shouting so the whole courtroom would hear. "…BUT THAT STATEMENT YOU GAVE. THAT FIRST STATEMENT, which is almost always the truth. That first statement, Mr. Bates, would have received twenty-five to life with no parole. That's what the district attorney told you. Now, we all know you knew that the threat of a *life sentence* was hanging over your head, Mr. Bates, when you signed that second statement. But wait a minute…you said it yourself that when Mr. Matt came out with Mr. Rickerson a half hour later…while you waited in the car, Mr. Rickerson was already deceased. Isn't that correct?"

Bates squirmed uncomfortably in his seat, confused by the misdirection. His trembling became visibly worse. "Mr. Bates!" Roberts yelled in expectation. Bates shook his head nervously and shifted his wide girth in his chair which creaked loudly in the quiet courtroom.

"…All I know is I told the truth," he said softly.

The eager defense lawyer sprung back. "Was that the second time or the first time, Mr. Bates?" he asked. "Because if it was the second time, then everything you said to prosecutors up until February twenty-fourth of 1998 would have been a flat out lie. Would that be correct, sir?" An uncomfortable silence filled the courtroom.

"Yes, it would be, sir." The prosecution's star witness answered. Roberts raised his hands and slowly approached the jury. "Mr. Bates has absolutely no credibility here, ladies and gentlemen. Once a liar, always a liar. You've all heard the phrase."

At the prosecutions' summation, the lead attorney reiterated that all the witnesses brought forward painted a pretty clear picture of the type of person Richard Matt was. "It showed him to be a master manipulator and a ruthless thug capable of committing horrible crimes. His former friend, Lee Bates, was merely an unfortunate pawn who was swept up in Mr. Matt's scheme to steal money from William Rickerson. When that plan went awry, so did Richard Matt who showed his true colors. He violently attacked and tortured seventy-six-year-old William Rickerson, eventually murdering him in cold blood by snapping his neck.

To hide his deed, he cut William Rickerson's body up with a hacksaw and disposed of the body parts."

The prosecutor emphasized that Richard Matt, in his own words, helped dig his own grave. "He provided self-incriminating evidence by telling friends and associates things about the crime every time he opened his mouth. You heard the collective testimony of all the witnesses. When Mr. Matt was serving time in a Mexican prison, he also wrote a letter to Bates' family indicating that if they brought him ten thousand dollars, he would clear Bates of any involvement with Rickerson's murder. Richard Matt wrote in that letter, *I was there. Bates is just as guilty as me of killing B. Rickerson.*" The special prosecutor threw up his arms. "How do you ignore that admission?"

The summation for the defense took place on April 14, 2008. Roberts vilified the prosecution's case, which was all based on empty talk. "There was not one piece of physical evidence that backed up the claims of Lee Bates. There was no evidence Ricky had brought a shotgun into the house that evening. There was no proof that William Rickerson was tied up with duct tape. There was no proof he had been stabbed in the ear with a knife sharpener. There was no knife sharpener. There was no evidence of torture, and there was no evidence of murder. There was no body! Nobody could say how William Rickerson had died.

"The bulk of the prosecution's case rested on Lee Bates a star witness who had changed his original statement to one that incriminated Richard Matt to a ghastly crime only after being told he would be tried as the sole defendant in the case and receive a mandatory twenty-five to life sentence. The letter written by Richard Matt from Mexico to Bates' family afterwards was simply the act of a desperate man willing to do or say anything to get money to survive another day in a brutal Mexican prison."

In his final summation, Roberts offered an alternative theory to what had happened that night. "Mr. Matt was never even there that night at Mr. Rickerson's. How could he be? He had already gone down to Angola to collect the money his cousin owed him from the day before." The lawyer further stated, "Mr. Bates went alone to Mr. Rickerson's house to collect money owed. When things went awry, Lee Bates killed William Rickerson and tossed his limp body into the trunk. It was a frantic Lee Bates who met up with my client later that night after he came home from Angola and begged him for his help. Feeling badly for his friend, Richard Matt went back to Mr. Rickerson's house with Mr. Bates and cleaned up the mess. The two men subsequently drove twenty-four hours looking for a place to bury the body. Unable to find one because of the snow, they came home, and my client dismembered the body discarding the remains into the Niagara River."

The late ploy by the defense to offer an alternative theory painting Lee Bates as the lone killer seemed to backfire immediately. No one in the courtroom or jury believed it, considering the personalities involved and the witness testimony that had come beforehand. It seemed by many to be an underhanded move by the defense to try and avoid a conviction and point the finger elsewhere. Neither Ricky, Nick, nor Vee understood why the public defender had added it to his summation. It only added an element of confusion and seemed to devalue their argument against the prosecution. As Nick angrily exited the courtroom that afternoon, he felt his dad's fate had just been sealed. The sixteen-year-old had been correct. It took the jury only four hours to reach its verdict, GUILTY on all counts. Three charges of second-degree murder, two charges of first-degree robbery and three charges of first-degree kidnapping.

A month later, Ricky appeared back in court for his sentencing hearing and was given a twenty-five to life sentence. Afterwards, he sat at the defense table and signed the necessary paperwork to file an appeal. Ricky was led out of the courtroom shackled and wearing handcuffs. On his exit, he glanced back to the judge. "Thank you, Your Honor," he said to her. "You've been very fair to me." The judge smiled in contempt and waved him off. Twelve weeks later, his appeal verdict came back while he sat in jail. It read: DENIED.

CHAPTER 34
THE ROAD TO PERDITION

As hot dogs and hamburgers sizzled on the backyard grill, their appetizing aroma filled the air. It was Independence Day at the Harris household, and the holiday celebration was in full swing. The front and back yards were packed with an eclectic mix of partygoers and boisterous revelers. Near the pool, several female teens strutted their stuff in bikinis, admired by teenage boys standing around in groups, hoping to get noticed. The underage crowd openly drank from beer cans and liquor bottles which was one of the biggest perks of a Harris party. It was even more loose than usual. Vee was working a double shift, so Nick was in charge of the festivities.

Wendy pulled into the driveway in her Jeep Wrangler. The top was off, and a handsome teenage boy occupied the passenger seat. Nick glanced over from his spot in front of the grill and noticed her immediately. He watched as she exited the jeep in her bikini bottoms and pink sarong wrap which hugged her curvy frame. Nick lowered his head as she approached and began fidgeting with a new iPhone his mom had recently purchased for him. A redhead was snuggled up next to him, amazed at the new high-tech gadget that was all the rage. Sadly, Nick knew Wendy had only stopped by as a friend. His drug habit had created a wall between them despite their mutual feelings. He had tried to stop, but the problem had only gotten worse.

It had been several months since his dad had been sent to the state prison at Dannemora. The month-long trial and lengthy phone conversations that had started up again with Ricky had taken a huge toll on Nick. He sometimes felt like his life was out of control and he was sinking into an abyss. At the same time, his weed habit had increased along with his drinking. He even showed up drunk for two exams. Vee had become alarmed at Nick's impulsive behavior and his inability to stay focused on anything. She took him to the family doctor who diagnosed him with Attention Deficit Hyperactivity Disorder. Nick just laughed when he was told. The physician had prescribed a stimulant called Adderall to combat the behavior. It seemed to work but only when Nick took it as prescribed.

Wendy kissed Nick on the cheek and introduced him to her new boyfriend. "Nick, this is Tyler. Tyler, this is my best friend, Nick," she said.

"Pleasure to meet you, Nick," Tyler said respectfully as he extended his hand in friendship. Nick glanced up at the six-foot tall blue-chip athlete with chiseled looks and blond hair. His first impulse was to drop him with a right hook, but he put a check on his jealousy and only smirked.

"Yeah, good to meet you too, man," Nick said. "Grab a beer. And thanks for coming." Nick nonchalantly turned away and continued his conversation with the redheaded beauty.

They were soon joined by two other girls who wanted to see the new toy. As Wendy walked away with Tyler towards the pool, she glanced back at Nick. He looked up, and their gazes locked for a moment. Nick knew his introduction to Tyler had been Wendy's way of sending him a message.

⚒

The party finally wound down in the late evening as most of the remaining guests had wandered off and left. Nick walked behind his garage with two other men in their late-twenties, Jimmy and Mike. Jimmy removed a bottle of prescription pills from his leather jacket and handed it to Nick. Nick opened the bottle and poured ten Xanax tablets into his hand. He put them back into the bottle and licked his lips. Out of his side pocket, Nick took out a bottle of his Adderall prescription which he had been hoarding instead of taking. He handed it to Jimmy who tossed a six-ounce bag of weed to Nick to complete the deal. Both parties seemed satisfied with the downers for uppers swap.

Out of the shadows, Jake Donald joined the group. Jimmy recognized him right away and approached. "Hey, you're awesome on that board, man... I'm Jimmy," he said. "It's really an honor to meet you."

"Yeah, well, I think you and your boy here should take off now. Okay, Jimmy?" Jake responded coldly.

"You heard the man," Nick said. "Time to go." The two men snickered as they walked away.

"That little prick will be crawling on his knees for this shit inside a week," Jimmy commented quietly to his partner.

Jake turned towards Nick. "I told you, I don't mind you smokin' weed once in a while." He said. "I do it too bro, okay? But any of this other shit... I can't take you to parties or anything else if you're on that stuff. I told you that before Nicky." Nick lowered his head dejectedly and tossed the Xanax bottle into a puddle. Jake put his hand on Nick's shoulder and the two walked side-by-side back to the house.

Three months later, in late October, as the sun was setting at the end of a peaceful day, chaos suddenly erupted in the Harris household. Vee stood in the kitchen ranting at Nick who was sitting at the table. A cell phone bill was swinging wildly in Vee's right hand. "We had a deal, Nicky...that you would never speak to that deranged son-of-bitch again!" she yelled.

"...Whadda you want me to do, Mom? He's family!" Nick sniped back. "The only fath—" He cut himself off sharply and put his head in his hands. Nick hadn't slept in three days, and it showed. He looked horrible.

Vee slammed the phone bill onto the table and raised her hand high into the air. Before she could strike, Nick stood up and grabbed his mother's arm. He held it tightly, holding it in place. Nick looked her in the eye, his body shaking fiercely. "Don't you ever try to hit me again, you fuckin' bitch!" he shouted. The room drew silent. Even Frankie peeked in from the living room. Vee's jaw dropped. She ripped her arm out of Nick's grasp and glared at her son.

Overcome by anger and shame, Vee grabbed her cigarettes and fled out the side door, screaming, "You're becoming just like your fucking father!"

A week later, Nick stopped talking to Ricky altogether. Vee completely cut off giving him spending money, so he could no longer afford his phone or anything else. Trading his Adderall for Oxycodone and Lortabs didn't earn him enough money for his habits either. He thought about selling drugs but fearfully remembered the threat his dad had made when they had talked. Deep down, Nick felt Ricky could always get to him if he really wanted to, even if the man was locked inside a maximum security prison.

Nick had felt remorseful about how he had treated his mom during their argument. He decided he would try to smooth things over by throwing himself into his schoolwork, starting with the AP math exam slated for the following day. Nick had already missed ten days of school, and it was only November. Failing out of high school was not an option. He had enough self-respect left in him to make sure that would not happen, so he headed upstairs to hit the books.

The next day, the silence in the classroom was deafening. Two dozen high school juniors were hard at work on their quarterly math test, nervously glancing up at the wall clock every few minutes to see how much time they had left. With twenty minutes remaining, a low, muffled rumble began to slowly echo through the room. At first, the sound did not disturb the test takers, but it grew louder until it became noticeably boisterous. Even the teacher stood up to locate the source of the disturbance.

Asleep in a back row seat was Nick. His head rested between his arms laying atop a wrinkled test paper. He was in a deep slumber and snoring thunderously. Some of the students laughed while others anxiously tried to waken their classmate. Nothing worked. As the teacher approached, Trip finally rushed over and shook him awake. Nick slowly opened his eyes to the scornful frown of his math teacher glaring down at him. The groggy teen was promptly escorted to the principal's office and lambasted for coming to school drunk. Nick received a one-week suspension and ordered to undergo a mandatory psych evaluation. Ironically, he had scored a ninety-four on the math exam.

Three days later, Nick and Vee visited Dr. Willard Edgecombe, a child psychiatrist in the city of Buffalo. Nick had undergone a series of psychological tests, and now the two waited patiently in the doctor's office, sipping their coffees. The sixty-five-year-old physician entered the room and sat down at his desk. In his preliminary findings, Dr. Edgecombe said that Nick was suffering from depression and recommended he be started on a daily regimen of antidepressants. He also said Nick's ADHD had become progressively worse compared to previous reports, so he wanted to up his dosage of Adderall.

Dr. Edgecombe indicated that he had also reviewed Ricky's medical history, which had given him great cause for concern. "Mrs. Harris, genetics often plays a significant role in mental illness," he said. "Your son's father has been diagnosed and treated for an extensive list of serious mental health issues throughout his life." Vee could only sit there silently, dreading the news. "In my opinion," the doctor continued, "it is more likely than not that Nick will develop some form of bipolar disorder sometime in his mid-twenties and have other issues later on, given his father's history and your son's current mental health."

"But the medications you're prescribing will control his symptoms. Right, Doctor?" Vee asked.

Dr. Edgecombe tore three scripts from his prescription pad and handed them to Vee with an encouraging smile. "They should but let's just see how things go. Okay, Mrs. Harris?" he said. "One day at a time."

Nick sat in his chair full of anguish. It was one thing to think about a fearful possibility. It was another to be told about its reality directly to your face. He had no idea what to think. A month earlier, the teenager had stumbled onto a gossip website which led him into a chatroom discussing famous murderers and serial killers. One of the topics was

Richard Matt. Nick had followed the conversation with curiosity. He grimaced when one of the chat members suddenly blurted out, "I think Matt's son should be murdered too...or at least he should commit suicide. Five to one, he inherited his old man's killer gene." Looking back as he sat in the doctor's office, Nick thought to himself, maybe it was true.

—•— ▣◆▤ —•—

Nick stayed clean from drug use for most of the winter, except for weed which he didn't consider a drug. He even took up snowboarding with his new girlfriend, an athletic eighteen-year-old preppy name Kirsten. The two hit the slopes in mid-February and, for a few months, were inseparable. The young girl was enamored with Nick and willingly lost her virginity to him during one of their ski excursions at a local resort.

In late spring, two days after Lake Shore High School's graduation, the relationship between Nick and Kirsten abruptly ended. Shelby Nicolson, a gorgeous classmate Nick had always harbored a crush for, had suddenly become available according to a mutual friend. That same friend had also told Nick that Shelby was interested in him, very interested. Nick unceremoniously dumped Kirsten after a quick meet-up and raced over to Shelby's high school graduation party going on that evening.

At the party, Nick downed several shots of vodka until he summoned the courage to approach his crush. Two friends who were with her had stepped away, so Shelby was standing alone. It was the perfect moment. "Hi, Shelby," Nick said nervously. She looked at him and smiled.

"Hi, Nick," she said.

"Congrats on graduating," Nick added as he kissed her on the cheek. Shelby stood there with a sexy grin. Nick leaned in again and kissed her on the lips. He put his hand on her waist and pulled her closer. Shelby leaned in, and the two melted into a passionate kiss. Nick reached down and squeezed her ass.

Without warning, Nick was blindsided by a thunderous hit to the side which knocked him violently to the ground. "What the fuck are you doing?" he heard a voice yell. The stunned teen lifted his head from the moist grass and gazed up at a huge member of the senior class standing above him. Nick recognized him from school. He was an offensive lineman on the football team and a friend of the quarterback who had been Shelby's boyfriend. Nick stood up and immediately dodged two wild swings from the clumsy giant. Nick quickly countered with an uppercut and two powerful right hooks to the jaw which dropped the 250-pound lineman to his knees.

Three teammates in the crowd rushed to the aid of their bloodied friend and helped him to his feet. The four athletes surrounded Nick and rushed him. There was a sudden flurry of punches. Nick fought ferociously, quickly connecting with several solid hits, knocking two of the attackers down. They got back up and went at him again. Eventually, the four larger teens overpowered Nick with a stream of pummeling blows. A last round of punches to his face and midsection finally sent the exhausted teen to the ground. Most of the partygoers just watched in curiosity, but no one offered to help him.

A battered Nick glanced up from the ground. It felt like his nose was broken and some ribs were cracked. Through the pain, he could see Shelby was looking at him with a mischievous grin on her face, shaking her head. She turned towards someone in the crowd. Nick followed her glance. He could see their mutual friend, Juliet, standing off to the side with a smug look on her face. She turned towards Nick and extended both her middle fingers. "That fucking bitch!" Nick said to himself angrily. He immediately knew the whole thing had been a setup.

Juliet had been the girl who had told Nick about the party. She had also fed him all the apparently bullshit information on Shelby. *"She has the hots for you Nick!"* Juliet had now apparently exacted some form of warped revenge. At a house party several months back, Nick had given her some ecstasy pills which he claimed would let her enjoy the party more. Twenty minutes later, the normally demure teen was suddenly, and eagerly, going down on Nick in a small side room. The next day,

Juliet felt ashamed at what she had done. She told Nick the pills he had given her had made her lose control. Nick only laughed and said everyone used them, and that there was nothing wrong with what they had done. Juliet told Shelby and a couple of other friends about what had happened. Soon after, the word had spread out around school which only made her more embarrassed.

With his face in the grass, Nick laughed to himself at the sudden turn of events. He clenched his fists as a wave of rage surged through him. The bloodied teen slowly rose to his feet and cried out, "You can't hurt me motherfuckers...don't you know I'm invincible!" Nick stared wild eyed at Shelby who was no longer grinning—and at the four big teens who had fought him. With a quick motion, Nick flipped open his switchblade. "Come and get it, boys," he said quietly. The four athletes stood motionless. None were interested in ending their careers before they had even started.

"You're a fuckin' psycho, you know that, man," one of them said.

"I know that if you come at me again, I'd be obliged to cut your balls off and hang 'em on that tree," Nick said pointing to a small maple. The group backed off.

"Get out of here, or we'll call the cops!" someone yelled from the crowd. Nick grinned and slowly pocketed his knife. He walked up to Shelby with his bloodied face and gave her another forceful kiss on her lips. She pulled away in disgust and spat on the ground.

"I can't wait for the next party," Nick said grinning. He turned around and walked out the driveway.

A mile down the road, Nick stopped and took a knee. The painful throbbing of his ribs causing agonizing discomfort with each step. It hurt just to breathe. As he rested, a rusted up old Ford Focus pulled up alongside him. The window rolled down, and Jimmy stuck out his head. "What the fuck happened to you?" he said. "Looks like you could use a ride, my brother."

"No, I'm good man," Nick said, catching his breath. "I think I'm just gonna hoof it back to the house. Thanks just the same."

Jimmy took out a small vial of white powder from inside his jacket and held it out. "Gotta lot more of this fine China White back at my place if you're interested?" he said with a smirk.

"How much?" Nick asked about the popular, designer, synthetic opiate. "On the house, my man. On the motherfuckin' house," Jimmy said smiling. He opened the back door, and Nick gingerly slid his throbbing body into the back seat.

CHAPTER 35
CHASING THE DRAGON
AND THEN SOME

Nestled between two sizable livestock farms sat an old, two-story shack that had seen better days. The windows were boarded up, the siding was coming off, and the lawn wildly unkempt. The forgotten structure and its small patch of surrounding trees stuck out like a sore thumb in the open fields, even in the dark of night. Building inspectors on the reservation would go out to the house once a year to put up condemned signs listing the house as unsafe. That did not stop squatters and other transients from taking up residence.

During the last week, it had been turned into a crack house after being taken over by Jimmy and his small crew. People would be coming and going at all hours of the day and night. The inside was in complete disarray with garbage strewn about haphazardly, and the sparse furniture was old and ratty. The floor in the front room was covered by mattresses spotted with dark stains and burn marks. There was just enough space between the makeshift beds so people could walk. Several were occupied, others waited for a new client. The rooms stunk of urine and rotten eggs mixed with the smell of burning plastic.

Nick followed Jimmy and Mike through the front door. He was instantly hit by the foul stench and overcome by a feeling of nausea. Nick dropped to one knee and began to dry heave. Mike sprayed a can of air freshener, but the effort was futile. Nick placed a handkerchief over his mouth, which was still bloody from the fight. Jimmy helped him up, then guided Nick down a long hallway to a back room. A huge bouncer with an enormous girth stood at the entrance door and waved Nick in after a slight nod from Jimmy.

Inside the room, the tin foils were red hot, the China White flowing. Nick sat down at an open spot by the wall. Jimmy handed him a foil with a white dab on top and a small plastic tube. He took out a lighter and lit under the foil. As the powder began to boil, Nick placed the plastic tube above it and deeply inhaled the vapors. He let out a deep sigh as he was enveloped in a deep wave of sweet euphoria.

The minutes turned into hours as Nick came in and out of dreamy highs. Jimmy kept the teen's steady supply of paradise coming. At some point, Nick began inhaling from a crack pipe. He looked at it but could not remember when he had upgraded. Nick glanced around the room; there were more people than when he had entered. He recognized some. A former classmate, Brian Harden, had been smoking next to him for the past hour. He had been expelled from a prestigious Ivy League college and banned from home by his affluent parents after chasing the dragon became his main occupation. The same with his tripped-out girlfriend, Sue, who sat next to him. She just graduated high school and decided to take a year off to find herself. Nick guessed she was still looking.

As Nick tried to take another hit from the pipe, Mike suddenly took it away. "Are you fuckin' crazy?" Nick snapped. He shot to his feet and went after him. The bouncer at the door quickly rushed in and pinned Nick to the floor under his large frame. "Give me some more of that shit, dude!" Nick screamed.

"That's enough for now," Jimmy said. "We don't need you dyin' here, Nicky." The bouncer slowly released Nick who raised himself to one knee.

"Jimmy, I'm fuckin' invincible, man!" he said boldly. "I could smoke all the shit you got in here for breakfast!"

"Yeah, well the kitchen's closed, my man." Jimmy replied. "You just put down two grams of 60 percent pure in three hours."

Jimmy looked at Nick with satisfaction. The kid had a high tolerance for the potent smack with no adverse symptoms. He would be a good customer. Tonight's free taste of heaven had been a test while simultaneously a business investment. Jimmy knew Nick was popular at school. He would be an excellent supplier of new customers when the money ran dry.

"Give me another hit, Jimmy!" Nick pleaded.

"I'll tell you what, my man," Jimmy said. "You bring me money and some of your friends, and the trips to paradise will never stop." Nick shook his head in frustration and went after the pipe in Mike's hand again. The bouncer and Mike grabbed Nick roughly as Jimmy nodded towards the door. The two big men dragged the combative teen along the floor and through the hallway as Jimmy yelled angrily from the back room, "And don't come back till you bring me two new B clients and some cash, you little prick!" Nick was unceremoniously dumped onto the front porch. The door behind him slammed shut in his face.

Nick lay in a motionless heap on the porch. He was roused by a rumble of thunder and a sudden flash of light. Nick wiped his face with his hand, then forced himself up into a sitting position. Another burst of lightning illuminated the dark night. He could see it was pouring. "Fuck. Just what I needed," he whispered to himself.

"Hey, Nicky, you need a lift home or something?" a voice off to the side asked nervously. Nick turned and could see Brian quietly standing back against the wall. Sue was next to him.

"Yeah, that'd be cool if you don't mind?" Nick said groggily as he slowly stood up.

"I'm right over there," Brian said eagerly, pointing to an SUV parked on the lawn. The three ran off the porch to the vehicle through the heavy rain.

Inside the SUV, Brian tossed a towel to Nick so could dry himself off. "...Uh, listen...Nicky, umm...you think it would be okay if Susie and me stayed at your place tonight?" he asked. "I'll be honest with you, our credit cards are maxed, and we just gave our last dime to Jimmy."

Nick rubbed his hair with the towel and grinned. "Yeah, sure," he said. "I got some weed and beer back at the house."

"Thanks, man!" Brian said smiling. Sue leaned over from the back seat and gave Nick a quick peck on the cheek. Brian started the engine and slowly drove the SUV down the long gravel driveway.

Several hours later, Nick sat in his recliner smoking the last remnants of a joint. Brian and Sue lay in the lower bunkbed quietly fondling each other, still high as kites. It had been a nice after-party considering the shit with Jimmy. "Pay it forward, my man. Pay it forward," Nick said to himself as he gestured towards the TV and shut it off. The clock on the wall read 3:45 A.M. Barely able to keep his eyes open, Nick waved goodnight to his guests. He climbed into the top bunk and passed out.

The alarm clock went off and Nick slowly awakened. The time read 3:00 P.M. He had gone to sleep nearly twelve hours earlier. He jumped down from the top bunk naked, strange since he could not remember taking his clothes off during the night. He opened a small oak case on the dresser to get his iPhone. It was empty. The phone was gone along with several hundred dollars he kept on a money clip. "Oh, shit!" Nick said out loud as he hastily put on a pair of shorts. The anxious teen began a frantic search for his money and, more importantly, his phone. All my fuckin' contacts, he thought desperately to himself. And where the fuck were Brian and Sue? Nick walked into the bathroom. A note written in red lipstick beamed off the mirror. "Thank you for the orgasms last night!" it read. "A.M.Z.!!" At first, Nick grinned with pride but then violently punched the wall in a rage. "Those silver-spooned fucks stole my phone!"

After a quick shower, Nick ran downstairs and dialed up Jimmy on the landline. He hoped Brian had gone back there for another fix. There was no answer, and the agitated teen slammed down the phone. As he walked through the living room, he saw Wendy's jeep quickly pull into the driveway through the window. Filled with unease, Nick stepped onto the porch and was greeted by a hysterical Wendy. "... He said he was your friend, Nicky!" she screamed. "He said he was your friend…"

Nick grabbed her arms. "Wait, wait…calm down, Wendy, okay. Calm down," he said. "Who said he was my friend?"

"The guy who answered your phone and said you were working together!" she said with a trembling voice. "I called you around noon. My girlfriend was in town and wanted some ecstasy pills. I thought you would have some."

Nick stood there dumbstruck. "Okay, just tell me what happened," he said. Wendy sat down on the steps and took several deep breaths to calm herself. "I met the guy on the beach behind Mickey Rat's beach club. It was that preppy kid, Brian. I remembered him from school a couple years ago. I handed him three hundred dollars for the pills, and he just smiled at me, Nicky. He turned to leave without giving me anything. The money wasn't mine, so I jumped on his back and began pulling his fuckin' hair. That's when it happened," Wendy said shaking. "Oh God! Oh God...!" Nick looked at her in alarm.

"What happened, Wendy?" he asked calmly.

"He threw me to the ground and ripped off my shorts..." Wendy said trembling. "He jumped on top of me and tried to..." Nick stood motionless trying to contain his growing frenzy. "...I screamed," she continued. "A man ran up from the beach and threatened to call the police. Brian ran off. It was humiliating, Nicky!" Wendy burst into tears and rested her head on Nick's shoulder.

"I'll take care of it," he seethed. "You just go home and rest." She hugged him tightly. Nick walked Wendy back to her jeep and helped her in. As she backed out, he waved to her before turning to go back into the house.

Once inside, Nick angrily dialed up his cell phone from the landline. There was no answer. He dialed up Jimmy. This time he answered. "Jimmy, this is Nick. Do you know where Brian is?" he said forcefully.

"I might," Jimmy said. "Then again, I might not."

"Well, that motherfucker stole my phone," Nick yelled. "It has my contacts...maybe some of your new fuckin' clients. You understand?"

"My man, I am at your disposal," Jimmy said eagerly. "I know where your friend Brian's at."

"The phone's locked," Nick added. "Only I have access to it."

"It's all about trust, Nicky," Jimmy said. "You give me what I want. I give you what you want. I'll be over with Mike to pick you up. We'll get your phone back."

An hour later, an old Gran Torino pulled in front of a beachfront home along the lake. The upscale residence was isolated and well hidden by an array of foliage and fenceline. The property belonged to Sue's parents. She and Brian would squat there on weekdays during the summer months. As the setting sun began to create deep shadows along the drive, the horn from the car sounded twice. Brian emerged impatiently from the front entrance. Jimmy had phoned and told him a shipment of 90 percent pure freebase had just arrived. He knew that would send the little prick into a full-blown lather.

Jimmy and Mike got out and stood by the side of the Torino. "Where's Sue?" Jimmy asked.

"She went into the city," Brian replied as he approached.

"Okay then, my man. Let's go inside and see what we got," Jimmy said with a grin. As the three turned towards the house, Nick snuck out from behind the car carrying a shovel. He raised it and swung it at Brian, hitting him in the back of the head. The stunned teen crashed to the ground. He lay there motionless for several seconds, then groggily struggled to his knees. A powerful right hook to the jaw from Nick sent him back to the ground again.

Nick stood over the hapless teen in a wild-eyed rage. "You molested my girl, you piece of shit! You stole my phone, and you stole my fuckin' money!" He bent down and madly dug through Brian's pockets. Nick found $six hundred dollars in cash and shoved it into his pocket. He could find no phone. He held up Brian's head and delivered two vicious punches to his face.

"I didn't take your phone, Nicky!" the battered teen cried out. "I don't even know who Wendy is!"

Nick glared at him. "I don't recall telling you her name, you stupid fuck." The petrified look on Brian's face said it all.

As Nick straddled over Brian, pinning him to the ground, Mike tossed him a roll of duct tape. He placed a piece over Brian's mouth and secured his hands and feet. Nick and Mike stood him up as Jimmy approached. He slapped Brian across the face several times. Jimmy leaned in close and looked the terrified teen in the eyes. "You're in some deep shit, man," he said. "Still have no idea what happened to my phone, spoon-fed?" Nick asked one more time. Brian shook his head. "Suit yourself." Nick chuckled. He hoisted Brian onto his shoulder and carried him to the car. Nick threw him into the open trunk and slammed it shut. The three young men got into the car. Jimmy cranked up the stereo as the Gran Torino spun its wheels and shot out the driveway.

The car traveled down a long, bumpy road until it got to Rt. 5 and headed south. As Mike drove, Brian's incessant pounding from inside the trunk blended nicely with the beat of the music. Jimmy laughed and started drumming on the dashboard. Nick, with a cigarette dangling from his lips, grinned at the antics from the back seat as he carefully loaded a twelve-gauge shotgun. They exited the highway after fifteen minutes and headed inland, into the densely wooded hills. The car moved cautiously along the winding roads, the headlights illuminating a small path through the bleak darkness. Mike slowed the car as they approached their destination, looking for the wooded post that marked the turnoff. He saw it, and the Gran Torino made an abrupt right turn onto a long-forgotten road encroached by vegetation on both sides. A quarter mile in, the car bounced over two sets of railroad tracks before entering a small secluded valley. They finally came to rest at the entrance to an old abandoned fairground.

In front of them stretched a large collection of old, rusted carnival rides from years past. Many were overrun by high grass and wild vegetation which covered up their former splendor. Everyone exited the car. Nick grabbed the shotgun off the back seat as Jimmy popped open the trunk. He and Mike pulled Brian out from inside. A rising full moon lit up the night sky with its dazzling light, but it would not suffice for what they had to do. Mike reached into the front seat of the car and flipped on the high beams. They lit up a small clearing next to a merry-go-round a short distance ahead.

Nick took out his knife and cut the duct tape off Brian's feet. He placed the shotgun at the back of Brian's head. "Let's take a little walk," he said. "It's justice time for you, scumbag!" Brian nervously walked forward, followed by the others. The group stopped near the merry-go-round. Nick turned him around and cut the duct tape off Brian's hands. Mike handed him a shovel. Brian's eyes widened in terror. He reached up and ripped the duct tape off his mouth. "Please don't kill me like this! Please, I beg you, Nicky!" he pleaded. Nick viciously thrust the butt end of the shotgun into Brian's face, knocking him to the ground.

"Start digging you piece of shit," Nick said as he pumped the shotgun. Brian crawled towards Nick and raised himself to his knees, clasping his hands.

"Okay…uh, uh, I stole your money and your phone," he confessed, "…but I never touched your girl. I swear. I took her money, but that was it. Your phone must have fallen out of my pocket on the beach. It's got to be there." Nick glared at Brian and slowly lit a cigarette.

"Never touched Wendy, huh? Then that would make her a liar. I don't think so." Nick moved forward and forced the shotgun barrel into Brian's mouth. "Dig! …Or I swear to God I'll blow your head off!" Nick growled. Horrified in sweat, Brian picked up the shovel and started digging. Nick sat on the edge of the merry-go-round and was joined by Jimmy and Mike. Jimmy lit up a joint, and the three took turns taking hits as they watched Brian dig his own grave.

After an hour, Nick stood up and walked over to the exhausted teen. "Strip down, spoon-fed!" he said. Brian began to weep and slowly removed his clothes until he was left standing only in his underwear. Nick took out his knife and with a quick flick of the wrist cut the elastic band, so the shorts fell to the ground. "You'll be leaving this world the same way you came into it, scumbag," Nick said. "Now turn around." Brian turned, and Nick kicked him violently in the back. The naked teen went crashing headfirst into the shallow grave. "Now get on your knees with your back towards me," Nick continued. Brian did as he was told and began to visibly tremble. Nick placed the barrel of the gun at the back of Brian's head and began to count. "One…two…three." Nick raised the barrel so it pointed up into the sky and pulled the trigger. A thunderous blast echoed in the night as Brian fell face first into the grave, screaming. Nick and the others burst out laughing.

Satisfied with the night's effort, the three picked up their belongings and headed back to the car. As they walked away, Brian climbed up to the edge of the grave. "You cocksuckers are gonna pay for this!" he yelled out angrily. Nick stopped in his tracks and quickly turned around. He started to walk back towards Brian with the shotgun. The fearful teen retreated back into the grave.

Nick approached and looked down at him with wrath in his eyes. "You ever go near Wendy again and I'll fuckin' kill ya," he said. "And you better hope to God we find the phone on the beach; otherwise, we'll be paying you another visit. Understand?" Brian nodded his head sheepishly.

CHAPTER 36
LIKE FATHER LIKE SON, ALMOST

It was a hot summer afternoon, and the courtroom in North Collins was packed. Nick stood before the judge, relaxed, composed, and sure of himself. He had initially been charged with felony kidnapping and assault with a deadly weapon. However, the charges had been reduced to a misdemeanor after a year of plea-bargaining. Today the sentence would be handed out. Anxious friends and family sat behind him offering their support. Vee was in the front row with Trip and Frankie on each side. Jesse and Shawn were present as character witnesses should they be needed.

Standing next to Nick at the table was famed Buffalo defense attorney, Tommy Eoannou. He was dressed in an Armani suit and looked every bit the sharp, seasoned pro that he was. Vee had secured his services courtesy of his association with her late mother. In the far back of the courtroom sat Jimmy and Mike. They had escaped prosecution because Nick had taken the fall alone. He had done so at their behest with the promise of future considerations. He was the only one underaged at the time of the incident, so his record would be sealed. Nick's sentence would most likely be lighter as a juvenile, probably probation. The only sticking point was his ninettenth birthday was the following Monday. Any jail time the judge did impose would now be in the big boys' prison. It was at his discretion.

All eyes focused on the judge as he came out of his chambers and took a seat at the bench. The seventy-five-year old opened the document in front of him and rendered his decision. "The sentence of this court is five years' probation or six months in a state correctional facility. What's it going to be, counselor?" he said. A thankful mother cried out in the front row as deep sighs of relief enveloped the courtroom. Nick's lawyer was looking at his nineteen-year-old client with an uneven brow as they conferred.

"I can do six months standing on my head, Tommy," Nick said brazenly. "It's in my fuckin' genes!"

"Think of your mom, Nick," Tommy said. "You can walk out of here today a free man."

"I can't do a five-spot on probation," Nick continued. "I just can't do it."

Tommy shook his head at his stubborn client. "Okay. It's your call," he said and nodded for him to answer the judge.

"I'll take the six-month stretch, Your Honor," Nick said loudly. "If that's okay with you, sir."

The judge cracked a slight smile. "That's fine with me, son," he replied. Vee let out a cry of shock as the crowd behind her gasped. The judge banged his gavel for silence before continuing. "You'll need to report to the Erie County Correctional Facility in Alden on September tenth at nine A.M., Mr. Harris. Do you understand, sir?" he said.

"All set, Your Honor," Nick replied.

Nick stood motionless staring straight ahead, contemplating the rationale for his decision. If he had taken probation, he would be subjected to random drug tests. He knew he would not be able to stay clean for five years. Any breech of his probation would send him back to prison to serve out his full sentence. It was six months in jail and be free or in and out of prison for the next five years for violating the rules of his probation. Nick weighed his options quickly; he didn't have a job, a girlfriend, or even a pot to piss in. He was a college dropout hooked on opioids and crack. Perhaps jail would clean him up. From his vantage point, it looked pretty good.

Thirty-five-year-old Dennis Morgan had long blond hair and a beard to match. The gaunt, repeat offender stood over six feet tall but weighed a mere 160 lbs. His prison jumpsuit appeared oversized and gangly on his slender frame. He had a laidback personality and, for the most part, was very congenial. While in prison, he had suddenly found God. Photos of the Pope, Jesus, and the Virgin Mary decorated the south wall of the small cell. A dark-blue rosary always sat on the bed beside him.

Dennis lay in his lower bunk and had just finished singing "Happy Birthday" to his new cellmate on the bunk above. His cellie laughed and jumped down onto the concrete floor. He poked his head into the lower bunk. "Thanks, roomy," he said. It was Nick. The grinning teen was now serving his first day in Alden. It also happened to be his nineteenth birthday. Nick was dressed in an orange jump suit and white sneakers. He was still trying to get used to his new surroundings, but it felt strange. He had landed at the same facility Ricky had been sent to twenty-five years earlier. They had even been about the same age. Knowing his dad had once walked these same halls made Nick feel more connected to him than ever before.

A buzzer sounded and the two-inch thick steel door opened. Nick and Dennis stepped out from their cell as a burly prison guard casually checked them off his sheet. They and the other prisoners were escorted to lunch. The interior of the cafeteria hall was massive. Four hundred inmates occupied forty tables. Nick glanced around and realized this was no movie. This was a real prison. Those were real criminals, and he would be sitting amongst them. He nervously got in a food line. At the serving station, an inmate tossed some processed turkey and mashed potatoes onto his plate along with a dinner roll and waxed beans. Nick grabbed a milk from the bowl of ice and headed off to an open table.

A number of veteran inmates soon joined him. Nick sat in his chair with a look of angst. His dad had told him all the stories and what to expect in the event he was ever incarcerated. Right on cue, he would now be tested. A degenerate looking man in his late forties with missing teeth and an odd haircut approached his table. He sat down next to Nick and began sliding closer, too close. The newbie inmate stared down the toothless predator. "You come any closer, old man river, and I'll cut your balls off and knock out the rest of your teeth so you can suck your own dick," he said loudly. A boisterous laugh emanated from the nearby tables. Nick had passed his first test, but he had a slight advantage. The word had already spread among the prisoners that he was the son of Richard Matt. His brazen escape was still considered legend among many at the maximum-security prison. Nick's bloodline instantly afforded him some hard-to-earn prison *cred*.

Nick's first week in prison went by quickly. He received three square meals a day and had money in his account from his mom for snacks. Withdrawing from the drugs was rough, but eventually, he came out from the darkness. An inmate from the prison gang MS-13 had befriended him in the yard. The twenty-five-year-old street thug had heard about his dad's relationship with Cardenas back in Mexico and soon began treating Nick like a kid brother.

On the second Saturday of his incarceration, Vee sat across from her son at a small table in the visiting area. She had been crying the entire first half hour of the visit. Thirty minutes later, Nick finally convinced her his incarceration had nothing to do with his upbringing. Nor did it have anything to do with Vee choosing to let him visit his dad in prison four years earlier. "The choices I made were mine, Mom," Nick said forcefully. "Not Ricky's...and certainly not yours. That jerk Brian assaulted Wendy and stole the phone you got me. I did what I had to do." Nick reached across the table and held her hands warmly. "Besides, I'm clean now," he added. "And I plan on staying that way."

"That's good, Nicky...that's good." Vee replied, half-heartedly.

Nick studied his mom. Something didn't seem right. "What's wrong, Mom?" he asked.

Vee looked at him nervously. "I've been losing my voice off and on over the last few months," she said. "I was worried, so I went to see a doctor. An MRI shows I have several polyps on my vocal cords. The ENT suggested I have them removed and biopsied for cancer." Nick looked at Vee, his face filled with unease. "...They're just polyps, Nicky," Vee continued, "...extra tissue on my vocal cords. The doctor thinks they're benign."

"Okay. Okay," Nick said anxiously.

Vee briefly pointed to her left shoulder with her finger and made a circular motion. "I also have two small growths on my shoulder and neck," she added. "The doctor's feel pretty confident they'll be fine too."

Nick sat there in disbelief. Almost trembling. "You might have cancer?" he asked with concern.

"Nicky, I have the best doctors," Vee said. "I've worked with these people all my life. It's not emergent. The growths are probably benign. I may even postpone the surgery until you get out in March."

The officer on duty nodded to Nick who let out a muffled groan. "I gotta' go, Mom," he said. The two hugged, said goodbye, and Vee grabbed her son's hands.

"Don't worry, Nicky, I'll be fine." Nick glanced back at her with a nagging uneasiness as he was led away.

Later that afternoon in the prison yard as Nick stood alone thinking about his mom, he was approached by three MS-13 gang members. One of them had seen his cellmate's rosary and wanted Nick to get it. He said he would try. That night, Nick anxiously broached the subject as he and Dennis lay in their bunks. "...Look, man, the dude wants it, or they're gonna' kick your ass and mine too," Nick said desperately. "I didn't think it was right to steal it from you, so I'm just telling you straight up." He glanced down at the rosary sitting on the desk below and the religious icons on the wall. A picture of Jesus dressed in a white robe and majestic colors stared back at him. It made him feel anxious.

Nick jumped down from his bunk in a hurry. He implored his pious cellmate to hand over the rosary. Dennis lay in his bunk smiling and shaking his head. He wouldn't budge. Now in the fourth year of a mandatory five-year sentence, he had revamped his life on the inside. The despondent, former crackhead had willingly turned his life over to God one day at prison Bible study. He had suddenly been shown the way. He believed Jesus was directly responsible for his transformation. Dennis took the rosary in hand and glanced up at Nick. "Long before me, there were followers of Christ who gave up their lives for what they believed in," he said. "While it would distress me should anything happen to you, please tell that gentleman I refused to give it to you. Tell him I'll be waiting here should he want to discuss it."

"Dude, he'll fuckin' kill you!" Nick exclaimed.

"Then so be it," Dennis replied with a benign smile.

The next afternoon, Nick met up with the gang leader. "He just wouldn't give it up, man," Nick tried to explain. "He said it was personal. His connection to God. I just couldn't beat his ass and steal it. It didn't seem right." The gangster stared at Nick in disbelief. With one nod, he could have had Nick and Dennis killed, but something seemed to touch the hardened criminal. His initial anger subsided. He looked at Nick and said, "Bueno," then walked away with his henchmen in tow. Nick glanced after him and noticed a multicolored tattoo of a cross decorating his bare back.

＊＊＊

A month later, with Nick finally settling into the dull routine of prison life, some good news came his way unexpectedly. He was informed by prison officials his name had been put at the top of the list for early release. Since Nick was a juvenile at the time of his offense, he was accorded an *early release distinction* should there be overcrowding in the prison. There was overcrowding, and he was told he would be out in two weeks. Nick was ecstatic. He would wind up serving less than two months in jail. Vee was overjoyed as well. She rescheduled her surgery for the day after his arrival back home.

CHAPTER 37
MALPRACTICE 101

Vee awoke in a hospital bed. She glanced around her antiseptic surroundings to get her bearings. It was her post-op patient room. A friendly nurse smiled down at her and waved. Vee tried to gesture back, but the pain on the left side of her face and neck was too great. Vee suddenly felt scared. The doctor had assured her the simple laryngoscopy procedure would be the least invasive way of removing the lesions from her vocal cords. At worst, he said, she might experience a very sore throat that would be mildly uncomfortable. This felt far worse.

The ENT specialist who had performed the surgery entered the room. Vee tried to shift her head to look at him. The simple movement caused her unbearable pain, and she moaned. With her right hand, Vee reached up to her neck and could feel a large gauze bandage wrapped around it. She could also feel her once long brown hair had been cut just above the neckline. Vee tried to sit herself up in bed but couldn't. The right arm worked, but the left was limp. She tried to move her left hand and fingers. They still functioned normally. Thank God for that, she thought. Despite the positive sign, Vee knew something had gone terribly wrong in the surgery.

Nick and Frankie entered the room following the doctor. Nick approached his mom while Frankie hung back. She began to cry. Vee felt a pit in her stomach. The doctor stepped up to her bedside. "Ms. Harris," he said with a sterile tone, "I removed the three lesions from your vocal cords. However, one of the tumors was more intrusive than the X-rays originally showed. Because of that, I had to probe deeper than I had intended. In the process, I inadvertently clipped a nerve bundle. Specifically, the spinal accessory nerve leading to your trapezius muscle. It has resulted in left-sided trapezius paralysis."

"Until the nerve damage is repaired or compensated for," the doctor continued, "you will likely experience pain and paralysis in the shoulder and neck area. Your left arm mobility will also be severely restricted. I've already consulted with an orthopedic specialist. He has recommended we schedule a follow-up surgery as soon as possible to repair the damage." Vee looked at the doctor in horror. "Unfortunately," he added, "unexpected complications can occur with the procedure you had. It is a small percentile, but it did happen in your case. We have to make do the best we can and move forward."

"Make do the best we can?" Nick angrily shouted. "You fucked up, and now my mom is paralyzed! Fuck that shit!" The fiery teen rushed impulsively toward the doctor who stepped back in surprise. He fell back awkwardly against the wall, knocking over a large piece of equipment. It fell to the floor with a loud crash. A nurse rushed in and watched Nick jump on top of the doctor, forcefully pinning him down by the collar. She called for security. Two large guards entered and quickly pried Nick off. "Anything permanent happens to my mom, you're fuckin' dead!" he yelled, struggling to get free. Still dazed, the doctor got up from the floor slowly.

"Let him go," he said in an uneven voice. "He's understandably angry." The guards reluctantly let Nick go. He kicked a medicine cart in anger and ran out the door, swiftly forcing his way through the curious crowd that had grown outside the room.

"Frankie, go after him. Make sure he's okay," Vee said in a muffled voice to her daughter. The young teen silently exited the room.

The doctor stood facing Vee with a solemn look. "I'm sorry you have to go through this, Ms. Harris," he said before turning to leave.

A few moments later, another doctor entered the room and approached Vee's bedside. "Hello, Ms. Harris. I'm Dr. Langley, an orthopedic surgeon here at the hospital. I've been in consult with your ENT and have been apprised of your situation." Vee grunted in acknowledgment. "I'm going to recommend you undergo the Eden-Lange procedure, Ms. Harris," he said. "It is a surgical treatment that involves transferring localized muscles to replace the anatomical function of the denervated segment of the trapezius muscle.

"The end result," Langley explained, "will allow you to twist your head, move your shoulders, and support your left arm again. It should also provide adequate relief of pain. The success rate of this procedure is excellent. The one negative aspect of the surgery is the healing time. You would be required to wear a half-body cast for at least six months. The upper left portion of your body needs to remain immobile for that period to facilitate healing. Physical activity must be limited. You would not be able to work."

"I understand," Vee said weakly through her tears. Dr. Langley's beeper went off. He checked it and grimaced.

"I have to go, Ms. Harris. Please talk things over with your ENT and your primary physician. We can schedule the repair surgery as soon as you feel you're ready." Dr. Langley let out a polite smile and left the room.

Vee watched him exit as she lay helpless in her bed. She felt devastated. Detachment and disbelief mixed freely with anger and fear. She calmly tried to think about what she was going to do. It wasn't just about her health but also her finances. She had no catastrophic medical insurance. Her doctor bills and physical therapy would be covered up to a point by health insurance. Beyond that, nothing. She would be out of work and have no money coming in. Maybe I could apply for disability, Vee thought desperately to herself. She still had eight weeks of vacation she could use, but that was it. There was also no guarantee she could go back to work after six months either. Suddenly feeling overwhelmed, the mother of two cried harder than she had in a very long time.

CHAPTER 38
SIX MONTHS OF HELL

If there was a silver lining to Vee's botched surgery, it was that the tissue samples taken from the biopsies were all negative. There was no sign of cancer. It was one less problem Vee had to deal with. Through the pain and paralysis, she devoted all of her efforts to getting back to the way she had been. The follow up surgery to repair the damage was performed shortly after the initial operation. Afterwards, Vee was fitted with an upper body cast which covered her chest, back, and neck. It also wrapped around her left shoulder and arm. The latter protruding out to the side and bending forward. Her entire upper body was immobile except for her right arm.

The rigid cast made any movement very awkward and limiting. Vee could no longer drive and had to be transported wherever she went. She required help standing up, sitting down, and just getting around from room to room. Simple daily functions such as dressing, using the toilet, making dinner, and lying down in bed to go to sleep suddenly became stumbling blocks requiring assistance. For the independent Vee, it was very humbling to have to rely on others for aid to do routine things.

The cast was also heavy. It instantly added sixty pounds to her slender, 120 lb. frame. Without additional support, she would tire quickly from the constant effort needed to carry the extra weight and maintain stability. The uneven weight distribution affected her balance, causing her to tilt to the left and lean forward. This was especially pronounced when she was fatigued. It constantly made her back and neck sore. Vee thought the plaster rig was a monstrosity, but she gritted her teeth, took her pain meds, and endured it for the duration of the healing period.

After six months had elapsed, Vee finally got the word from Dr. Langley the cast was ready to be removed. She and Nick eagerly arrived early for her appointment. The two were escorted into one of the examination rooms in the doctor's office. While they sat and waited nervously, both felt hopeful about the outcome. Dr. Langley had been very confidant of the success of the operation. A nurse and an orthopedic technician entered the room. The nurse assisted Vee onto the examining table as the technician grabbed a small, hand-held circular saw from one of the cabinets. After positioning her properly, the technician slowly began cutting through the plaster cast.

A short time later, Vee was finally free of her albatross. She smiled and let out a sigh of relief, no longer encumbered by the weight or the smothering feeling of being encased in plaster. Dr. Langley entered the room. "Hello, Ms. Harris," he said. "Let's take a look at how you're doing." The surgeon quickly examined her neck, shoulder, and arm. Seemingly satisfied, he pulled up a stool and sat directly in front of Vee so they were face to face. "Try moving your head to the left," the doctor said. Tentative at first, Vee slowly turned her head to the left. "That's good. That's very good," he said. "Now to the right." Vee slowly moved it to the right. "Now up...and then down," he continued. Vee did as she was told. Dr. Langley smiled. "You just passed the first test with flying colors," he said.

The doctor gently grabbed Vee's left arm and examined it. She stared at it with noticeable alarm. It had become physically smaller than its counterpart. The thickness of the upper arm was half its normal size. "Don't worry about that," the doctor said calmly. "Atrophy is normal. The muscle mass will return when you start to use it again. Now, try gradually raising your left arm as high as you can." Vee had difficulty at first but slowly managed to elevate the arm up to her shoulder. "Excellent," Dr. Langley said. "That's a good baseline. With a few months of physical therapy, you should get much of your functionality back."

The doctor stood up and began examining Vee further. He checked her back. For the first time, he noticed she was sitting hunched forward. "Ms. Harris, could you sit up straight for me?" he asked. Vee tried to push up but suddenly felt a sharp pain in her back.

"Let me try standing," she said. "I think I was sitting too long. Sometimes my back gets sore." The nurse helped Vee off the table. She stood hunched over at an angle.

"Go ahead and give it a try now," Dr. Langley said. "Stand up straight but go slowly." Vee tried but could not. She anxiously made several more attempts, but whenever she reached a certain point, the back pain became too great.

"I can't do it, Doctor!" Vee cried out in distress.

Two days later, X-rays revealed four herniated discs in Vee's spine. Dr. Langley called to give her the bad news. "...The weight of the cast must have placed a tremendous amount of stress on your upper back and shoulders," he sadly commented. "The damage sustained by the vertebrae was irreparable. The surgical risks to repair were too great. I'm sorry to have to tell you the likelihood of you walking or standing fully erect again is very low. For patients with your condition, the chances are one in five." Vee sunk into her chair, devastated by the news.

The bad news piled up. Shortly after, the devasted mother of two received a text from her malpractice attorney. She had filed a lawsuit several months earlier against the doctor who had performed the initial surgery. The final offer on the settlement had just come in. The text read, *$325,000. Final Offer.* It was the maximum amount allowed by the doctor's homeowner's insurance. He had no malpractice coverage. Vee would receive that amount minus the lawyer fees. That would be it. She knew it wouldn't last long considering the mounting medical bills and her inability to work. Vee took it in desperation.

CHAPTER 39
FOX ON THE RUN

The outside of the Harris home was now different. Two years of neglect had brought about a drastic change. The once flawlessly manicured yard was now a mere shadow of its former self. The grass was overgrown and filled with weeds. The driveway had started to become pock marked with unfilled potholes. Even the pool had been ravaged after being left open and unprotected through two harsh winters. The rusted interior had a foot of black standing water in it filled with old, dead leaves. The same decay had befallen the large wooden picnic tables in the front yard which were now unusable. The inside of the home had followed the same path. The rooms were unkempt and had the general look of being unattended. It was made worse by the putrid stench and filthy grime of cigarette smoke which had seeped its way into every nook and cranny, ruining the once meticulously kept interior.

Vee sat on the living room couch hunched over in pain. She lit a cigarette and stared indifferently at the burn marks dotting the leather seat of her latest walker. The expensive habit had also burned a significant hole in her pocketbook. Since becoming disabled, Vee's chain smoking had gone through the roof. She had started spending six hundred dollars a month on cigarettes, with Nick adding another two hundred of his own to the bill. The expense had become so great they were forced to switch from their preferred Marlboro Reds to the much cheaper, tax-free, Indian brand cigarettes from the reservation. The brand name change had reduced their total monthly bill to $250 and still provided the same level of nicotine kick they both craved.

The Harris household needed to economize. From the malpractice suit two years earlier, Vee had only received $165,000 after the legal fees had been taken out. Most of the money had gone towards the monthly mortgage payments on the house, paying off Vee's SUV, and medical bills not covered by insurance. The settlement money and Vee's savings were almost gone. They were now on Medicaid. The only money coming in was Vee's social security disability and Frankie's few shifts at a local coffee shop in between classes. Nick could not hold a job. Still, their monthly expenses continued to mount. With no more cash reserves to draw from, they were rapidly falling in the hole.

Vee looked at the plastic bag full of pills on the table beside her. They were the end result of two weeks of doctor shopping. In what had become part of her regular routine, she had visited multiple doctors and received a variety of prescriptions from each for the same conditions, chronic pain and depression. This allowed her to always have an abundant mix of pills on hand to choose from. Vee would take them indiscriminately as her moods and needs dictated. Dangerously, she often took different medications simultaneously or in excessive amounts which frequently led her to experience blackouts, disorientation, and a host of other side effects. Vee had even overdosed on three separate occasions over the last year. Nick calling 911 for paramedics had become routine.

Frankie entered the living room. She looked at her mom with despair in her eyes. The nineteen-year-old college sophomore had watched her mom rapidly deteriorate after the successive medical blunders. Their lives had suddenly been turned upside down. The two had always been best friends but now couldn't even maintain a simple conversation because of her mom's constant pain. It tore at Frankie's heart. She walked over to a chair and quietly sat down. With a feeling of helplessness, Frankie watched her mom put a Fentanyl patch on her arm and quickly swallow three pills from her plastic bag to mask the next wave of agony.

There was a noise in the kitchen as Nick entered from outside with Trip. While Nick walked over to the fridge, Trip stepped into the living room, and Vee's eyes lit up. She adored the young man. Trip had been Nick's best friend all through school and remained so afterwards. They hung out together frequently. Vee felt comforted when they did because, of the two, she knew Trip was the more responsible one. He had recently graduated from a two-year college. Trip was now working full-time at a local factory. He rarely drank liquor and only smoked weed on occasion. Nothing else. Trip would often keep Nick from getting into trouble. The unofficial member of the Harris family reciprocated Vee's affection and made it a habit to check on her whenever he could.

Nick walked into the living room holding two beers. He tossed one to Trip and kissed his mom on the cheek. "You look better today. How you feelin'?" he asked. Vee looked at him with discomfort.

"You gotta' get me to the doctor for the Ketamine infusions, Nicky. We missed two appointments already," she said desperately.

Nick threw his beer can against the wall and shouted, "I got it, alright, Mom…fuck! I'll get you there, next time. Give me a friggin' break, will ya." Trip, Vee, and Frankie looked at Nick in silence and waited for him to calm down. They were used to his sudden, angry outbursts.

Nick nervously ran his hand through his hair. He picked up the smashed beer can and plopped onto the couch. On the coffee table in front of him, a number of bills begged for his attention. The property and school taxes were overdue. The gas and electric bills, the car insurance, cell phones—all needed to be paid. Nick sat there with the weight of the world crushing down on him. He grabbed the stack of bills and glared at the mortgage. "Forfeiting our home is not an option here, guys," he uttered waving the bill.

"Things would be better for you kids if I wasn't here," Vee said gloomily.

"That's not an option either, Mom," Nick yelled. "Stop talkin' shit!" He watched as she hung her head down dejectedly. Nick walked over to his mom and gently gave her a hug. "Listen, I'll take care of everything," he said reassuringly. "Don't you worry." Vee let out a weak smile and nodded her head. Nick looked at her with bleary eyes before heading up to bed.

Early the next morning, Nick eagerly came running down the stairs and into the kitchen. He warmed two waffles in the toaster and was extra careful not to spill any syrup on his new jeans and button-down shirt. Nick wanted to look good. Today was a big day. He quickly ate his breakfast, checked on Vee, and rushed out the side door.

In the driveway, Nick raised his arms as if in mock celebration and took a dramatic bow as if in front of a large crowd. Today was his birthday. He had officially reached twenty-one years of age. He could now buy and drink alcohol legally, among other things. More importantly to Nick, the day marked the real beginning of being an adult and taking responsibility. It represented independence and freedom of choice. He wanted to take the reins.

To mark the right of passage, Nick decided he would start providing for the family. If they were going to survive financially, he was going to have to pick up the slack. His mom could no longer work, and Frankie was too busy with school. Nick knew he could never hold a nine-to-five job. With his mood swings, he would fuck up sooner or later and get canned. Nick decided he would go into business for himself. It was the only way. But before he started his new enterprise, he needed to talk to his dad face to face. That would necessitate a four-hundred-mile road trip to upstate New York.

Nick jumped into his sports car and cranked up the music. He drove a short distance and pulled into the parking lot of his favorite coffee shop. Nick parked the car and ran inside. Waiting in one of the booths was Wendy. Her attention was consumed by her smart phone as she sat texting. Nick approached anxiously. He could feel his palms perspiring. A few days earlier, he had called Wendy and told her he was going to drive up to Dannemora on his birthday to visit his dad. He asked if she wanted to go for the ride. Maybe talk again like old times, provide some emotional support. He felt on edge going up to see him alone. Surprisingly, she said yes.

Wendy had been seeing another guy for quite a while. Nick knew and felt apprehensive calling her out of the blue. They had not spoken much since his release from prison. Wendy had always felt responsible for his incarceration because her phone call had started the whole unfortunate chain of events. The first time they did talk after he returned home, Nick had reassured her none of it was her fault. He had made his own choices. Besides, it was all in the past now. Nick had also told Wendy that, in retrospect, his time spent behind bars had been the best thing that could have happened to him. He had not used drugs at all during his confinement and had come out clean as a whistle. While that was true at the time, Nick had begun using again soon after. Yet he was convinced he could give up drugs anytime he wanted. Going cold turkey in prison had proved he could. For now, he just didn't want to. They made him feel better and helped him cope with all the shit that was going on at home.

Knowing how Wendy still felt about it, Nick purposely hadn't ingested any drugs for the last couple of days so he would at least appear clean and fresh-faced. As he approached the table, Wendy glanced up and smiled. She got up and gave him a careful hug. "You look good, Nicky," she said.

"Thanks. You do too, Wendy. You look fantastic," Nick replied.

Wendy grabbed her things. "We better fly if you're going to make those visiting hours," she said. "It's a long trip."

"We'll make it. You know how I drive." Nick laughed. "I'll grab a couple coffees before we go."

<hr />

Nick opened the passenger side door of his car and moved to help Wendy inside. As he did, she gave him a passionate kiss on the lips and whispered in his ear. "Happy birthday, Nicky." He stood there silently and a little stunned. She had never kissed him that way before.

Nick looked her in the eyes and grinned. "Thanks," he said, then closed the door behind her. He walked around the car to the driver's side filled with a sense of euphoria. It was better than any opioid high he had ever felt. Nick sat down behind the wheel smiling.

The first part of their trip was uneventful. It was a boring, straight run east on the state thruway. The former best friends and high school sweethearts had started off with some small talk but soon retreated into their own private cocoons. Wendy began texting back and forth with her girlfriends while Nick listened to his gangster rap music. Two hundred miles out, Nick pulled off into a service area around Syracuse. He topped off the gas tank and picked up some burgers and shakes at McDonald's.

They continued on, heading north along Route 81 which would take them upstate. Nick slipped an Alison Krauss CD in the player and "Whiskey Lullaby" began playing on the sound system. He took a bite of his cheeseburger and started singing the lyrics to the sweet country ballad. Wendy stopped texting and glanced over at Nick with a smile. "You know the words, Nicky?" she asked.

"You're damn right I know the words," He said grinning. "I don't just listen to Lil Wayne, ya' know." Wendy laughed and started singing the lyrics with him. In unison, they belted out another five ballads from the CD. Each song drawing them closer in spirit and soul. It was just like old times.

When the CD ended, Wendy pressed the playback button again. She grabbed Nick's milkshake and took a sip from his straw. As the music played again, Wendy laid her head on Nick's shoulder and closed her eyes. Nick felt a deep sense of elation. He slowed the car down and set the cruise control to 65 mph. Normally, he drove like a bat out of hell, but he couldn't help himself. He just wanted this moment to last.

Two hours later, Nick came out of his peaceful reverie. The overhead sign along the highway read: "Dannemora 30 miles." Nick felt a sudden wave of apprehension that made him feel anxious. He had good reason to be. Nick was only thirty minutes away from seeing his dad. Plus, he had not told Wendy everything about the trip. When he had called the prison in advance to make the arrangements, he had put his name on the visitor list but not Wendy's. Nick did not want her there when he actually talked to his dad. If she knew the real reason for the visit, she would never want to see him again.

As Nick tried to think of what to say to her, the car slowly meandered its way through the wooded hills into the small town. He had never been to Dannemora before. He was surprised at how enormous the prison actually was. The imposing structure seemed to rise up out of the ground and take up half the township. He drove down the main street along-ide the thirty-foot high concrete prison walls which appeared to extend all the way across town. Nick saw the main gate and parked his car in the lot across the street. Wendy was still asleep next to him. He carefully placed her head on the headrest and quietly exited the car.

Wendy awakened. She let out a yawn and rubbed her eyes. "Sorry I woke you up," Nick said. "I was going to let you sleep." He pointed through the windshield. She stared at the prison and was awestruck by its size.

"Oh my God. What a terrible looking place," she said.

Nick could see the angst in her eyes. "I was thinking," he said. "Maybe it'd be better if I went in and saw him alone."

"...Yeah, maybe that would be best," Wendy replied nervously. "I'll just hang out here. Probably grab a coffee next door so I can wake up." Nick grinned. He offered her his car keys and a twenty-dollar bill. She took the keys but declined the money. She leaned over and gave him a kiss. "Good luck," she said.

"I think I'm gonna need it," he replied back.

Nick stepped away from the car and walked across the street. He paused in front of the titanic main door of the facility. Wendy beeped the car horn and stuck her head out the window. "Just tell him how you really feel!" she shouted. Nick spun around and gave a thumbs up sign. He turned back around with a frown. "How I really feel..." Nick nervously whispered to himself, "...is that Ricky's gonna' wanna kick my ass after I tell him what I came here to tell him." Nick glanced up at the guard tower ominously perched way above the entrance door before going in.

In the lobby, Nick stood in line to sign the visitors log. As he waited, he thought about what he was going to say to his dad. He had come all this way to get his approval to sell drugs. Nick knew Ricky staunchly disapproved of drug dealers. He claimed they had destroyed his parents and robbed him of a normal childhood. At the desk, Nick showed his ID and signed the visitors' log. He walked over to the entrance of the visitors' center and stood in line for the metal detector at the first checkpoint.

Nick thought about his family's dire situation. They were out of money and would soon lose the mortgage. Next, they would be struggling to find a low rent apartment. Even worse, many of the meds his mom was now taking were not covered by Medicaid. They had to pay out of pocket. That included the multiple doctor visits when she went *shopping* for the meds. The only way Nick could quickly get the sums of money needed to cover all their expenses was selling drugs. He had all the connections and he had Jimmy and Mike, who owed him. It was the only way.

Nick was next in line for the metal detector. Standing there silently, Ricky's anticipated words reverberated inside his head. "Stay the fuck away from drugs, Nicky! Get a job. Two if need be. Do whatever it takes to take care of your family." Empty words of advice. Nick knew Ricky never applied them to his own existence. His answer was always to go rob or steal from someone. How did that work out? Nick suddenly found himself unconcerned about his dad's flawed upbringing.

Halfway through the metal detector, Nick abruptly stopped and shouted out loud in an angry voice, "You ain't never been there for me, Ricky Matt! There ain't no reason for me to ever be there for you!" Nick turned around and briskly started walking back through the lobby towards the entrance. "Why the fuck am I even here?" Nick continued to shout. "Ask for your permission! Who the fuck are you? I'm old enough to make up my own fuckin' mind!" He stormed out of the entrance and across the street to the parking lot. The correctional staff watched Nick leave but seemed unconcerned. Arguments between visitors and inmates were a regular occurrence.

Off to the side, Wendy was having an argument of her own. She was pacing back and forth near a small gazebo, yelling into her phone.

Her ex had called in an attempt to rekindle their relationship. Instead, it had opened old wounds. Five weeks earlier, Wendy had found out her boyfriend of two years had been cheating on her. The two had been just days away from heading off to Los Angeles together where he would be attending medical school. Everything had suddenly been dashed. Outside of her parents, Wendy hadn't told anybody about it except some of her close girlfriends. She was still reeling from the whole thing. As Wendy continued to yell into the phone, she suddenly saw Nick walking back into the parking lot and sharply ended the call.

The ride back was quiet and filled with tension. Both were visibly upset, but neither could tell the other the reason why. Nick had explained there had been a paperwork snafu and he had not seen his dad. That was the reason he had come out so quickly. Besides the brief interchange, the two barely spoke the entire ride home. Nick turned on his radar detector, and they made it back in record time. He even slipped himself some uppers on the sly to keep awake.

Nick's sport car pulled into the driveway of Wendy's affluent home just before ten o'clock that night. Nick walked Wendy to the front door, and she gave him a quick kiss on the cheek. Nick boldly leaned forward to grab one more. They touched lips. It soon turned into a kiss of heated passion as they tightly embraced. Wendy's dad suddenly opened the front door, and the disheveled pair separated. Nick knew it was his exit cue. He waved goodbye and left.

CHAPTER 40
HOME SWEET HOME, WITH A TWIST

Nick smiled through his weariness as he recalled the sweet kiss with Wendy that ended his first-round trip to Dannemora two years earlier. This time, he had made the journey alone. It was after midnight when Nick finally arrived home and pulled into his driveway. While he had come back empty handed, he felt the trip had been worth it. Agent Maggio had given his word he would try to get Nick his dad's painting and other personal effects from his cell when the dust settled.

The exhausted twenty-three-year-old exited the car and sluggishly climbed the front steps. Standing on his porch, he suddenly realized something was different. Nick turned around. The media vultures had all packed up and moved on to their next victim. Not even one straggler was camped on the roadside, waiting for an exclusive interview in case something broke on the story. Nick shook his head in disgust. He wondered how those rat bastards could live with themselves, making the lives of innocent people a living hell for the sake of sensationalized bullshit. Nick stared up at the full moon and yelled out angrily, "Calling it your job don't make it right, boss!" He turned around and entered the house.

Inside, Nick walked into the living room. The TV was on, playing an old movie. Vee lay curled up on the couch in a deep slumber, a half-spent cigarette dangled from her fingers. Her plastic baggie of prescription pills was on the coffee table in front of her. They had done their job for the evening. Nick extinguished the cigarette as sadness filled his eyes. He placed a small piece of tissue paper in front of his mom's nose and watched it flutter. She was still breathing, albeit slowly. Nick kissed her on the forehead and covered her with a blanket before heading upstairs.

At the top of the stairs, Nick suddenly tensed up. The door to his room was ajar and the TV was on, the opposite of how he had left them. His mom could not have paid a visit while he was gone; she could no longer get up the stairs. Someone was in his room, right then and there. Nick's private sanctuary was a forbidden zone for others. It was made especially for the stashed drugs and the fifteen thousand dollars in cash in the attic. He pulled out his knife and flicked it open. Sweat trickled off his forehead as Nick cautiously entered the room, ready for anything. Almost immediately, the nervous intensity on his face turned into a relieved smile.

Asleep in the recliner was Wendy. Nick stood there gazing at her angelic beauty. He moved in closer and gently touched her hair. Sensing his presence, she opened her eyes and waved him onto the chair. They embraced each other, and Nick held her tightly, refusing to let go. He always felt secure with Wendy. They had a mutual comfort level that stripped away any emotional barriers. "We're soulmates for life, Wendy. Just you and me," Nick whispered. He reached for a kiss, but she abruptly pulled back and raised her hands in defiance.

"Remember what I said, Nicky," she said forcefully. Nick's face soured. Months earlier, Wendy had put the clamps on their relationship when she found out Nick was doing drugs. She had read him the riot act. They would remain friends, but it would never go beyond that until Nick gave up selling and using for good. Wendy lowered her hands. "You're halfway there, Nicky," she said. "You're halfway there."

Wendy stood up and moved toward the window. A text message bell sounded on her iPhone. She responded back and turned towards Nick. "I have to get going. I just wanted to make sure you made it back in one piece." Wendy waved goodbye and quickly headed downstairs for her ride. Nick glanced somberly out the window as a luxury SUV pulled into the driveway. He watched as Wendy climbed into the front passenger seat and received a quick kiss from the young man at the wheel. As the SUV backed out of the driveway, its bright lights flashed through the second-floor window, briefly illuminating Nick and his room before leaving him alone in darkness and disillusionment.

Nick stood silently with disappointed eyes. The pain ran deep. He was losing Wendy through his own stupidity and weakness. There was a growing chasm between them that seemed impossible to stop. It only pushed him further into the abyss. Nick could feel himself buckling under the weight of his own inner demons and swirling paranoia. He decided to fight the only way he knew how to ease his heartache. Nick reached into the hidden crawlspace under the rug and removed a Fentanyl patch and some foil. He sat down in his recliner and lit up. After two deep inhales, Nick was on his way to euphoric oblivion.

CHAPTER 41
BACK TO LIFE, BACK TO REALITY

Nick abruptly woke up from his drug induced stupor. Something was wrong. As he fought to clear the mental haze, he could smell smoke. Something was burning. Nick jumped out of his recliner in panic and looked around the room. Nothing. He rushed out the bedroom door and down the stairs. Nick could see smoke coming from the living room. "Holy shit!" he said under his breath. Nick ran into the room. His mom was lying face down on the floor in front of the couch. The throw rug next to her was smoldering badly. Part of it was on fire.

Momentarily startled, Nick quickly snapped into action. He raced into the kitchen and opened the fridge, searching for the large pitcher of ice water they always kept on hand. Nick grabbed it and ran back into the living room. He quickly poured the contents on the flames. It doused the fire, but the rug was smoking profusely. Its pungent smell filled the room. Nick pulled at the rug, but part of it was still under his mom. He gave it a steady tug, and it slowly came out from under her. He dragged the smoldering mess out the back door and dumped it in the yard. Nick ran back in the house to check on Vee. He knelt down next to her. His mom was breathing deeply but okay. She was in one of her deep *self-medicated* sleeps. Nick breathed a sigh of relief and surveyed the mess. It appeared Vee had passed out on the couch while smoking. She rolled forward onto the floor and her cigarette went on the rug. "Fuck," Nick said to himself in exasperation.

Trembling with nervous tension, Nick hovered over his mom who was lying defenseless in a fetal position. The horror of what may have transpired, had he not awakened, finally registered in his mind. The house, along with them inside, could have gone up in flames. Nick looked up at the ceiling and stared at the round impression left by the old smoke detector. He had removed it from the living room because it kept going off from the cigarette smoke. Maybe it had not been such a good idea. Nick cradled his mom's head and gently pushed back her hair. He didn't want to risk moving her alone with her bad back and shoulder. He would wait until she woke up. By then Frankie or Trip would be there to help. Nick placed a small pillow from the couch under his mom's head and threw a blanket over her. He stood up. In an effort to clear some of the smoke out of the room, Nick opened some of the windows and turned on a fan. He would clean up the remainder of the clutter later.

For the first time since he had entered the room, the TV caught his attention. Vee had been watching CNN as she always did. The prison escape was still the top story. A picture of Ricky in his prison greens was featured in the background as reporter Don Lemon and Dog the Bounty Hunter were spewing out more silliness. For the umpteenth time, they were going over all the alleged sightings of the escapees since the breakout two weeks earlier. "With Richard Matt's pedigree," Dog shouted. "They could be anywhere! In Pennsylvania. In Canada. Even Mexico. Remember, Matt is fluent in Spanish..."

Nick glared at the TV, "You fuckin' morons don't know what the hell you're talkin' about," he sniped.

Despite being furious, Nick was starting to feel numb to all the constant coverage. He was surprised at the degree of fear and hysteria whipped up across the country by the news shows like CNN. *There's a monster on the loose! Lock your door!* So far, millions of taxpayer dollars had been spent. Over 1,400 New York law enforcement officers were out looking across the state. Yet all their efforts had been in vain. Nick looked drearily at the TV and started to sing in a drowsy voice, "Oh, where, oh, where could Ricky Matt be, oh, where, oh, where could he be…" CNN cut to a commercial, and Nick stood up to go into the kitchen. "Inept bastards," he added with venom.

The tired son of Ricky Matt grabbed two beers from the fridge and a pack of cigarettes off the counter. He returned to the living room and sat back in the recliner across from his mom. She was still sleeping in a peaceful heap on the floor. Nick kicked back and opened a cold beer. He glanced at his glum face staring back at him from the wall mirror. How did everything go off the rails so fast, he thought to himself. Nick took a sip from his beer and closed his eyes.

CHAPTER 42
ENTREPRENEURIAL LEADERSHIP

It had been six months since Nick had made his trip to Dannemora. The time had not been wasted. He had established a working arrangement with Jimmy. The long-time drug dealer would teach him the ropes in exchange for taking ownership of the contact list in Nick's phone. The prime list of names was a goldmine of potential customers. Many of Nick's friends, especially from school, came from affluent families who had the money and ripe mindsets to become regulars. However, it would take time to mine through the contacts and develop a solid customer base. In the meantime, Jimmy fronted Nick money. It was enough to live on but did not cover all his family's monthly expenses. Their finances were still spiraling out of control. Nick needed to start making money fast. Jimmy found a way for him to make a quick score and get the ball rolling.

—+— ⊠◆⊠ —+—

Dozens of patients waited inside the large waiting area of the pain clinic. The facility housed several physicians specializing in pain management and physical therapy. Among those waiting impatiently for their name to be called was Nick. He was dressed casually in a gray sport coat. His demeanor was quiet with discouraged eyes. A pretty blond nurse in her early twenties called out his name. Nick glanced at her and stood up slowly. She took his file and escorted him down a hallway towards a series of examination rooms in the back. Nick followed, walking slower than normal. He appeared guarded in his movements and seemed to wince in pain as he walked along.

Nick was seated on an exam table inside one of the rooms. The nurse took his vitals and glanced down at his chart. She smiled at him, and he smiled back as they waited. There was a quick knock at the door, and it opened. A hurried Asian doctor entered. He placed Nick's MRI on the screen. The doctor looked closely at the scan and shook his head. It showed advanced degenerative disease in three vertebrae of the upper spine. "What your pain level, scale one to ten?" he asked Nick in broken English.

"I can't take it anymore, Doc!" Nick stated tensely. "I can't work. I can't do things around the house. I can't even sleep at night the pain gets so bad."

"Sorry to see in one so young. What number please? Pain number?" the doctor asked persistently as he glanced at his watch.

"Number?" Nick said. "Oh. When it gets bad...at least a nine... maybe even close to ten! It's unbearable."

The doctor gave Nick a quick cursory exam. "You have trouble with drug addiction before?" he asked.

Startled, Nick looked at him with a questioning glance. "Me? No, sir," he replied. "I ain't never taken an illegal drug in my life."

"Sorry. Required to ask," the doctor said. He nodded to the nurse who handed Nick a document to sign, swearing he would not see other pain doctors while being treated at the clinic. Nick signed it, and the doctor handed him a script. "This is prescription to help manage pain," he said. "Important to follow regimen. Do not exceed daily dose. Also never chew on tablets. Must swallow whole. Call my office if pain still bad. Otherwise, see you three months." Nick gingerly slid off the table and stood up.

"Thanks, Doc," he said.

As Nick walked down the hallway, he glanced down at the script. "Office of Victor S. Chang MD. 180 OxyContin at 30mg." Nick let out a big smile. The street value on that amount of Oxy's was five thousand dollars. Half of that would be his. Nick felt an elated wave run through him at the thought. He also couldn't believe how easy it had been. Jimmy had been spot on about the whole con.

Since Nick had qualified for healthcare under his mom's Medicaid plan, he would be covered until age twenty-six. Jimmy had figured out a way to take advantage of the coverage so Nick could obtain pain meds at virtually no cost. Those in turn could be sold at premium rates to his customers. The crafty drug dealer had obtained a falsified MRI for Nick showing degenerative disc disease. All Nick needed to do was to add some supportive background info on the patient questionnaire and, most importantly, convince the doctor he was in physical pain. Nick laughed as he walked out of the clinic. When he had taken an introductory acting class in high school, this was not how he imagined he would put the skills to use.

Later that afternoon, a dozen customers pressed up against the backdoor entrance of Jimmy's latest trap house. All waiting impatiently to gain entry. Nick walked by them and waved at Mike who stood in the doorway. He let Nick walk in, much to the chagrin of the others. Nick covered his nose briefly as he made his way through the maze of people lying about. He still could not get used to the foul stench of these places. Two scantily clad prostitutes stood along the wall, waiting to escort anyone interested in their services to the second floor. Nick nodded to them as he passed and went into the kitchen.

Inside, Jimmy was sitting at the table organizing small plastic bags filled with product. He glanced over at Nick. Nick smiled and reached into his inside coat pocket. He pulled out the large prescription bottle of OxyContin and shook it, so the pills rattled inside. "Pay dirt," Nick said. Jimmy took the bottle and examined it. "What'd I tell yah." He grinned. "And it's just the beginning my man." Jimmy reached into a leather bag near his seat and took out a wad of cash. He counted out twenty-five one-hundred-dollar bills and handed them to Nick. Nick smiled from ear to ear. The Harris family would not worry about money again.

Over the next eighteen months, Nick became the firm's top salesman. He worked his contact list until he developed a solid base of repeat customers. Splitting the proceeds with Jimmy. For Nick, buying and selling drugs became second nature. He also played it smart, knowing the volatile nature of the business. He cultivated enough contacts to keep his relationship with Jimmy solid but always kept a few high-end leads on reserve just in case things went sour. He also stayed away from selling heroin and cocaine.

Nick knew the DEA kept tabs on all the major suppliers of the hardcore drugs in the area. Usually, it was only a matter of time before some coke addict turned on their supplier to save his own ass. It was high stakes. By sticking with opioids and keeping the operation small, Nick figured he would fly under the feds' radar. He deliberately kept the supply loop spread out and low key. Nick connected with the attractive nurse at the pain management facility. From time to time, she would supply him with blank scripts in addition to some bonus sex on the side. Jimmy also introduced Nick to a few willing Medicare recipients who needed the extra cash to put food on their table. They executed the same scam he had carried out on Dr. Chang. He would give them cash for the pain medications they procured.

As the months progressed, Nick had a steady supply of opioids coming in from multiple sources. Besides OxyContin, he added Fentanyl, Demerol, and Lortab to his growing inventory. The Fentanyl scripts he copied directly from his mom's which he flipped and sold on the street at half price. Nick made a killing. It was not uncommon for him to make as much as three thousand dollars a week. Amusingly, however, Nick considered himself to be *Hood Rich*. While he always seemed to be awash in money, it went out as fast as it came in. Most of his earnings went towards bills and his mom's meds. He also kicked in for Frankie's schooling.

At home, Frankie became suspicious at the sudden influx of cash. When confronted, Vee told her the money had come from her dad. That worked for a short while, until Frankie actually talked to him on the phone. She eventually guessed the real truth. It wasn't hard to figure out. Her brother was a drug dealer. That realization, combined with her mom's own unrelenting addiction to painkillers, pushed the bewildered young woman to the edge. She had had enough. Frankie found a job downtown in a local restaurant and moved out permanently.

Profits continued to grow for Nick. He now had plenty of extra cash and began to flaunt it. Nick started to buy exclusive brand name clothes and cultivate expensive tastes. He loved to buy dinner and drinks for everybody. His popularity soared. The opioid king had a sudden influx of newfound friends and always seemed to be surrounded by a throng of pretty girls. His fast rise was fueled by his lavish spending, and most importantly, everyone around him knew his drugs were safe. Nick inspected everything that came in and went out. Even with Fentanyl, he only sold gel he had extracted from the patches himself. Nick was careful to sell in single dose levels that would not provide too much bang for the buck. It was too easy to overdose. He did everything he could to prevent that from happening to his clients.

Despite the bevy of new people, Nick felt lonely. All of his relationships were superficial. The more women he slept with, the emptier he felt. He still drew pleasure from buying things and taking care of his mom, but it wasn't the same. She was zoned out most of the time, and Frankie was no longer in the house. He could not even contact Wendy on the phone just to talk or text. She had blocked him. Wendy found out he'd been selling drugs. After that, she refused to see or talk to him. The *Hood Rich* kid from Angola suddenly felt dirt poor inside. The sense of isolation extended deep into his soul.

Nick sat alone in his bedroom. He rose up slowly and stood in front of the mirror. Nick stared at his reflection. In the background, he could see his stash of money strewn across the bed. It was twenty thousand dollars. Not something to be laughed at. *It was twenty thousand fuckin' dollars!* Nick looked back at his reflection and shouted out loud, "Nick Harris in the house everybody!" Fuck this self-pity shit, he thought. He had a boatload of cash and beautiful women at his beck and call.

Turning around, Nick did a quick dash over to the bed and grabbed wads of cash in each hand. He returned to the mirror and gazed at himself triumphantly, extending the fistfuls of money outward as if they were on display. His boastful excitement suddenly stopped, and he stepped closer to the mirror. Nick dropped the money to the floor and reached up to his face with his hands. For the first time, he noticed his eyes had deep circles under them, and his face looked pale. It was even beginning to get inundated by acne. All side effects of the shit he was using. "I'm starting to look like a fuckin' junkie," Nick said under his breath. He retreated back to his bed, demoralized at what he had just seen.

A small portion of a Fentanyl patch sat on the night table next to the bed. Nick grabbed it and lit up. He inhaled the last remaining vapors. Instead of feeling the usual euphoria, he felt overwhelmed by a wave of emotion. Nick leaned his head back on the pillow and stared up at the ceiling. A small cross hung on the wall above his bed that his mom had put there long ago. He stared at it with a focused intensity, and his hands began to tremble. Nick suddenly began crying uncontrollably. "Why you gotta do this to us, huh, old man?!" he shouted. "Abandon my mom like that. What gives you the fuckin' right to punish innocent people like that?! You've never dealt my family a legit hand to play, you son of a bitch!" Nick grabbed an alarm clock on the table and threw it up at the cross. It ricocheted off the wall and ceiling before crashing to the floor. Overwrought, Nick abruptly sat up and stuffed a wad of cash off the bed into his coat pocket. "Fuck this shit!" he yelled, wiping the tears from his eyes. He hustled downstairs and out the side door.

Nick hopped in his car and lit a cigarette. He cranked up the music and leaned back to listen. It made him relax. He began to feel better.

After a few minutes of calming himself down, there was a sudden knock on the driver's side window which startled him. Nick turned to see a man in a sport coat standing next to his door looking down at him. He was holding a gold shield against the window with his left hand. It read, "Evans Police Department: Detective."

What the fuck? Nick thought nervously to himself as he powered down the window. "Something I can help you with, officer?" he asked.

The detective smirked. "Yeah, Nicky. Just wanted to let you know that we know who you are, and we know what you've been doing," he said flatly. "You needn't bother packing a toothbrush—oh wait, that's right, you've done time before haven't you? I don't need to tell you how to get ready for prison." Nick glared at him without saying anything. "Oh, and make sure you tell Jimmy Detective Horvath says hello," he said smiling. The detective tapped on the hood of the car and slowly walked over to his unmarked vehicle parked in front of the house. Nick watched him get in and drive off down the street. He sat behind the wheel shell-shocked. In the back of his mind, Nick always knew the gravy train could come to a screeching halt at any moment. He also knew the detective didn't have enough to arrest him. For now, he would just have to be more careful.

CHAPTER 43
DEATH IN THE AFTERNOON

Nick stretched back on the recliner and yawned. He could still remember the day Detective Horvath had come up to him in the driveway. That was the first time he really felt like he was in deep. The law was now keeping an eye on him. There was a sudden noise in the kitchen just as the outside door banged shut. Trip walked into the living room with a startled look. He looked at Vee lying on the floor. "She's okay," Nick said. "Just sleeping off her meds. Cigarette started the rug on fire. If I didn't wake up, this whole fuckin' place would've gone up."

"Jesus," Trip exclaimed shaking his head.

"Let's get her up on the couch," Nick said as he rose from the recliner. The two of them stood on either side of her and gently hoisted her up, lifting under her arms and using the gait belt around her waist for support. Vee let out a groggy moan as they placed her in her usual spot on the couch near the arm so she could lay her head down. The two cleaned up the remaining mess from the fire. "You gonna' stick around awhile?" Nick asked.

Trip nodded. "I'll watch some TV and keep an eye on her," he said.

"Thanks," Nick said. "I need to do some shopping. I'll be back in a little while."

After cleaning himself up, Nick went out to the car and headed to Walmart. He drove along quietly, trying to put the incident with his mom out of his mind. Instead, he tried to think of what to buy his dad. Today was his birthday. Ricky would be forty-nine years old. When Nick was at home watching CNN, they had a breaking news update. Police had found his dad's and David Sweat's DNA in a remote cabin in the woods, twenty miles east of Dannemora in Owls Head, New York. Evidence in the cabin suggested the two escapees had been there within the last forty-eight hours. Authorities were converging on the town and surrounding area. Nick felt sorry for his dad knowing he was running for his life out in the wilderness somewhere. Going out to buy something for him took away some of the feeling of helplessness. It almost felt normal.

Nick emerged from Walmart a couple hours later. He had spent all that time wandering the aisles aimlessly, not knowing what to buy. He finally went into the arts and crafts section and settled on a pack of oil paint brushes. Ricky could make good use of them since he liked to paint portraits. Before checking out, Nick went over to a bin of music CDs. He rummaged through them and pulled out a CD of *Johnny Cash from Folsom Prison*. Nick thought his dad might get a kick out of it. On a whim, he slipped the CD into his pocket before paying for the brushes.

In the parking lot, Nick looked at the contents of the bag and threw in the CD. "Happy birthday, Ricky," he said. He figured with the law closing in, his dad's capture appeared imminent. When Ricky was back in prison, Nick would visit and give him his presents. He could at least say he had bought them on his birthday. As Nick placed the bag in the car, he looked at the Walmart logo and grinned. According to CNN, the prison seamstress who had helped his dad and his cellmate escape had smuggled them tools and two hacksaw blades. She had purchased them from a Walmart as well. For some reason, the common connection to the superstore made Nick laugh.

Sitting in the driver's seat of his car, Nick rubbed his temples. He still felt hazy from the beer and Fentanyl he had used earlier. Nick took a swig of water from a bottle he had in the cup holder. Before inserting the keys in the ignition, the inside of the car was lit up bright red by flashing lights from behind. Nick looked in the rearview mirror. It was a police car. He could see three more police cruisers turn into the parking lot and pull up behind and in front, blocking him in. "Oh, fuck!" Nick yelled nervously. He looked over at the blanket in the back seat. It covered a loaded .22 caliber rifle he used for protection.

Nick's thoughts raced. He didn't have any drugs or alcohol in the car. The rifle, that wasn't illegal. Maybe Detective Horvath's hammer was finally about to come down. Nick decided he would just play it cool. He powered down the window and put his hands on the steering wheel. An officer approached the driver's door along the side with a flashlight. He flashed it in Nick's face. "Could you step out of the car, sir?" he said. Nick opened the door and stepped out. Other officers approached. Nick was frisked and placed in handcuffs. One of the uniforms escorted him to a police cruiser and placed him in the back seat.

Through the side window, Nick watched the police search his car. Across the hood, they placed his wallet with three thousand dollars cash, his knife, the rifle, and the Walmart bag with the contents on top of it. The cocky twenty-three-year-old yelled out from the back seat of the police cruiser with disdain, "You guys ain't got nothin' on me... I'm just tellin' you."

An officer near the open front door entered the front seat and turned around to look at Nick. "Sir, you're under arrest for shoplifting," he said.

"What?" Nick yelled out in disbelief. "You gotta' be fuckin' kiddin' me."

"No, I'm not," the officer replied flatly. He read Nick his rights and asked if he would also submit to a breathalyzer test. Nick just shook his head in aggravation.

Fucking Walmart security, Nick thought to himself. A five-dollar CD. He was going to argue with the officer but then thought better of it. He was tired. Why not just sleep it off on the police department's dime? He'd get a nice hot breakfast and a free shower in the morning. Checkout would be at noon. Nick leaned his head against the window. He looked up at the bright moon and started to howl. His shoulders shook as he convulsed with laughter. This would be one for the books.

Late the next morning, Nick prepared for his release. He finished his coffee and Danish and waited patiently in his cell. It was well past noon when the duty officer finally entered. The sergeant had heard about Nick's performance last night and was not amused. "Your paperwork is done," he said. "You're being released from custody. Follow me." The officer escorted Nick from his cell to a small waiting area in the jail. "Have a seat while I get your appearance ticket." Nick slid down into a chair as the officer walked over to his desk.

As Nick waited, a disheveled looking cabbie entered the room from outside. "Somebody call for a cab?" he inquired.

Nick looked around the room and smirked. He was the only one there. "I guess that would be for me," he said flippantly. The sergeant approached slowly with a small piece of paper and handed it to Nick. He looked at him with a sudden somber expression.

"Mr. Harris..." he said with hesitation. "I think there's something you need to see." Nick looked at him with curiosity. Now what? he thought to himself. He followed him back to his desk. The sergeant nodded to his computer screen.

On the monitor was a live feed of CNN. A large banner filled the bottom of the screen: BREAKING NEWS! Above it was the prison lineup photos of his dad and David Sweat. Written over Ricky's face in bold red letters was the word: DEAD. Nick stared at the screen in disbelief. He read the closed captioning as it scrolled across the screen. *Escaped fugitive Richard Matt shot dead in armed confrontation with elite Border Patrol unit.*

Tears welled up in Nick's eyes as he continued reading the news stream. *Shot in the head three times!* Flashed across. The sergeant put a comforting hand on his shoulder. "I'm sorry, son," he said.

"...It's okay...it's okay," Nick replied. "Didn't you know?"

"Know what?" the sergeant asked.

"My dad can't die," Nick said with confidence. "...He's immortal... my dad's immortal." The distraught son of Ricky Matt smiled weakly and grabbed his things off the seat. He hurried passed the cabbie and out the exit door. Outside, Nick walked a few steps before suddenly stopping and clenching his fists. He started to tremble. "No!" he screamed as he looked up tearfully into the afternoon sky.

After getting his car out of impound, Nick quickly drove home. When he arrived, a horde of media was camped out on the front lawn. Their vans clogged the street. Nick maneuvered his way around two large vehicles and managed to squeeze into the driveway. He parked and exited the car. The reporters converged on him. Nick tried to push his way through as questions came at him from every direction. Microphones were thrust in his face waiting for a reply. They were relentless. "Leave me alone!" he shouted angrily as he forced his way through to the porch. Nick entered the house and slammed the door shut. "Fucking vultures!" he exclaimed in frustration.

Inside, the chaos continued. Nick could immediately hear crying. The phone was ringing non-stop, and the TV was on loud. It was broadcasting the news. Nick walked into the living room and was surprised to see Wendy was sitting next to his mom on the couch. She was trying to comfort the grieving woman as she sat sobbing uncontrollably. Trip was there with Luke Donald. Frankie sat alone on the recliner. They all looked at Nick when he entered. Nick rushed to his mom. "They shot 'em in the head, Ma…" he cried. "They shot 'em in the head three times!" Vee reached over to him. Mother and son embraced, trying to console each other's pain. Nick looked over at Wendy and their eyes met. "Thanks for being here," he said.

"I'm sorry about your dad, Nicky," she replied. The small group huddled quietly in front of the TV the rest of the day watching the news, simply trying to get the details of what had happened. There was nothing else they could do.

Ricky had been killed in a wooded area about ten miles north of the cabin where his DNA had been discovered two days earlier. A state trooper had heard a cough in the woods where no one should have been. It was relayed to border agents who began a tactical search of the area. One of the agents saw movement in the woods and approached. Separated by ten to fifteen yards. He saw a man lying on the ground attempting to conceal himself behind a log. The agent identified himself and asked the person to step out into the clear. When there was no response, the agent moved in closer. He suddenly could see the barrel of a shotgun pointed directly at him. The agent immediately opened fire with his automatic rifle. It released several rounds. Agents converged on the scene and found the person dead. Three rounds had instantly ripped through his head. They removed the shotgun and lifted the person's shirt. A Mexico Forever tattoo was revealed on the back. They had positively identified Richard Matt.

In the early evening, Nick thanked everyone for coming. They all left, except for Trip who stayed behind to watch Vee. She had taken an extra dose of pain meds and had fallen asleep on the couch. Nick went upstairs to his room to be alone. He sat in his recliner for hours, staring blankly at the wall. He felt numb to everything. It was as if he had been hit by a bolt of lightning, suddenly desensitized and made immobile.

As the shock of the day wore off, Nick began to think deeply about his dad, his mom, and his own fucked up life. Everything. Long buried feelings of pain and anger quickly overtook him. The swirling angst intensified to a crescendo and the floodgates opened. He cried long and hard, just like a baby. When the tears finally subsided, Nick felt a great sense of relief. As if a fog was lifting and he could see clearly. It felt transformative. Layers of bullshit had finally been stripped away and his thoughts began to crystallize. Nick's eyes focused ahead like a laser, filled with a steely resolve.

Nick rose from the recliner and walked into the bathroom. He lifted up a floorboard to reveal the concealed space underneath. Nick took out two duffle bags. He sat on the edge of the tub and opened the bags. Nick pulled out a bottle of OxyContin. He opened it, poured the contents into the toilet, and flushed it down the drain. He pulled out another bottle and did the same. Nick emptied bottle after bottle until his entire inventory of prescription drugs and contraband meds was gone. Afterwards, he grabbed a small paper bag containing all of his blank scripts and dumped them in an ashtray on his night table. Nick took out a lighter and lit them up. "Never again," he said to himself as he watched the pile of paper burn.

Still feeling dirty, the now fatherless child showered and cleaned up. An hour later, he came down the stairs dressed in his best clothes and a sport coat. Despite the evening being late, most of the media were still outside. Nick stepped out on the front porch. He was quickly surrounded by reporters again. This time, he graciously answered their questions as best he could. He repeated the performance multiple times over the weekend. Periodically coming outside to field questions while he stayed at home taking care of his mom. Wendy had even stopped by twice to see how he was doing. It had lifted his spirits greatly.

Over the coming days, Nick also knew he would soon be experiencing withdrawal symptoms after abruptly stopping his drug use. He wasn't looking forward to it. The sweats, the stomach pain, the nausea and paranoia. It was just the tip of the iceberg. Nick had witnessed several of his clients go through their own private hell. He himself had experienced it to a lesser degree the time he went to prison and went cold turkey. However, Nick figured if his dad could survive the horrors of a Mexican prison and a host of other things throughout his life, he could survive a few days of pain and suffering. They were of the same blood.

— ⚏◆⚏ —

Amid much speculation by the media as to who would claim Richard Matt's body, Nick stepped in. He would not let his dad be buried in a pauper's grave in some remote upstate cemetery. Five days after his death, he drove 350 miles to the Franklin County coroner's office in Malone, New York where the body was being stored. It was thirty miles south of Dannemora. On the way up, Nick braced himself for what he would see. CNN had been circulating a graphic photograph of Ricky at the scene of his death. He was laying twisted on the ground with part of his head blown away.

Nick showed up at the county morgue and filled out the paperwork to claim the body. A heavyset attendant eating a sandwich escorted him to a room containing the refrigerated storage units along the wall. He opened one of the doors and pulled out the horizontal slab with Ricky's lifeless corpse. It was covered in a sheet. The attendant lifted the sheet part way. Nick grimaced in horror at the gaping hole at the top of his dad's head. He clenched his jaw and tried not to look at it. Nick glanced down at Ricky's face which, to his surprise, lay in a peaceful repose. "Could you pull him out a little farther, please?" he asked. The attendant did so.

"Take all the time you need," he said. "I'll leave you alone for some privacy." The attendant walked to his desk in the back.

Standing alone next to his dad, Nick reached out and held onto his dad's large, cold hand. "They didn't win, Ricky," he said in a gentle voice. "You died a free man. With no shackles to hold you down." Nick grabbed a rag from a nearby table and tried cleaning off his dad's arms and shoulders. There was still some mud and debris caked on his body. "Those bastards couldn't even clean you up right," Nick grumbled angrily. He started to cry. Grieving for a man he had only seen face to face a handful of times in his life. Yet he was proud of him. Grateful. He was the man who had bought him his first bike. The man who had taught him how to throw a flip knife. The man who had bought him an oversized pair of Air Jordan sneakers. Ricky would now have to answer to his maker for his actions, but no one else could ever judge him. Not with all the bad cards he'd been dealt in life.

Nick bent down and kissed Ricky's cheek. He turned and approached the attendant. "Sir, would it be possible to have a piece of my dad's hair?"

The attendant set down his coffee and stood up. "Why don't you wait in my office?" he said. "I'll see what I can do." The attendant escorted Nick to a room around the corner. He returned with the facility administrator a few minutes later. The latter handed Nick a lock of hair in a sealed plastic bag and a small vial of blood. He also sat down with Nick to discuss the final arrangements. It was confirmed; a local funeral parlor in Plattsburgh would take charge of the body and coordinate its transportation to a funeral parlor in Tonawanda, the town where Ricky was born. The body was to be cremated per Ricky's wishes. Nick paid $2,500 in cash and left for home.

Two days later, a small service was arranged locally for family members and close friends. The family included Nick, his mom, and Frankie in the front row with Ricky's half-brother Wayne behind them. Ricky's ashes were handled by the same funeral parlor that had said farewell to Herb, Elvira, and Johnny Mangano years earlier. After the service, Nick and Trip headed out to Angola with the urn. Trip had procured a small motorboat from a friend, and the two journeyed out a few hundred yards off shore. They spent the afternoon fishing. As the sun began to set over the horizon, Nick opened the urn and spread his father's ashes into the tranquil summer waters of Lake Erie.

CHAPTER 44
RUNAWAY TRAIN

It was a hot, hazy afternoon in August. Nick stood fidgeting over the grill cooking hot dogs as Wendy, Trip, and Vee sat at a picnic table in the Harris front yard. When the hot dogs were done, Nick placed them in buns and brought a filled plate to the table. He went over to the cooler. "Anybody else wanna another beer?" he shouted eagerly. Wendy and Trip raised their hands. Nick brought the cans to the table and sat down. Everyone dug into the food and chit-chatted at leisure.

Nick slapped some mustard on his hot dog and took a big bite out of it. As he chewed, he turned to Trip and began speaking fast and furious. "...you see, it's my destiny..." Nick exclaimed. "I'm the one who's supposed to single-handedly save the world of skateboarding. In the process, I'll wind up helping Jake and the rest of my boys." Trip looked at him quizzically. "The thing is," Nick continued. "the pros don't wanna be in the next Olympics because of the politics. It's all fuckin' bribery and scandals, just like World Cup soccer. You know what I'm gonna do? I'm gonna write a book exposing the Olympic committee for what it really is. A cartel of greedy assholes. When it comes out, I'll be world famous for exposing all the lies and corruption! Probably win the Nobel Prize for literature!"

Trip and Wendy looked at each other and laughed. "Maybe after the book is a bestseller, you can turn it into a movie," Trip said with a mischievous grin.

"You're damn right!" Nick exclaimed. "I'll win the Academy Award for best picture!"

"Great, Nicky," Trip said. "Just make sure you save a part for me when you make it, okay?"

"Me too!" Wendy squealed.

"Absolutely!" Nick yelled. "You guys will both be in it. We'll all be in it!" Nick took another bite from his hot dog but then sat back with a perplexed look. "We're gonna need to join the actor's union first," he said thoughtfully. "Probably need some acting lessons too."

"Whatever you say, Nicky," Trip said. He and Wendy laughed again. Even Vee chuckled. Their hysterics seemed to incite Nick. He stood up and flung the rest of his hot dog against a tree excitedly. Then lifted up the heavy wooden bench he was sitting on and smashed it hard into the ground with great fervor.

"I'm gonna win every fuckin' award there is, you'll see!" he screamed enthusiastically. Everyone chuckled at Nick's wild behavior. While Vee smiled at her son's antics, it thinly veiled a sense of worry. She knew something was wrong. She had seen this same behavior before...from Nick's dad.

Nick himself knew that something was not right. Crushed by the loss of his father and going cold turkey had taken a toll. It had been a month since Ricky's death. Nick had remained clean the whole time, but the transition to normalcy was still a work in progress. Withdrawal had not been smooth. Despite the lapse of time, he wasn't sure if he was over the drugs or not. All he knew was that he constantly felt nervous and fidgety, like he was wired. He also could not keep his mind focused on one thing for any length of time. The relentless bombardment of swirling thoughts made him feel confused and out of touch with reality. It was driving him mad. To help himself concentrate, Nick began listening to a small portable radio he had in his room. He would listen to it at all hours of the day and night. He would take it everywhere, focusing all his attention on the speaker—the voice on the radio. Doing this seemed to help corral his thoughts. It became an obsession. After a week of listening, Nick thought he could discern hidden messages and meanings from the voices on the radio. After two weeks, he was convinced the messages were meant for him. By the third, the talk show hosts were talking to him directly. He was certain of it!

After the cookout, Nick took Wendy and Trip for a joyride along the lake in his car. He sped over several bridges on Route 5 at a blistering speed. Nick glanced at Wendy in the front seat who appeared nervous. He looked at Trip in the rearview mirror. "This morning," Nick shouted, "Steve Harvey told me on his radio show that I was here to save the world...I'm to save this lowly-ass place from its own ugly self!"

Trip shouted back, "You can save it later, Nicky. Just slow the fuck down!" Nick laughed and continued to increase his speed. He barreled past several cars. Without warning, Nick slammed on the brakes. The car skidded forward, sending Trip forward into the front headrest. "What the fuck are you doing?!" he yelled. Nick pulled the car to the side of the road and shifted it into park. His eyes were glazed over, and his breathing was heavy. He slumped forward, his head on the steering wheel.

"You guys can't see it," he mumbled, "...but Nick Harris is here to help the masses. I'm meetin' up with Lil Wayne and Jazzy Jeff later tonight down at the radio station. We're gonna' put on a show you won't believe. You'll see." Wendy and Trip looked at each other in bewilderment.

Over the next few days, Nick began to feel worse. He was getting the sweats and couldn't sleep. Nick was besieged by the side effects of withdrawal, and they would not subside. To make matters worse, his physical cravings for a fix was off the charts. He even thought of going through his mom's bag and grabbing an OxyContin or a Fentanyl patch for a quick hit. Nick resisted. He would not go down that path again. Letting the symptoms wear off over time wasn't working. Nor was his attempt to satiate his cravings by loading up on caffeine and nicotine as an alternate. He needed help. Nick confided in Wendy. Together, they arranged for Nick to go to a local state-run drug clinic that specialized in medical detox. The facility arranged for an outpatient treatment plan. As a requirement, Nick also had to sign up for mandatory drug counseling.

On the day of his first medical treatment, Nick sat nervously in the waiting area. He felt desperate and was literally shaking in his seat. Wendy sat beside him almost in a panic herself. She had never seen him this way. "...It feels like I'm fuckin' drowning, Wendy," Nick said, his face racked with tension.

"Just hang on a little longer, Nicky," Wendy said. "This shot they're giving you is supposed to work right away."

"I sure the hell hope so," the desperate man replied back.

A nurse came out and called Nick's name. He jumped up immediately and was escorted into the doctor's office alone. A young woman doctor in her late twenties greeted him as he entered. "Per your treatment plan, Mr. Harris," she said directly, "I'll be administering a dose of Vivitrol to you today."

"This is gonna end those cravings right, Doc?" Nick asked. "They're killin' me."

"It should," she replied. "The drug acts as an opioid antagonist. It blocks the cravings and the pleasurable side effects so there is less chance of a relapse." The doctor grabbed his chart and looked at the lab results of the urine sample Nick had given an hour earlier. "You've been clean at least five days," she stated.

"I've been clean since June twenty-sixth," Nick shot back.

The doctor smiled. "Good. We want to keep you that way." She readied the needle and gave him the shot. Nick began to feel better almost immediately and gave a big sigh of relief. "I'll see you back here in ten days for a follow-up exam," the doctor said.

⚊⊷⚌⟐⚌⊶⚊

A dozen diehard Bible-thumpers gathered that evening at the chapel. Nick and Wendy were seated in the front row, much to Wendy's embarrassment. Nick had insisted. It was important. While religion had never played a prominent role in his life, he did remember going to church as a kid. Over time though, the whole family had drifted away from it. That was especially true after his grandparents had died. The only other occasion was when he was in prison in Alden. His cellmate Dennis had convinced him to attend a Bible-study group. However, one session of boisterous singing and thigh slapping praising of Jesus by inmates was all he could handle. Nick thought it was just a bunch of hokey nonsense.

Lately, the voices on the radio had convinced him otherwise. They had told him to reach out to God and embrace religion. He must learn about the teachings and lessons found in the Bible. Only then could he find personal enlightenment and be open to his own special life path. Nick immediately searched online for any local Bible study classes. He found several but chose one in a church nearby and signed up. He even convinced a reluctant Wendy to attend his first class with him.

For the first half hour, Nick had listened intently to every word the zealous pastor had delivered. The eloquent communicator continued with an impassioned reading of Matthew 24:4-5: . "…watch out that no one deceives you. For many will come in my name, claiming that I am the Christ, and will deceive many. And many false prophets will appear and deceive many people. And at that time if anyone says to you, look, here is the Christ, or, there he is! Do not believe it. For false Christ's and false prophets will appear and perform great signs and miracles to deceive even the elect…"

While Wendy yawned, Nick sat mesmerized, his hands shaking involuntarily. The preacher pressed on with another verse. "They will see the son of man coming on the clouds of the sky with power and great glory. And he will send his angels with a loud trumpet call, and they will gather the elect from the four winds, from one end of the heavens to the other." Nick suddenly began to cry in his seat. It turned into loud, uncontrolled sobbing. Wendy looked at him in surprise, not knowing what to do. The pastor stopped his reading. He looked at Nick and stepped forward. "Let it out, brother. Let it out," he said with great compassion. Several parishioners approached Nick in his seat. They laid hands on him and began to pray. Nick became the center of a circle of prayer. Several minutes passed. Nick's crying abated. A sudden stillness overtook him. He raised his head slowly, a newfound sense of purpose beaming from his eyes.

The following evening, Nick showed up at the local restaurant where Wendy worked. Her twelve-hour shift had just ended, and she joined Nick at a table drinking coffee as was their usual custom. Nick appeared worried. Wendy noticed it right away and looked at him with concern. "Nicky, you didn't start using again, did you?" she asked.

Nick shook his head. "No," he said. "I've been feeling fine ever since I got the Vivitrol injection."

"Then what's the matter?" she pressed.

Nick clutched her hands. "They've been communicating messages to me again, Wendy," he said in a peaceful voice.

Wendy leaned in and mouthed in amusement, "What kind of messages, Nicky?"

Nick looked at her with a deadpan stare. "I am a disciple for the son of man," he said. "Sent here by God to help save the world from its indiscretions."

Wendy sat back up. "Knock it off, Nicky," she said angrily. "It ain't funny!"

"You don't believe me?" he asked in a surprised tone.

"Of course, I don't believe you, you fuckin' idiot!" Wendy screamed.

"Then at least believe in the good works I do," he implored.

"Please stop it, Nicky," she begged.

"Okay," he said softly.

"Is that guy bothering you, Wendy?" a husky voice butted in from the side. "… because you sure don't need no Jesus freak hittin' on you like that." Nick and Wendy looked over. Two, hulking ex-jocks Wendy recognized from her college, and who were regular customers, sat in the booth next to them. They were just finishing up their meal of Texas hots and French fries. On their tabletop also stood several empty beer bottles.

"Everything's fine, Paul," she replied.

Nick raised his hand and smiled. "Bless you, sir," he said.

Paul scowled at him a moment before turning to Wendy. "Why don't you ever call me back?" he asked.

"Buzz off." Wendy yelled. She grabbed Nick by the arm and whispered to him, "Let's get out of here." They both got up and exited. The two tipsy young men threw some money on the table and followed them out the door.

Outside in the lot, Paul caught up to the pair and grabbed Nick from behind to slow him down. He playfully walked in front of him, so they stood face to face. The former lineman slapped Nick hard across the cheek. Nick's eyes were filled with a momentary rage which quickly dissolved into a sedate calm. He smiled at Paul. "Peace, brother," he said. The two big men were taken aback. They started to laugh.

"Fuckin' wuss," Paul blurted out.

"Leave him alone!" Wendy shouted. "...or I'll call the cops."

Paul's friend grabbed him by the arm. "C'mon, let's clear out. He's not worth it," he said.

Paul gave a sigh of resignation and threw up his hands. He looked at Wendy. "Farewell, your ladyship. If that's the kind of guy that turns you on..." He shrugged his shoulders. "And you, preacher man," Paul said turning towards Nick. "You better thank your girlfriend here, 'cause she just saved your fucking ass from a beating!"

⊷ ⊠◆⊠ ⊶

In the late afternoon on the following day, Nick stepped out the front door of a seedy looking home on Buffalo's lower east side. The house was a safe haven for stolen property. He remembered selling Lortabs to the guy who owned the place a while back when he was dealing. It was a great place to fence valuables for quick cash, although you almost never received the amount you were hoping for. Today, Nick had made $1,100 for several items he had brought from home. They were worth four times as much, but Nick didn't mind. He now had enough money to buy Wendy's engagement ring.

Nick loved Wendy with his whole heart and soul. He felt it was preordained she was to be his wife. It was simply meant to be. He was sure she felt the same way. To prepare for the occasion, Nick had been to a local jewelry store and preselected a beautiful diamond ring which would formally seal their bond. He even *borrowed* one of Wendy's current rings to show the jeweler to get the proper ring size for her finger. Everything had to be perfect. The ring cost several thousand dollars, but he finally had accumulated enough money to pay for it.

During the night, several hours later, Nick drove his car through a well-to-do neighborhood along the lakeshore. He was on his way to the home of Wendy's parents. As the subdued street lighting flickered past, Nick's mind conjured up a series of beautiful images of his bride-to-be and their life together in the near future. Nick could see himself and Wendy gazing into each other's eyes at the altar in Our Lady of Victory Basilica. He could visualize the happy smiles of his family and friends in attendance, rejoicing at their union. Nick could even see himself standing next to Wendy in a hospital delivery room, gently holding their first child together in his arms. The sweet, swirling images filled Nick with indescribable joy. For the first time in his life, he felt truly happy.

The house came into view. Nick pulled up out front and parked along the curb. Nervously, he grabbed the stately looking envelope sitting on the front passenger seat. It contained his marriage proposal letter which was to be hand delivered to Wendy's dad. Nick had spent hours at home working on a perfect draft. He had handwritten the final words on a sheet of high-quality linen paper and signed it. It looked elegant yet had a nice personal touch, he thought.

Nick stepped out of the car holding the envelope and carefully adjusted his new suit. He looked up into the evening sky. "Thank you, Grandma," he whispered. Her old tailor had given him a huge discount for the fancy threads. Nick walked up to the front door and knocked. A few moments later it opened, and Wendy's dad stood in the doorway.

"Hello, Nick," he said with a smile and shook his hand. "What can I do for you at this hour?"

"Mr. Masterson," Nick stated formally. "I would like to ask your permission to have your daughter's hand in holy matrimony." Nick handed him the letter and continued. "Here is a letter I've drawn up stating my honorable intentions." Wendy's dad looked at Nick with a bemused smile. He had been exposed to Nick's embellishments before.

"You have my permission, Mr. Harris," he said. But then pointed a finger at him. "...if that be my daughter's wish."

"Thank you, sir," Nick said smiling. "That's all I can ask for. I'll be on my way now."

The two shook hands again. "Good luck, Nick." Mr. Masterson said. The ecstatic young man walked back to his car grinning from ear to ear.

With the hour approaching midnight, it was getting late, but Nick was certain Wendy would be home. Her shift ended at 11:30 P.M. sharp, and she covered the short distance home in ten minutes. She was like clockwork. Despite his impatience, Nick took his time driving the twenty miles to Wendy's apartment. He wanted nothing to spoil the evening, so he drove carefully and within speed limits. There would be no speeding tickets tonight. Nick felt like he was floating on air. To him, the hardest part of the evening was already done. When he finally arrived, Nick parked out front and gave the horn a brief tap which was their signal. As he walked to the front, Wendy peeked out the side window and opened the door. She practically pulled him inside.

"You would not believe the night I had!" she said loudly. Before she could get in another word, Nick took a knee in front of her. He pulled a ring from his coat pocket and held it up. Nick looked up at a Wendy with a big grin. "Wendy Masterson, will you marry me?" he asked. "Oh, and I already asked your dad for permission. He granted my request."

Wendy stood there speechless. At first, she thought Nick might be joking, but after looking at him, she realized he was being sincere. She let out a distraught sigh and slowly dropped down to her knees so she and Nick were eye level. She reached for his outstretched hand and held it. "I can't marry you, Nicky," she said gently.

"...But we love each other," Nick said in a stunned voice.

"I do love you," Wendy said. "...but as a friend. We've talked about this before."

"But I stopped dealing," he said.

"That's not the only thing, Nicky," she exclaimed. "You said yourself you needed to get your life in order. Well, you need to do that before you do something like this." Nick slowly lowered his hand and slipped the ring back into his pocket. "Besides," Wendy added, "you already know I have a boyfriend I like very much. I'm sorry, Nicky." She slowly rose to her feet. "I'm gonna make some coffee. Would you like some?"

"No," Nick said as he stood up. "I'll take a rain check. I should be going."

"You're not mad at me, are you?" she asked.

"Of course not," he said. "Why would I be mad at you? It's just me being me." Nick turned and walked out the door.

CHAPTER 45
REJECTION GOD'S PROTECTION

Nick walked out of Wendy's apartment like he'd just been sucker punched in the gut. His brain could not process what had just happened. Wendy *had rejected him!* Nick walked tersely to his car, and as soon as the door closed, he let out a prolonged scream of agony. It felt like his world had just crashed down around him taking all his hopes and dreams with it. Nick pounded on the steering wheel several times with his hand and began to sob. After several minutes, his pain turned to numbness. Nick forced himself to move. He started the car and raced off down the street.

Twenty minutes later, Nick brought the car to a skidding halt in his driveway. He entered the house and went into the living room. Vee lay on the couch in a deep slumber. Nick sat down beside his mom and gave her a long hug, burying his head in her shoulder as he cried. When he finally let go, Nick took a handful of pills from her plastic bag and slipped them into his suit pocket. He went into the kitchen and grabbed a six-pack from the fridge before heading upstairs.

Inside his room, Nick threw the pills on the night table. He popped two of them into his mouth and washed them down with a beer. What they were didn't matter. In a whirl, Nick changed into jeans and a T-shirt. He threw his new Petroni suit into a crumpled heap on the floor.

Nick glanced around the room in a quiet frenzy. He needed to escape the pain he felt. It was unbearable. Nick knew his mom had Fentanyl patches, but they were only moderate dose. They would not fit the bill. He wanted something stronger.

Clenching his fists, Nick now regretted flushing his entire cache down the toilet when his dad died. Still, he felt sure there had to be something left behind somewhere. Nick looked around the room in desperation. He rushed into the bathroom and opened up the secret compartment in the floor. It was empty. Nick ran back into the bedroom and searched through every nook and cranny, tearing his room apart. He found a few pills but nothing that would be of use. Nick sat on the edge of the bed in frustration, slowly rubbing his forehead with his hand. Suddenly, he paused and glanced up.

Nick went to his DVD collection near his TV. He found *Robin Hood* and opened the case. Under the DVD inside was a small packet. Nick unfolded it to uncover a small gel tab. It was Fentanyl gel mixed with high grade heroine, 90 percent pure Colombian Tar. *Thank Christ!* Jimmy had given it to him when they were working together. He had told Nick to save it for a special occasion. "It will blow your mind, my man," he had said. Nick had put it in the DVD case for safe keeping but had forgotten about it.

Filled with a sense of urgency, Nick found a foil and sat down in his recliner. He lit up and inhaled the vapors until the gel was gone. The anguished young man leaned back in readiness, opening his mind to the massive wave of ecstasy that would soon hit. He waited in eager expectation as the seconds ticked by. It didn't come. Nick could suddenly feel his breath becoming labored. His skin felt cold and clammy. He looked around in distress. A painful stomach cramp caused him to crunch forward. It was followed by a wave of intense nausea. Nick felt like throwing up. He tried to get up but fell back, unable to stand. The room seemed to warp and spin. Nick closed his eyes and forced himself to stand up but was soon overcome by an enveloping heaviness. He fell to the floor and passed out.

When Nick woke up, his eyes looked across the rug at eye level. He could smell a pungent odor. He raised his head from a small pile of his own vomit off the floor. Nick looked at the clock. He had been out for a couple of hours. Feeling weak, he tried to steady himself as he slowly stood up. He sat down on the edge of the bed. "What the fuck was that?" he said to himself. Nick sunk his face into his hands. He suddenly remembered the Vivitrol shot. It remained active for a month. With a gloomy face, Nick shook his head and started to laugh. He had taken an opioid with an opioid-blocking drug in his body. It had taken away the bliss but let him experience all the nasty shit. *Absolutely fucking brilliant!*

Nick walked over to the mirror and gazed into it, seething at the pathetic image of a man looking back at him. "You're a fuck up, Nick Harris!" he screamed. Nick punched the mirror with his hand. It splintered. Several pieces fell to the floor. He walked over to his night table and snatched his car keys. Nick rushed out of his room and down the stairs. He stopped in the living room to take another look at his mom. Wiping away tears, Nick grabbed a framed photo of Vee and Ricky together in happier times, a bottle of vodka on the shelf below, then exited via the front door. He hopped in his car, started the engine, and cranked up the music.

CHAPTER 46
A FATHER WHO DOESN'T GIVE UP

The wind gusts fluctuated wildly in the cool night air. Nick held tightly onto the construction girder to maintain his footing atop the retainer wall. His heart raced as he stared down into the swirling black waters below. The city lights made glittering reflections in the undulating currents. Nick reached into his pant pocket with his free hand and pulled out Wendy's ring. He glared at it in anger and made a motion to throw it into the water but checked himself at the last second. Nick slowly put it back in his pocket. "Better they find it on me," he said bitterly. "Something to think about when you're screwing your preppy boyfriend, bitch!" Nick took a deep breath and released his hold on the girder. It was time to go. He shuffled sideways along the narrow foothold a short distance until he stood free and clear on the retainer wall, a hundred feet above the river. Nick slowly spread out his arms and closed his eyes. "I'm callin' you out again, old man!" he shouted at the night sky. "Send me to the heaven or send me to hell. Cause I ain't stayin' here!"

Nick could feel the gusts building again. He had trouble maintaining his footing. Nick was scared, yet he also felt calm, securely resigned to his fate. His jacket began flapping wildly as the wind became strong and steady. It started to swirl. Nick steeled himself as the gusts began making him unsteady. He lost his footing. Nick yelled out in terror as he fell. Instead of plummeting forward, he fell backward. He dropped four feet onto his back, hitting the pavement with a painful smack. It knocked the wind out of him. Nick lay on his back trying to catch his breath. "You can't even kill yourself right, you dumb fuck." He grunted loudly in a painful laugh. He remained motionless, looking back up into the night sky.

"Fuck this shit," Nick said in frustration. He rolled onto his side and slowly stood up. Nick reentered his car and forcefully slammed the door shut. He popped the last two pills he had on him into his mouth, downed them with vodka, then stepped on the accelerator. The car bolted forward, smashing the right fender against the retainer wall. It dragged against the wall a short distance until Nick finally swerved the vehicle off the shoulder and into the lane. He chuckled loudly as he stuck his head out the sunroof. "King Kong ain't got nothin' on me motherfuckers!" Nick raced over the remainder of the Skyway and into the city below.

— ✠ —

A few minutes later, the beaten-up sports car stopped in front of a radio station near the waterfront. Nick knew Wendy's boyfriend worked the early morning shift there as a disc jockey. He gazed out his front and rear windows. Not a soul was around. Nick exited the car and pulled out his skateboard from the back seat. He flipped it onto the ground and skated to the front entrance of the building. Nick rang the doorbell repeatedly. "Easy on the wakeup call," a pissed off voice responded on the intercom. "What can I do for you buddy?"

"Listen motherfucker," Nick shouted, glaring into the security camera. "You tell that little prick DJ dating my girl that I'm here to kick his ass right now! And tell Lil Wayne to get out here so we can talk about my show on Friday!" The intercom went silent.

Nick rang the doorbell again and again. There was no response. Upset at the silent treatment, he punched the camera, cracking its lens.

"You wanna' fuck with me?!" Nick screamed. He jumped back on his skateboard and raced around to the back of the building. Nick looked up at the second floor with a menacing gaze and shrieked at the top of his lungs. "Show yourself, you cock-blockin' bastard!" He picked up a small rock from the ground and whipped it at the building. It hit a second story window with a sharp clank before falling back down to the pavement. "You chickenshit little pussy!" Nick yelled. The back door suddenly flung open.

An incensed security guard with an enormous girth stepped out. Nick snarled at him. "You wanna a piece of me, lard ass, let's do it!" He rushed the big man at full speed. The security guard met Nick head on and easily tossed him up high in the air and into a hedge of rose bushes along the wall. Nick quickly jumped back to his feet, his face and hands bleeding from the prickly stems.

"You want more of that, you drugged up little shit?!" the security guard snapped.

"You're lucky I got a rap session coming up with Lil' Wayne," Nick said with a boisterous air, "or I'd finish you off right here!" He jumped back on his board and skated around to the front. The guard followed with a slow jog. Nick hopped back in the car and took off down the street. He could see the huffing giant in the rearview mirror standing at the curb hollering into his cell phone.

"Call the cops, you fat fuck!" Nick said as he sped away. "Ain't gonna do you no good anyway." He barreled through the city streets, weaving in and out of any traffic he encountered. Drivers honked their horns in anger or flashed their lights as he passed. Even pedestrians fled away in fear. Nick would zoom in close and veer away at the last second, beeping his horn. Two drunk teens flung their beer bottles at the speeding car in retaliation. One hit the back window, causing a large crack. Nick abruptly slammed on the breaks and hopped out of the car. "Which one of you little bastards threw the bottle?!" he shouted at them. The two large teens laughed and moved towards him.

"Time to take Jeff Gordon here off the streets," one of them uttered. Nick reached into the back seat of his car and pulled out a .22 caliber rifle.

"Fuck all you all motherfuckers!" he yelled. Nick pointed the gun at the two young men who stopped dead in their tracks. "What, nothing to say now, snowflakes?" Nick chuckled. The two teens backed off and took off down the street. "That's what I thought."

Nick got back in the car and banged the door shut. His side view mirror fell off and smashed onto the street. He laughed as he tried to run it over with his back tire. The car hurtled down the street. After a short distance, the red gas light suddenly lit up on his dashboard. "Fuck!" Nick groaned in exasperation and pounded the steering wheel with his hand. "End of the road, Nicky Boy," he uttered to himself. "End of the motherfuckin' road." The warning light had been on the whole time. Nick hadn't noticed it until now.

He puttered into an empty, dimly lit parking lot of a closed department store. He rolled into a space below a burned-out light tower. Nick reached for the rifle in back and carefully placed it across the passenger seat. "Eventually, I'll get this right," he said. "Even a broken clock's right twice a day." Nick grabbed the Alison Krauss CD he and Wendy had listened to on the drive up to Dannemora. He put it into the player. The sweet, melodic sound of "Down to the River to Pray" filled the air. Nick sang along with the sad elegy in a heartfelt voice. "As I went down in the river to pray. Studying about that good old way. And who shall wear the starry crown. Good Lord, show me the way." Nick curtly stopped the CD. "Fuck that!" he hollered. Hot tears trickled down his face. "Just send me to hell old man!" Nick pointed the rifle directly at his right temple. He closed his eyes and prepared to fire.

A car horn suddenly went off nearby. Nick opened his eyes and looked out the driver's side window. A white van had pulled up alongside him facing in the opposite direction. Five feet separated the two vehicles. Nick powered down the window. A nice-looking woman in her fifties glanced over at him. She waved a friendly hello. "It's good to see you again, Nick," she said. Nick gave her a perplexed look.

"How do you know my name?" he asked. The woman looked at him with a pleasant smile. "I laid hands on you and prayed for you that night in the chapel. Do you remember?" she replied. Nick stared at her as if in a fog, his finger still pressed tightly on the trigger.

"I remember the chapel," he said. "I don't remember you."

" I was there," she said warmly, "...among the other brothers and sisters, helping you release your pain."

Nick gazed around the empty parking lot in confusion then back at her. "What the hell are you doing here?" he asked.

"The Lord sent me here tonight..." the woman said. "He told me to intercede with your plans."

"What?" Nick said in agitation. "That's a bunch of bullshit!"

The woman smiled. "Why else would I be here, Nick? Right here. Right now," she said. "Earlier tonight, you tried to overdose with pills, you tried to jump off a bridge, and now this. Sooner or later you're going to get your wish." The woman leaned forward and added with a sly smile. "Even a broken clock's right twice a day." Nick looked at her in astonishment. *How could she know that?* He shook his head trying to clear his thoughts. Nick believed she was telling the truth. There was no other explanation.

"Are you saying God actually talked to you?" he asked with curiosity.

"Yes, Nick," she replied. "All of God's children can speak to him through the Holy Spirit at any time if you just let him into your life."

The woman stepped out of the van and slowly approached the car. The confused young man suddenly looked at her with suspicion. Nick grabbed the rifle and pointed it towards her. "How do I know you weren't sent by Satan?" he asked forcefully. The stately woman looked at Nick and the gun unperturbed.

"Killing yourself is a sin, Nick. I was sent here to stop you from doing that. Satan would want you to succeed. I rebuke him in the name of our Lord and Savior Jesus Christ." Nick held firm still not convinced. The woman continued. "Satan cannot rebuke himself, can he, Nick?" she said matter-of-factly. Nick swallowed hard and lowered the rifle. His breaths became short.

"If you were sent by God, then tell me why my life is so fucked up. I don't want to live anymore!" Nick cried out.

"Sometimes we have to suffer for the sins of others," The woman stated. "Just as Jesus did. Now you must carry your cross and fulfill your destiny here on Earth."

"Which is what?" Nick said sharply.

"You already know the answer to that in your heart," she said smiling. Nick lay the gun on the seat and buried his face in his hands. "You must be strong in your faith, Nick. It's God's will." The woman said firmly, placing her hand gently on his arm. Nick raised his head to speak. The woman and the van were gone. He stared blankly at the empty space where they had been.

Nick leaned back in his seat in stunned silence. His astonishment was counterbalanced by a feeling of growing tranquility. "You must be strong in your faith, Nick. It's God's will." Suddenly echoed in the car again. It was the woman's voice coming from the radio. Nick let out a serene smile.

"I am my father's son," Nick said out loud. He took a deep breath and glanced into the rearview mirror. The reflected image of Jesus smiled back at him. Nick lowered his head in humility. Out the front window, he could see two police cars traveling slowly along the street. They both turned into the parking lot and suddenly switched on their flashing lights. There was no siren. Nick watched the red flashers quietly approach as if it was some surreal dream. The cars parked quickly behind him. They turned on their spotlights which filled the car with bright white light. Nick covered his eyes with his hand. In the side view mirrors, he could see two officers walking towards his car, one on each side.

"Have a busy night, sir?" the officer near his window asked. Nick smiled at him without saying anything. The officer peered over Nick's shoulder and saw the rifle sitting on the passenger seat. He immediately drew his weapon and pointed it at Nick. "Put your hands on the steering wheel, sir!" he shouted. "Please put your hands on the wheel!" Nick complied. The second officer opened the passenger door and removed the rifle from the car. "Step out of the car, sir," the first officer said forcefully. Nick exited. He was quickly frisked and placed in handcuffs.

"Forgive them, Father," Nick uttered to himself as he glanced up into the dark night sky. He turned towards the policemen with a glazed expression. "Have you men talked to him about me, too?" Nick asked with a softness in his voice.

"Talked to who, sir?" One of the officers responded back.

"God," Nick replied. "I've been getting messages from him on the radio."

The two officers looked at each other. "Can you tell me your name, sir?" One of them asked.

"My name is Jesus Christ," Nick said with a smile. The officer tapped his shoulder mic.

"We're going to need an ambulance dispatched to the Target parking lot on..."

⊷ ⊨◊⊨ ⊶

The inside of the psych ward was similar to a medium security prison. The doors were always locked. Several large attendants guarded the halls. There was constant surveillance, and the routines of the patients were rigidly monitored. On the fifth floor, extra security measures were taken due to the extreme nature of the patients' behavior. They were all considered to be a danger to themselves or to others. In one of the rooms on this floor was the son of Ricky Matt.

Nick sprang up in his bed, held down by restraints holding his arms and legs. He let out a loud screech and rambled maniacally. "Those two bastards tried to kill me, Doc! Satan sent 'em. That son-of-a-bitch! Anybody comes at me again I'll kick their ass...I ain't takin' no shit."

Standing over Nick was a psychiatrist in his mid-sixties. "Mr. Harris, I'm going to give you a shot of Valium," he said. "It will calm you down and make you feel better."

"No!" Nick shouted as he fought to free himself from the restraints. Two large male orderlies moved in and held Nick's arms down securely. He continued with his rant. "You ain't tryin' to poison me, too, are you, Doc?! 'Cause me and my boy Jake gotta cancel the next Olympics. All the skateboarders are boycotting it...ain't no way we're lettin' that happen. It's just more money for the man. Those fuckers!" The doctor administered the shot. Nick tried to get free but could not. He

313

wrenched his body and struggled until his energy was spent. Nick finally lay back in exhaustion, drenched in sweat.

After a few days of treatment, a more sedate patient was allowed to receive his first visitor. On the designated day, Trip made the drive from Angola to the psychiatric ward in downtown Buffalo. Because of Nick's delicate condition, it was required that visitors first talk to his treating psychiatrist before seeing him. When Trip arrived, he was escorted into the office of Dr. Ann Shirley, a petite woman in her mid-thirties who eerily resembled Wendy.

"Please, Mr. Triphauser, have a seat," Dr. Shirley greeted Trip as he entered her office. "Mr. Harris has given me authorization to discuss his condition with you." Trip sat down across from her at the desk.

"Is Nick gonna' be okay, Doctor?" he asked. The doctor glanced through her notes.

"In time, he will," she said. "Mr. Harris is suffering from a general psychosis. He is experiencing hallucinations, delusional behavior, and dissociative disorder."

Trip grimaced at all the medical terminology. "What does the last one mean?" he asked quietly.

Dr. Shirley looked up from her file. "Sometimes Nick is Nick, and sometimes he thinks he's Jesus Christ."

"Holy shit!" Trip blurted out. He removed a Bible from his bag. "Nick asked me to bring this to him," Trip said. "He said his father in heaven wanted him to have it. He isn't talkin' about his dad, is he?"

"No," the doctor said. "A number of my patients suffer from the Messiah complex. Saviors sent from heaven to save the world."

"Why do they think that?" Trip asked.

"In Nick's case, he's been through a tremendous amount of trauma," she answered. "Believing he's the Messiah gives him a way to fix things. Hopefully, with the right levels of medication, he should be much better in a few weeks."

The doctor rose from her chair. "I've started him on a regiment of Lithium and Zyprexa for his psychosis," she said. "I also put him on Risperdal. That should help him sleep at night. He hasn't had much of that over the past few days."

Trip shook his head. "You think all that stuff can help him?" he asked.

"It should," Dr. Shirley said confidently. "But it will take the medications time to reach their optimum levels." Trip stood up, and the doctor walked him to the door.

"His mom is worried sick. Do you think she'll be able to see him?" Trip asked.

"I don't think Nick is ready to see Ms. Harris right now," the doctor replied. "Seeing his mom in her debilitated state might trigger unnecessary trauma. We'll wait to see how Nick responds to the medications."

An hour later, Trip sat fidgeting in a small, sanitized room. There were no windows except for an 8 x 10-inch glass partition built into the steel door. Nick entered dressed in a loose hospital gown and black socks. The two friends gave each other a strong hug. "How you doin', Nicky?" Trip asked nervously.

Nick saw the Bible lying on the table and smiled kindly. He sat down and placed his hand on the holy book. "I am Alpha and Omega," Nick said with conviction. "The beginning and the ending, saith the Lord, which is, and which was, and which is to come, the Almighty."

"What the hell does that mean?" Trip said jokingly.

"Do you not know who I am?" Nick replied.

Trip looked at him strangely. "Yeah, I know who you are..." he said. "We've known each other since high school. Are you fuckin' with me, Nicky?"

Trip stood up from the table. "I am the way," Nick said calmly. "The way to the truth. To each man's salvation."

"And what about your salvation?" Trip said with a bite in his tone. "You've done a lot of pretty fucked up things you know..."

Nick grabbed the Bible and held it in the air. "My salvation is secure!" he said loudly. "I've conquered death and have been sent here to save the world."

"Save the world from what?" Trip asked in confusion. He anxiously stepped towards the exit door.

"Eternal damnation," Nick responded.

Trip glanced back at him and yelled out, "I thought only God could do that?"

Nick stared at him intently. "I am his son. The Christ in the flesh," he said.

"Get the fuck out here with that shit, Nicky! You're scaring me man," Trip said nervously as he motioned to the attendant to open the door.

"There is no need to be afraid," Nick said softly.

"I hope you like the food in here, Jesus." Trip said with a mix of anger and fear. "Because unless you can really walk through walls, you'll be getting three squares a day of hospital food." He rushed out of the room. His face was cloaked with concern.

In the subsequent two weeks, Nick's behavioral incidents slowly dwindled down. Dr. Shirley had taken it upon herself to rigidly supervise his treatment. She had learned in depth of Nick's traumatic background and tried to be as transparent as possible with him regarding his diagnosis and treatment. In one of their sessions, the doctor had even showed Nick, per his request, the diagnostic list of things he was being treated for. It summarily showed general psychosis, depression, bipolar mania, dissociative disorder, sleep disorder, ADHD, anxiety, substance abuse... Nick shook his head and stopped reading. "I'm really fucked up, aren't I, Doc?" he said to her with a subdued laugh.

"You've suffered a great deal of distress in your life, Nick," Dr. Shirley responded. "Much more than most. But with that being said, your recovery is still totally up to you."

"You think I can do it?" Nick asked honestly.

"I think you can," she replied. "But you'll need to approach this one day at a time." A knock at the door interrupted their session.

A young female assistant popped her head into the room. "Your three o'clock is here, Doctor."

"Thank you, Cindy," Dr. Shirley responded back. Nick stood up. The doctor walked him to the door. "You need to stay on your meds, okay?" she said. "Promise me that."

"I promise." Nick smiled.

"You and your family have had some bad breaks, Nick," the doctor continued. "It's not what happens to you in life that matters, but how you react to what happens to you in life."

"I'll try my best," he said. "Thank you, Doctor."

By the third week of his stay, Nick had been showing steady progress. The prescribed meds had attained their optimum levels in his body. The stable combination had him functioning almost like normal. He was even sleeping soundly, which he hadn't done for months. The voluntary therapy sessions he attended also augmented his improvement. He still had outbursts of paranoia, but they were minor and infrequent. Nick's progress was such that he was even allowed more visitations. Trip soon began showing up regularly. Nick was overjoyed, as was Trip, who was glad to see the noticeable improvement in his friend. On one of his visits, Trip asked Nick if he still thought he was the Messiah. The latter had been clutching a Bible throughout his stay and was spewing out biblical quotes with the slightest of ease. Nick laughed. "No. I just find peace and solitude when I read *the word*, Trip," he said. Nick told him he had been reading the Bible voraciously every night. Immersing himself in the texts. He even started attending Bible class held at the hospital. Trip joked his best friend was officially becoming a Bible thumper.

Nick was soon told he was going to be released from the hospital. He would continue to be treated there as an outpatient. Just prior to his release, Nick went to attend his last Bible class at the facility. He sat down in his usual seat. The chair next to him was open but was soon taken up by a tall, lanky man. Nick looked at him in disbelief. It was his old cellmate, Dennis Morgan from Alden. The two men embraced and shook hands. Nick glanced at the blue rosary in Dennis's right hand. "Still see you got the same rosary, huh, brother?" Nick said with a big smile.

Dennis nodded in appreciation. "All thanks to you, brother. All thanks to you." The two spoke for several minutes. Nick found out Dennis had been out of prison for several years. He was teaching Bible study and giving sermons as part of an outreach program. The amiable ex-con was sorry to hear Nick had been having problems but at the same time was happy to see him holding a Bible.

When they were done talking, Dennis walked up to the podium. He began reading from scripture. Nick stood and read out loud with his friend. Others soon joined in. The group became wonderfully boisterous and unabashed. As the meeting went on, Dennis became more forceful and began reading with great conviction. "Is there anyone here today whose life has gone the way they didn't want? Is there anyone here who would like to make a change and allow God to ease their burden? Jesus took up his cross so that you could be witness to that event and take up yours as well. Who in here right now would like our Savior to lighten their burden and be their salvation?"

Nick dropped to his knees, flooded with emotion. He suddenly cried out, "Lord, I can't take it anymore...I can't take the pain! With all my heart, I wanna give my life and everything I have to you...just please don't let me suffer anymore, almighty Father! I beg you!" Nick curled into a ball on the floor, sobbing uncontrollably. Dennis instructed the class to keep reading as his friend purged his soul.

***

Nick Harris came out of the hospital feeling reborn. He spent the next month at home readjusting to his new life, helping his mom and staying out of trouble. There would be no more drugs. No more toxic people with bad situations. Nick was feeling good, ready to get on with things. Still, he knew maintaining his mental health would always be a top priority. Some of his meds might need to be taken for the remainder of his life to keep the symptoms in check. Nick would continue his outpatient treatment at the psych hospital and at the detox clinic. It would be a long and difficult road, but he was determined to persevere. He was also confident his new faith would carry him through.

Supported by members of his Bible study class, Nick was encouraged to try new things. Activities that would have a positive influence on him and enrich his life. He noticed an ad in the city arts paper for acting classes at a local theater. Nick immediately signed up for it. He had liked acting in high school but had never pursued it afterwards. Now might be the time. Nick thought it was a good way to meet new people and gain fresh experiences. He also thought pursuing the arts would be a viable means to express his feelings and inner thoughts. It was a small first step but still a step. God would show him the way.

·—· ·⊰◆⊱· ·—·

On a comfortable fall day, as the sun kept peeking through partly cloudy skies, Nick drove his car over the railroad tracks and through the old neighborhood in Tonawanda. He looked at the familiar streets with nostalgia and a sense of fondness. It hadn't changed much. When his old house came into view, he pulled off to the side of the road and parked. He stared wistfully at the home where he had grown up. It was just sitting there, abandoned and wasting away. Every place has its time, he thought.

Grabbing a small backpack from the passenger seat, Nick stepped out of the car. He glanced about before cutting through an open lot into the woods in the back. He walked a short distance through the thick brush before turning and cutting across parallel to the street. He wound up in the woods directly behind his old house. He looked around with great care until he found the old path. He began following it, walking deep into the woods.

A mix of memories flooded Nick's mind as he moved along. It was the same path he and his dad had walked together so many years earlier. The brush was a little fuller and the trees bigger, but it was still the same. Nick smiled when he noticed an old cut in a tree Ricky had made to serve as a marker. After traveling a quarter mile, he walked into the small clearing with the large oak tree. At its base was Beau's small grave. The handmade cross still marking the spot.

Nick walked over to it and dropped to his knees. He put the backpack down and began digging a hole in front of the marker. About a foot down, Nick came into contact with some old sack cloth in the mud. He pulled it out. Inside was the tightly bundled plastic bag he had buried so many months earlier. Nick opened it. The $2,500 and the cell phone he had left for Ricky were still there. His eyes began to fill with emotion. Nick reached over for his backpack. It held the stack of letters from his dad and a small baggie containing the lock of hair and vial of blood he had received from the mortuary. He carefully transferred each item to the plastic bag with the money and the phone. Nick closed the bag and wrapped it up tightly. He placed the bundle in the grave and covered it firmly with dirt. Nick gazed at the grave. *"Rest in Peace Beau 1975"* was still legible on the weather-beaten marker. A light rain began to filter down through the treetops. It made a gentle patter on the leaves. Nick stood up slowly and grabbed his backpack. "Goodbye, Ricky. I love you...*Dad*," he said proudly and with conviction. It was the first time in his life Nick had called Ricky dad. Nick gently touched the cross. Then disappeared back down the path.

THE END

VEE HARRIS

At the time of this publishing, Vee Harris had debilitated further in her struggles with opioids, RSD, and cigarette smoking. But despite all this, the former registered nurse still tries to maintain a glass half-full attitude and help her son on his journey.

NICK HARRIS

At the time of this publishing, Nick Harris had given up selling drugs altogether. The transition began with his father's escape from Dannemora. That still holds true today. Nick also continues to fight the good fight with his lifelong battle against drug addiction. After turning his life over to God that night in the psych ward, the twenty-six-year-old relapsed once, spent four months in a minimum-security prison, his crime, testing positive for drugs, but has since remained clean going on his second year now. Nick attends acting classes and remains dedicated to taking care of his mom in her time of need. He also recently started painting portraits.